HUMAN FORM & FUNCTION

Pamela Minett
David Wayne
David Rubenstein

Collins Educational

An imprint of HarperCollins*Publishers*

Published by
Collins Educational
An imprint of HarperCollins*Publishers*
77–85 Fulham Palace Road
London W6 8JB

First published 1989
Reprinted 1990, 1992, 1993, 1994, 1995

British Library Cataloguing in Publication Data

Minett, P. M. (Pamela Mary)
   Human form and function
   1. Man. Biology
   I. Title   II. Wayne, David
   III. Rubenstein, David
   599.9

   ISBN 0 00 322303 5

Artwork by Oxford Illustrators Limited
Typeset by August Filmsetting, Haydock, St Helens
Printed and bound in Great Britain by
Scotprint Ltd, Musselburgh

Contents

Preface

Humans do not live in isolation. They are part of the environment and interact with it; their actions affect it and they are affected by it. The importance of this fundamental truth is becoming more and more widely recognised and is receiving increased emphasis. There has been a very marked trend over recent years of people wishing to know more about their own bodies. Those who have an interest in human anatomy and physiology are better equipped to understand and evaluate the information and advice which they receive from their doctors, read in the press, and see and hear on television. This trend is reflected in the GCSE Human Biology and GCSE Biology syllabuses, and in the training requirements for nurses and the paramedical professions. Others working in the Health Services, Community Care and similar fields require comparable standards of knowledge.

Human Form and Function supplies a basic core of knowledge covering the GCSE Human Biology syllabuses and a large part of GCSE Biology. It also meets the needs of students of all ages who wish to acquire a good basic knowledge about the structure and functioning of the body and to understand their relationship to health. The aim has been to produce a book which will meet the needs of the classroom and the teacher as well as the general reader, and which is written in language that is comprehensible to lay people whilst maintaining the highest standard of physiological and medical accuracy. It is a book for a very wide ability range and provides a firm foundation for those who wish to go on to more advanced studies.

The book is divided into 100 Topics each of which is a two-page spread. This helps with a planned course of study and provides an easy source of reference. The text has been kept direct and succinct and the numerous illustrations form an integral part of each Topic. The presentation is designed to stimulate interest and curiosity and to encourage observation and questioning. It allows teachers a flexibility of approach which will suit their own methods and the needs of individual classes or students.

Many modern courses require knowledge wider than the structure and function of the human body. This has been borne in mind throughout the book and its final section deals more fully with a number of environmental aspects. This book has been produced by a team of an experienced practising school teacher in partnership with two consultant medical practitioners. All three have written books in their own fields which are recognised as standard works.

Acknowledgements

Preparation of a book such as this requires consultation with experts in many spheres ranging from design to specialised medical fields. The authors wish to thank all who have readily given help, advice and criticism. We would especially like to record our gratitude to:

Sir Edward Wayne FRCP and Stanley Minett for checking our work and for much valuable advice, Stanley Everiss for much detailed advice and information, Dr Elizabeth and Peter Griffiths for assistance with the environmental section, Peter Saunders of the UK Atomic Energy Authority, Clare Williams of Oxford Illustrators for the artwork.

The following staff at James Paget Hospital, Gt Yarmouth, Norfolk: Madelaine Borg, Department of Medical illustration, Reg Cooper, chiropodist, Pamela Higginbotham, diagnostic imaging (ultrasound), Sally Jevons, dietician, George Heyes Moore, consultant orthopaedic surgeon, Christine Thompson, librarian.

Staff and pupils at Cliff Park High School, Gorleston, Norfolk and The Hewett School, Norwich, where class-room research was carried out.

Human Form and Function: Revision Exercises, a companion book of photocopy masters which can be used in conjunction with this textbook, has been prepared by Pamela Minett and published by Stokesby House Publications. It is available from ASE Booksales, College Lane, Hatfield, Herts AL10 9AA.
ISBN 0–9514490–0–1

SECTION 1
Basic Structure

The human body

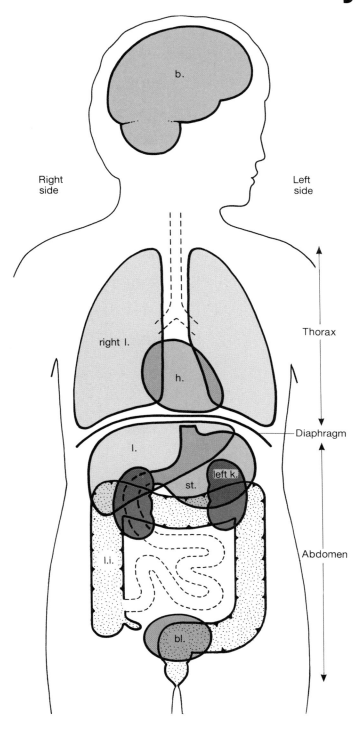

Right side

Left side

b.

right l.

h.

l.

left k.

st.

l.i.

bl.

Thorax

Diaphragm

Abdomen

Figure 1 Diagram to show the main organs of the human body. **Note** that this diagram shows the body as seen from the front – therefore when you are looking at the diagram, the left side of the body in the diagram is opposite to your right side

General structure

Head About half the space within the head is occupied by the brain. The brain and the nearby sense organs – eyes, ears, nose and tongue – are all partly or completely protected by the bony skull.

Neck The voice box (larynx) and the thyroid gland are in the front of the neck, and the gullet (oesophagus) and windpipe (trachea) pass behind them. The small bones (vertebrae) in the neck allow the head to turn in different directions.

Trunk The large cavity inside the trunk is separated into two parts by a thin, tough sheet of muscle and fibrous tissue called the **diaphragm**. The upper region – the **thorax** (chest) – contains the heart and lungs. The lower region – the **abdomen** – contains the main organs of digestion, excretion and reproduction. The small amount of free space within the trunk is filled with fluid which acts as a lubricant.

Organs and systems

Within the body there are a number of organs of different types which are grouped together into systems.

Organs An organ is a part of the body with a special function or functions. Examples are:
heart for pumping blood,
lungs for breathing,
stomach for digesting food,
bladder for storing urine.

Systems A system is a group of organs working in harmony so that the body can carry out a particular function or functions. The main systems are shown in **Fig 2, A** to **I**.

Main fields of study

The study of the human body is divided into:
Anatomy – the structure of the body (what it is like).
Physiology – how the body functions (what happens and how it happens).

Specialised fields of study include:
Cardiology – the heart.
Endocrinology – hormones.
Gastro-enterology – the digestive system.
Geriatrics – medical care of the elderly.
Gynaecology – the female reproductive system.
Haematology – blood.
Hygiene – the principles governing health.
Nephrology – kidneys and bladder.
Neurology – the nervous system.
Obstetrics – pregnancy and childbirth.
Ophthalmology – eyes.
Paediatrics – care and development of children.
Pathology – investigation of disease.
Psychology – how the mind works.
Radiology – X-rays and ultrasound.

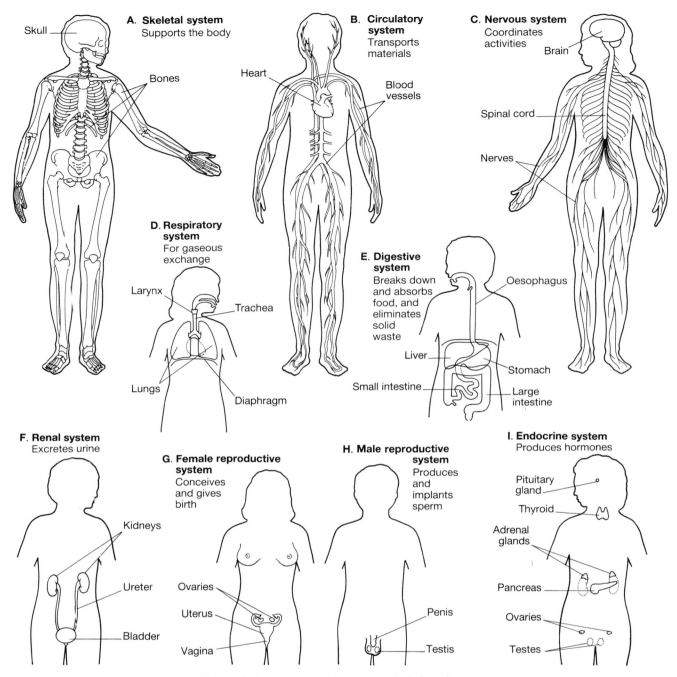

Figure 2 Systems of the body and their functions

QUESTIONS

1a Name the sheet of tissue which separates the trunk into two parts.
 b Name: (i) the upper part of the trunk, (ii) the lower part of the trunk.
2a What is meant by the terms: (i) organ, (ii) system?
 b Name nine systems of the body and give a function of each.
 c Study **Fig 2**, then name the eight organs in **Fig 1** which are shown by their initials.
3 Complete this chart using the information shown on the opposite page.

Field of study	What is studied
Anatomy	the structure of the body

FURTHER WORK

1 Copy the outline of the human body shown in **Fig 1**. Copy the organs separately on another sheet of paper. Cut them out and stick them in position on your outline of the body. In the **thorax**: place the lungs over the heart. In the **abdomen**: place the kidneys in position first, then the stomach, then the large intestine, then the liver, then the bladder.

2 Study the hospital signboard: **Fig 3**. To which of the departments named do patients go: (i) to keep an appointment with a paediatrician, (ii) for a blood test, (iii) to be X-rayed, (iv) when pregnant, (v) with heart disease? Give the purpose of each of the other departments on the signboard.

↖ **Antenatal Clinic**
↖ **Out Patients**
↖ **Cardiology**
↖ **Childrens Unit**
↖ **Haematology**
Pathology →
Radiology →
Pharmacy →
Stores →
← **Physiotherapy**
← **Geriatric Unit**
← **Neurology**
← **Administration**

Figure 3 Signboard in a hospital

3

The skeleton

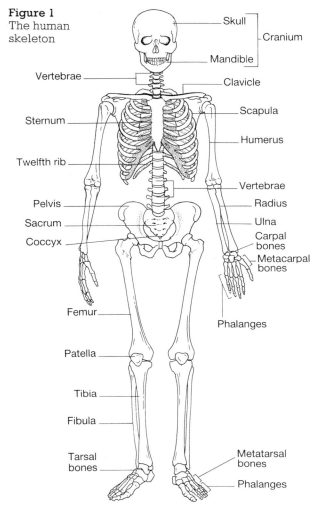

Figure 1
The human skeleton

Skull
Cranium
Mandible
Vertebrae
Clavicle
Sternum
Scapula
Humerus
Twelfth rib
Vertebrae
Pelvis
Radius
Sacrum
Ulna
Coccyx
Carpal bones
Metacarpal bones
Femur
Phalanges
Patella
Tibia
Fibula
Tarsal bones
Metatarsal bones
Phalanges

Cranium (brain box)
Fixed joint
Figure 2 Skull
Eye socket (orbit)
Nasal opening
Upper jaw (maxilla)
Ear opening
Lower jaw (mandible)
Jaw hinge
Position of large hole in the centre of the floor of the cranium for the spinal cord
Position of attachment of collar bone

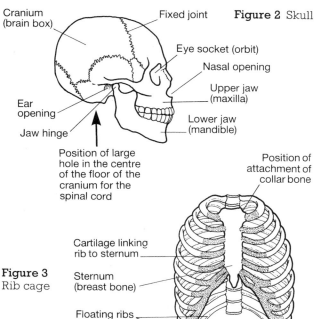

Cartilage linking rib to sternum
Sternum (breast bone)
Figure 3
Rib cage
Floating ribs

The human skeleton contains 206 bones. They fit together to form a framework for the body and are held in place by muscles and ligaments.

Functions of the skeleton

◆ **Supports** and gives shape to the body.
◆ **Allows movement** because:
   the skeleton is jointed,
   bones have places to which muscles are attached.
◆ **Protects** the internal organs:
   the skull protects the brain;
   the backbone protects the spinal cord;
   the rib cage protects the heart, lungs, liver, kidneys and spleen.
◆ **Makes blood cells** – all the red cells and some of the white cells are made in the bone marrow.
◆ **Stores calcium** so that there is always a supply readily available (p. 8).

Structure of the skeleton

The skull, backbone (vertebral column) and rib cage form the main axis of the body and are called the **axial skeleton**. The pectoral girdle, pelvic girdle, arms and legs are attached (appended) to the main axis and are called the **appendicular skeleton**.

Skull The skull consists of more than 20 bones which are interlocked to form a very firm structure, with the lower jaw being the only movable part.
   The largest part of the skull – the **cranium** – surrounds and protects the brain. The shape of the cranium follows the shape of the brain, and as the brain grows the cranium enlarges. The brain connects with the spinal cord through a large hole in the floor of the cranium. The **ear openings** in the sides of the skull lead to the middle and inner parts of the ears. These parts are inside the bones of the floor of the cranium.
   The bones of the **face** are arranged so that they surround the openings of the eyes, nose and mouth. Although some of these bones may seem very thick, they are hollow inside. These cavities (holes) – called **sinuses** – lessen the weight of the skull and give resonance to the voice. Each sinus has a narrow opening into the nose (**Fig 3**, p. 105).

Rib cage The sternum, ribs, and part of the backbone form a cage around the thorax. All the twelve pairs of ribs are joined to the twelve thoracic vertebrae of the backbone, and the upper ten pairs are also joined to the sternum. Although the other two pairs are firmly held in place by the muscles of the back, they are sometimes called 'floating ribs' as they are not fixed to the sternum.

Pelvic girdle (hip girdle; pelvis) The pelvic girdle consists of two hip bones – the **right pelvis** and **left pelvis** – and the part of the backbone – the **sacrum** – to which they are joined. Together they form a strong ring of bone – strong enough to support the weight of the upper part of the body and to take the strain of the attached muscles of the legs, spine and abdominal wall. The contents of the lower part of the abdomen are protected by the pelvic girdle, and the upper leg bones (femurs) fit into deep sockets at the sides.

The shape of the pelvis varies according to sex. It is wider and flatter in females and adapted to the needs of childbirth. Males are more muscular than females and have a larger and stronger pelvis to which their powerful leg muscles are attached.

The hip bones meet in the front at the **pubic symphysis**, where they are held together by tough, fibrous tissue. In males the pubic symphysis is rigid, but in females slight movement is possible during childbirth.

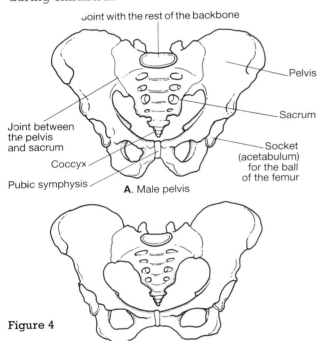

Figure 4

Joint with the rest of the backbone

Pelvis

Sacrum

Socket (acetabulum) for the ball of the femur

Joint between the pelvis and sacrum

Coccyx

Pubic symphysis

A. Male pelvis

B. Female pelvis

Pectoral girdle (shoulder girdle) The pectoral girdle is composed of four bones – two **clavicles** (collar bones) and two **scapulae** (shoulder blades). It is connected to the rest of the skeleton by joints between the clavicles and the sternum.

The functions of the scapula are to form a shoulder joint with the arms, and also to provide large areas of bone to which the muscles of the arm, back and chest are attached. The shoulder joint is held in position by these muscles. The scapula is able to move by sliding over the ribs, and when it does so it takes the arm with it, thus increasing the range of arm movement. The function of the clavicle is to support the shoulder joint.

Limbs The legs and arms are **pentadactyl** limbs (penta = five; dactyl = fingered) and they both follow a common plan. Moving outwards from the shoulder or hip:

◆ The upper part consists of a single bone (upper arm or thigh).
◆ The next segment (forearm or lower leg) has two parallel bones.
◆ Next comes a cluster of small bones (eight in the wrist, seven in the ankle).
◆ Then there are five parallel bones (in the palm or foot).
◆ At the end are five jointed digits (fingers or toes).

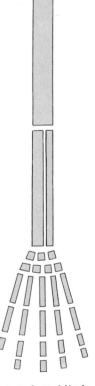

Figure 5 Diagram of a pentadactyl limb

QUESTIONS

1a Give five functions of the skeleton.
 b Name the parts of: (i) the axial skeleton, (ii) the appendicular skeleton.
 c How are the bones held in place in the body?

2 Give the technical names for:
 a brain box,
 b lower jaw,
 c collar bone,
 d shoulder blade,
 e breast bone,
 f wrist bones,
 g bones of the palm,
 h hip bone,
 i thigh bone,
 j knee cap,
 k ankle bones,
 l shoulder girdle,
 m the long bones in the foot,
 n the bones in the fingers and toes,
 o the bone of the upper arm.

3a (i) Name the two bones in the forearm.
 (ii) Which of these bones is on the same side of the arm as the thumb?
 b (i) Name the two bones of the lower leg.
 (ii) Which of these bones is on the same side of the leg as the big toe?

4a (i) How many pairs of ribs are joined both to the backbone and the sternum?
 (ii) Why are the other two pairs called 'floating ribs'?
 b Describe the difference between the male pelvis and the female pelvis.

5 Draw and label a diagram of the skull.

FURTHER WORK

1 Study a model of the skeleton: **a.** How many bones can you count? **b.** Which is the longest bone? **c.** What happens to the bones of the forearm when the hand is turned over? **d.** Where do: (i) the pectoral girdle, (ii) the pelvic girdle, connect to the rest of the skeleton? **e.** Find the hole in the skull through which the brain connects with the spinal cord. **f.** The ear opening leads to the middle and inner parts of the ear. Note where these parts are situated within the floor of the cranium.

2 Draw a diagram of a pentadactyl limb. On one side, label the bones as in an arm, and on the other side, label as in a leg.

3 List, in two columns, differences between the pelvic and pectoral girdles.

Vertebral column

Figure 1 Vertebral column
– side view

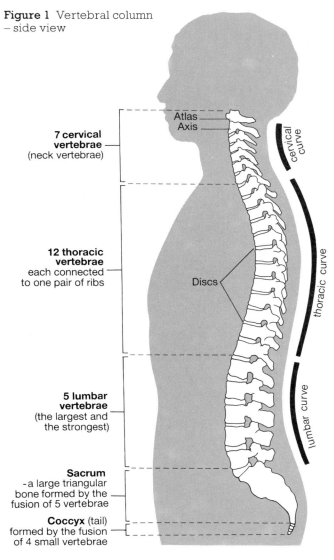

7 **cervical vertebrae**
(neck vertebrae)

12 **thoracic vertebrae**
each connected
to one pair of ribs

5 **lumbar vertebrae**
(the largest and
the strongest)

Sacrum
- a large triangular
bone formed by the
fusion of 5 vertebrae

Coccyx (tail)
formed by the fusion
of 4 small vertebrae

Atlas
Axis

cervical curve

thoracic curve

lumbar curve

Discs

Structure

The **vertebral column**, also known as the **backbone** or **spine**, is a column of thirty-three small bones called **vertebrae** (each is a **vertebra**). The top twenty-four are separate bones, the next five are fused to form the **sacrum**, and the lowest four form the **coccyx**, which is the remnant of a tail.

Fig 1 shows the natural shape of the backbone when seen from the side. It is held in this S-shaped curve by the **muscles** of the back and by the **ligaments** which link the vertebrae.

The backbone is protected against damage by jarring because:
◆ the shape of the spine makes it behave like a spring,
◆ the cartilage discs between the vertebrae act as shock absorbers.

Functions of the vertebral column

◆ **Supports** the upper part of the body.
◆ Encloses and **protects** the spinal cord.
◆ Provides points of **attachment** for the ribs, and for the muscles of the back.
◆ **Allows movement** of the head and the trunk:
  The joint between the skull and the top vertebra (**atlas**) allows the head to move backwards and forwards.
  The joint between the first and second vertebrae (**atlas** and **axis**) allows the head to turn from side to side.
  The joints between other vertebrae each allow a small amount of movement, and the combined movement of all the separate joints allows the trunk to bend and turn.

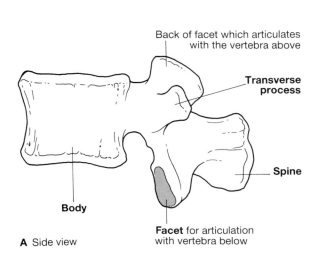

Back of facet which articulates
with the vertebra above

Transverse process

Spine

Body

Facet for articulation
with vertebra below

A Side view

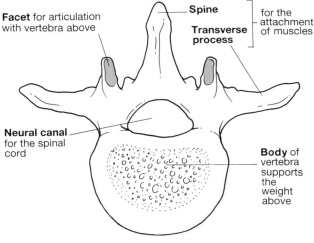

Facet for articulation
with vertebra above

Spine

Transverse process

for the attachment of muscles

Neural canal
for the spinal
cord

Body of
vertebra
supports
the
weight
above

B View from above

Figure 2 Diagrams of a lumbar vertebra

Discs

The discs between the vertebrae – **intervertebral discs** – make up about a quarter of the total length of the backbone. They join the individual bones (vertebrae) of the backbone together, making the whole structure flexible but strong.

Each disc is a tough pad of cartilage firmly attached to the vertebra immediately above, and to the one immediately below. It has a tough outer layer of strong fibrous tissue and a soft jelly-like centre. With every movement of the back, some or all of the discs become squeezed and/or stretched in different parts. They return to their normal shape when the back is straightened.

'Slipped' disc

When a great deal of strain is repeatedly put on the same part of the back, a disc may start to crack. If the strain continues, the crack gets larger and then opens so that jelly from the centre of the disc leaks through the crack. This is called a **'slipped' disc**, and when it presses on a nerve, it causes pain. **Fig 3** shows how close to each other the discs and the nerves are.

Pressure on the nerves in the lumbar region causes pain in the lower back – **lumbago**. Pressure on the sciatic nerve, which runs down the leg, results in the pain being felt in the leg – **sciatica**. When the nerves in the neck region are affected, pain may be felt in the arms, and 'pins and needles' in the fingers. Treatment of back pain, and ways of preventing it, are discussed on p. 21.

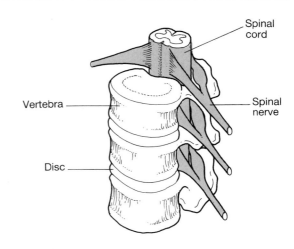

Figure 3 This diagram shows how close the discs are to the spinal cord and spinal nerves

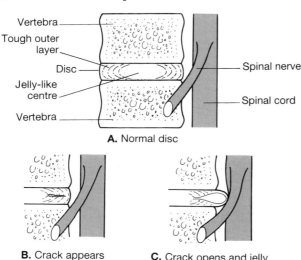

A. Normal disc

B. Crack appears

C. Crack opens and jelly bulges through

Figure 4 'Slipped' disc

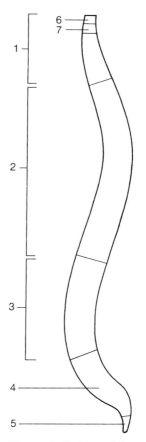

Figure 5 Outline of the vertebral column – side view

QUESTIONS

1a Describe the structure of the vertebral column.

2a Copy **Fig 5**. Label 1–7 using the information from **Fig 1**.
 b How is the backbone held in a curved shape?
 c Give two ways in which the structure of the backbone protects it from damage by jarring.

3a List four functions of the vertebral column.

 b How does the backbone allow head and trunk movements?

4a What length of the backbone do the discs occupy?
 b Describe a disc.
 c How is the shape of the disc affected by movement of the back?

5a Describe with words and diagrams the development of a 'slipped' disc.
 b What is: (i) lumbago, (ii) sciatica?

FURTHER WORK

1 Study the vertebral column of a skeleton, or a model of one. Note: the number of bones in the column; how they fit together; the shape and size of vertebrae in different parts of the column; the position of the discs and spinal cord; where the spinal nerves emerge.

2 Draw diagrams of a lumbar vertebra and indicate how its shape is suited to its function.

Bones

The bones of the body are living structures and are built and maintained by living cells. If damaged, they bleed and are painful; and if broken, they can mend. The main substance of bones is **bone tissue** (p. 27) and blood circulates through it in blood vessels in the Haversian canals. Bones only look clean and white when all the living tissues are removed: **Fig. 1**.

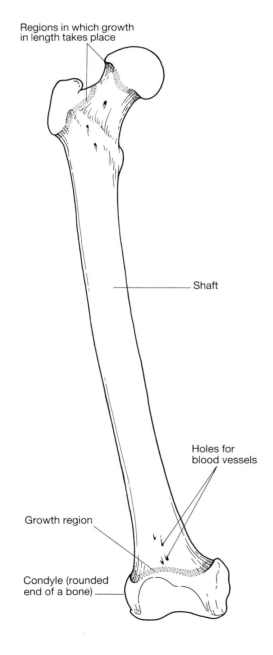

Regions in which growth in length takes place

Shaft

Holes for blood vessels

Growth region

Condyle (rounded end of a bone)

Figure 1 Bone (femur) with all the living tissues removed

Growth of bones

Length Growth in length occurs in special **growing regions** near the ends of the bone. These growing regions consist of cartilage and when they ossify growth in length stops (p. 158). **Ossification** is the replacement of cartilage by bone tissue.

Width Cells on the inside of the periosteum enable the bone to grow in width and also to repair damaged tissue. These cells are more active in children than in adults.

Requirements for growth Growth of bones requires an adequate supply of:
- **protein** – a type of protein called **collagen** forms the framework of the bone.
- **calcium** – to make the bone hard.
- **vitamin D** – to enable calcium to be absorbed from the intestine and deposited in bone.
- **hormones** – growth hormone, thyroid hormone and parathyroid hormone.

Activities within bones

The continuous activity which takes place inside bones includes:

Remodelling Throughout life, cells within bones are constantly at work rebuilding and remodelling. This enables young bones to enlarge and change shape as the body grows, and repairs to be made to damaged bones. Remodelling involves:
- **bone resorption** – the removal of bone tissue by **osteoclasts**, cells which remove bone tissue.
- **bone formation** – the growth of bone tissue by **osteoblasts**, cells which make new bone tissue.

Manufacture of blood cells Red cells, white cells and platelets are made in the bone marrow. At birth, marrow occurs throughout the skeleton, but is gradually replaced by fat in many of the limb bones as the child grows.

Movement of calcium There is continuous interchange between the large store of calcium in bones and the calcium in the blood. This allows the calcium level in the blood to be kept constant (see parathyroid hormone, p. 114), which is important for the healthy functioning of cells.

Bones need the stress of movement and gravity to keep healthy. For example, limbs which are paralysed tend to lose calcium, and when astronauts are weightless, calcium is rapidly lost from bones. The calcium enters the blood stream and is removed from the body through the kidneys in urine.

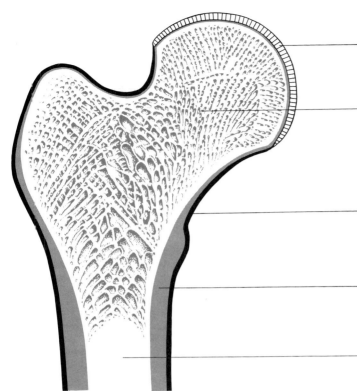

Cartilage covers the ends of the bone at the positions of the joints. It is also present in the growth regions of young bones.

Spongy bone gets its name because of the numerous small spaces within it and not because it is soft and sponge-like. It is neither as strong nor as heavy as compact bone because the spaces are filled with fat or marrow. The blood within spongy bone gives it a pinkish colour. Spongy bone is strengthened by a criss-cross network of **bony supports**. They form in places where extra strength is needed and follow the lines of stress.

Periosteum (peri = around; osteum = bone) covers the remainder of the bone that is not covered by cartilage. This thin, tough membrane is firmly attached to the bone and is almost impossible to remove. There is a network of **nerves** in the periosteum.

Compact bone forms an outer layer and is thickest in those places which receive the greatest stress. Its dense texture gives it strength but makes it heavy.

Central cavity is present only in long bones (those which have an elongated shape) and is filled with marrow or fat. There can be a cavity in the centre of a long bone because this region is not required to take any load or other stress. It makes the bone lighter without loss of strength and allows the space to be used for other purposes.

Figure 2 Inside a bone: When the inside of a bone is studied it shows a varied and interesting structure

QUESTIONS

1 Draw and label a diagram which shows a bone after the living tissues have been removed.

2a Draw a diagram to show the internal structure of a bone, Fig 3. Label 1–5 from the information given on Fig 2.
  b Whereabouts is cartilage found?
  c Describe the periosteum.
  d Whereabouts are nerves found?
  e Describe compact bone.
  f (i) Why is spongy bone so called?
    (ii) Why is it a pinkish colour?
    (iii) Describe how spongy bone is strengthened?
  g (i) Why can there be a cavity in the centre of a long bone? (ii) What is the cavity filled with?

3a How do bones grow in: (i) length, (ii) width?
  b Name four requirements for bone growth.
  c Describe the cells and processes involved when bones are remodelled.
  d Describe the part played by bones in keeping the calcium level in the blood constant.

4a How do bones grow in: (i) length, (ii) width?
  b List four requirements for growth of bones.

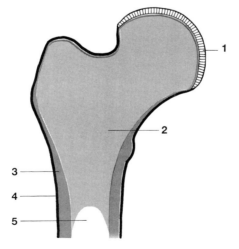

Figure 3 Diagram to show the internal structure of a bone

FURTHER WORK

1. **Examining bones**
a Study a fresh animal bone which has been cut in half. Identify the parts labelled in **Fig 2**.
1 Boil one of the halves of the bone to remove the soft tissues. (i) List the parts which have been destroyed and removed by boiling. (ii) Note the changes in colour of the different parts.

2. **Removing the calcium from a bone**
a Boil a bone to remove the flesh (a rib bone from pork or a chicken leg bone is suitable).
b Place the bone in a dilute solution of hydrochloric acid (2 M) to dissolve the calcium from the bone.
c Leave for a few days to give time for the calcium to be removed, then lift out the bone and wash in cold water to remove the acid.
d It should now be possible to bend the bone because only the flexible collagen remains.

3 (i) Describe, with the aid of a diagram, how a bone is constructed to combine lightness with strength. (ii) Many of the weight-bearing bones have the shape of a tube. Demonstrate, using a cardboard tube, how the strength of such bones is due partly to their shape and not to the material of which they are made. (iii) The skull has the shape of an egg. Demonstrate the difference in strength between a whole egg and a piece of eggshell.

Joints

Classification of joints

The place where two bones meet is called a **joint**. The joints in the body can be classified according to the amount and type of movement between the two bones:

Fixed joints The bones interlock where they touch each other and are firmly fixed together so that no movement can take place.

Slightly movable joints (cartilaginous joints) The bones are firmly joined together by cartilage. Although cartilage is tough, it is also flexible enough to allow a small amount of movement when it is squeezed or stretched.

Freely movable joints (synovial joints) These joints allow a considerable amount of movement between the two bones. Examples are:

Ball and socket joints. The end of one bone is rounded and fits into a hollow in the other bone and movement in nearly all directions is possible.

Hinge joints. These act like door hinges and allow movement in one plane only.

Gliding joints. The bones slide over each other.

Pivot joints. One bone rotates alongside the other.

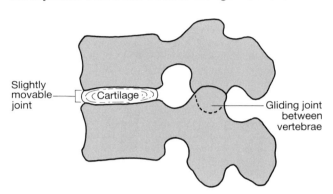

A. Vertebrae showing a slightly movable joint and a gliding joint

Joint between bones of the cranium (**fixed**)

Joint between atlas and axis allows head to turn (**pivot**) from side to side

Ribs and sternum are joined by **cartilage** (allows the chest to expand in deep breathing)

Jaw (**hinge**)

Shoulder (**ball and socket**)

Elbow (**hinge**) - see **B**

Finger (**hinge**)

Joint between pelvis and sacrum (**fixed**)

Wrist (**gliding**)

Hip (**ball and socket**) - see **C**

Cartilage disc between the vertebrae - see **A**

Knee (**hinge**)

Ankle (**gliding**)

Toe (**hinge**)

Figure 1 Joints in the body

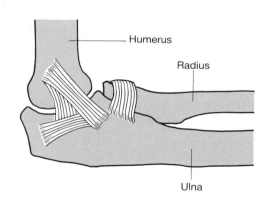

B. Hinge joint of elbow (4 ligaments shown)

Humerus

Radius

Ulna

Ligaments Ligaments are bands of tough, fibrous tissue linking the bones at a joint. The bones are mainly held in place at the joint by the muscles, but the ligaments also help to keep them in position. The ligaments bend as the joint bends, but they have little stretch and their main function is to limit the amount of movement which can take place between the two bones.

The term **double-jointed** means that the ligaments can stretch more than is usual and allow a larger range of movements. (The number of joints is still the same.)

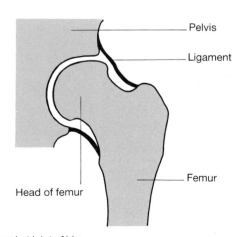

Pelvis

Ligament

Femur

Head of femur

C. Ball and socket joint of hip

Structure of a synovial joint

Synovial joints are the most common type of joint in the body. Smooth movement between the two bones is possible because:

- **cartilage** – smooth and slippery – covers the ends of the bones where they touch each other.
- **synovial membrane** – smooth and moist – lines the inside of the joint.
- **synovial fluid** – secreted by the synovial membrane – lubricates the joint.

The joint is strengthened by:

- **muscles** surrounding the joint,
- **ligaments** linking the bones,
- a **tough capsule** that encloses and seals the joint.

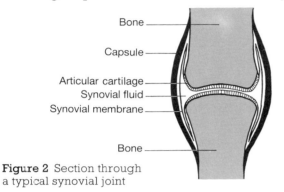

Bone

Capsule

Articular cartilage
Synovial fluid
Synovial membrane

Bone

Figure 2 Section through a typical synovial joint

Arthritis

Arthritis means inflammation of a joint. Inflamed joints are painful, may be hot and swollen, and movement at the joint is limited. Two common types of arthritis are:

Osteo-arthritis ('wear and tear' arthritis)

- This condition is restricted to the joints.
- The smooth covering of cartilage at the ends of bones becomes worn away by rough bone. This causes pain and stiffness when the joint is moved.
- The joints most affected are the weight-bearing joints of the hips, knees and spine.

QUESTIONS

1a What is a joint?
 b Describe a fixed joint and give two examples.
 c Describe a slightly movable joint and give two examples.

2a Draw and label a section through a typical synovial joint.
 b Name three factors which enable the bones of a synovial joint to move smoothly.
 c State three ways in which a synovial joint is strengthened.
 d Describe a ball and socket joint and give two examples.
 e Describe a hinge joint and give four examples.
 f What is the difference between gliding and pivot joints? Give an example of each.

3a What are ligaments?
 b Describe the main function of ligaments.
 c What is meant by 'double-jointed'?
 d Draw a diagram to show the ligaments at the elbow joint.

4a What is arthritis?
 b Name two common types of arthritis.

- Osteo-arthritis occurs mainly in elderly people and those who are overweight. It is more common in the joints of limbs which have been subject to undue stress in the past, eg injured joints or a badly set fracture.
- Once this condition has developed it remains and tends to increase with age. Symptoms are usually mild and respond to treatment.
- People who are severely disabled by painful arthritis of the hip, knee or elbow may be able to have the damaged joint replaced by an artificial one.

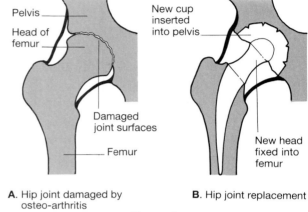

Pelvis

Head of femur

Damaged joint surfaces

Femur

New cup inserted into pelvis

New head fixed into femur

A. Hip joint damaged by osteo-arthritis

B. Hip joint replacement

Figure 3

Rheumatoid arthritis

- This condition affects other parts of the body as well as the joints. The sufferer may feel generally ill with exhaustion, weight loss and a fever.
- The fibrous tissue around the joints becomes inflamed, painful and stiff, and is generally worse first thing in the morning.
- The smaller joints such as fingers and toes are usually affected first.
- Younger people are affected, usually women, often before the age of forty.
- The condition follows an 'up and down' course with weeks or months when the joints improve, which is then followed by pain and stiffness again. This is why it is difficult to know whether any improvement is the result of treatment or would have happened naturally.
- Some people with acute (short-term) rheumatoid arthritis recover completely. Others may have permanent changes – usually seen in the hands. It is possible to replace some affected joints with artificial ones, especially the finger joints.

FURTHER WORK

1 **Arthritis:** Using the information above, compare osteo-arthritis with rheumatoid arthritis, listing the differences in two columns. Find out how these conditions affect the lives of sufferers, and how their life-style can be improved.

2 Complete exercise 2, p. 32.

Muscles

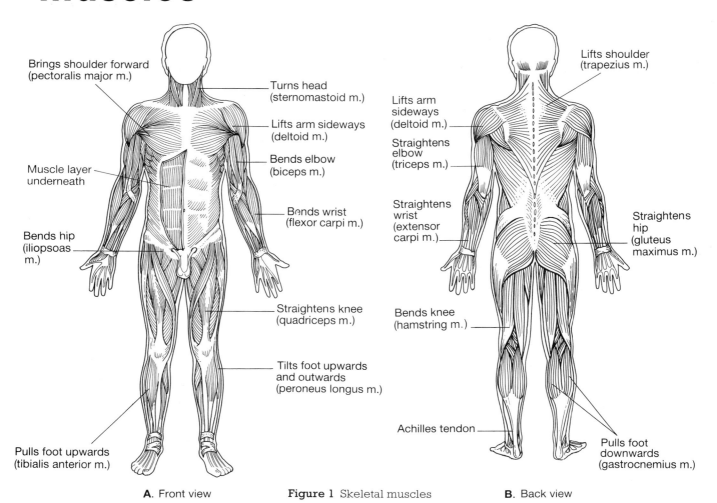

A. Front view   **Figure 1** Skeletal muscles   **B.** Back view

This topic deals only with the muscles that are attached to the skeleton – the **skeletal muscles**. They form the 'flesh' of the body – the lean part of meat – and their function is to hold the bones in position and to move them when required.

Skeletal muscles are also known as **voluntary muscles** as you can use them when you want to, for example, to eat, lift a bag or climb stairs. Other names for them are **striped muscles** and **striated muscles**, as the muscle fibres have a striped appearance when seen under a microscope (p. 27).

As can be seen from **Fig 1**, the individual muscles – there are about 600 of them – are arranged in a complex pattern.

Structure of a muscle

Each muscle is composed of long, thin muscle fibres arranged in bundles. **Fig 2** shows the general shape of a skeletal muscle. It is thicker in the centre because there are more fibres in this part. Usually there is a tendon at each end, although in some cases muscles are attached directly to the bone.

Tendons   A tendon is a tough cord which attaches a muscle to a bone. It is whitish in colour and is often known as **gristle**. Tendons are made of collagen fibres which are very strong but also flexible, so tendons can bend when the joints bend.

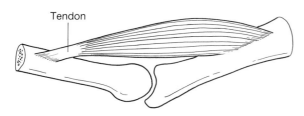

Figure 2 General shape of a skeletal muscle

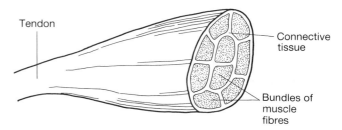

Figure 3 Section through a skeletal muscle

12

Movement

Movement is controlled by nerves Skeletal muscles are supplied with nerves from the spinal cord which relay messages from the brain. The nerves branch many times so that each muscle fibre has its own nerve endings: **Fig 4**. When a message from the brain passes along the nerve to tell the muscle to contract, each of the fibres receives the message. They then all contract to shorten the muscle, maybe by as much as half its length. When the message to contract ends, the muscle relaxes and can return to its former shape.

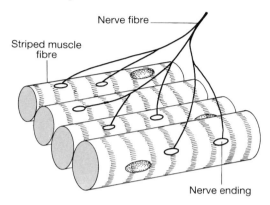

Figure 4 Nerve endings on muscle fibres (much enlarged)

Muscles always work in groups Because muscles can only pull bones but not push them, they always work in groups of two or more. One muscle pulls the bone to make it move, then after the movement has taken place, another muscle can pull it back to its original position.

All the muscles round a joint are in a slight state of contraction all the while. This is called **muscle tone**. Movement only takes place when the muscle on one side contracts more and pulls harder than that on the other side. The other muscle relaxes gradually and this keeps the movement smooth and under control.

Muscles which work together to produce movement in opposite directions are said to be **antagonistic**, and to form an **antagonistic system**. Examples of antagonistic systems are:

The **biceps** – bends the arm.
The **triceps** – straightens the arm.
The **hamstring** muscles – bend the knee.
The **thigh** muscles – straighten the knee.
The **shin** muscle – bends the ankle.
The **calf** muscles – straighten the ankle.

Flexors and extensors Muscles are called flexor or extensor according to whether they cause the joint to bend (flex) or straighten (extend).

A **flexor muscle** bends the joint.
An **extensor muscle** straightens the joint.

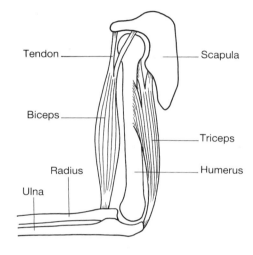

Figure 5 Diagram to show an antagonistic pair of muscles – the **triceps** and **biceps** – which cause movement at the elbow joint

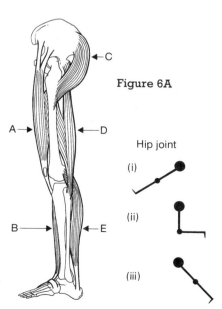

Figure 6A

Figure 6B Three movements of the leg

QUESTIONS

1a Why are the muscles which move bones called: **(i)** skeletal, **(ii)** voluntary, **(iii)** striped?
 b Draw diagrams of a skeletal muscle to show: **(i)** the general shape, **(ii)** a section through it.
2a What is a muscle composed of?
 b Why is a muscle thicker in the centre?
 c How are muscles attached to bones?
 d Describe a tendon.
3a How are muscles linked to the brain?
 b Describe what happens when a muscle receives a message from the brain to contract.
4a Why do muscles work in groups?
 b When are muscles antagonistic?
 c Give examples of antagonistic systems.

FURTHER WORK

1 Draw **Fig 5** as an example of an antagonistic system of muscles.
2 Fig 6A shows the skeleton of the leg and some of the muscles.
 a Name two bones to which muscle C is attached.
 b Give one effect of the contraction of muscle B.
 c Give one effect of the contraction of muscle E.
 d Muscles B and E are antagonistic to each other. Explain this statement.

Fig 6B shows three movements of the leg.
 e Which muscle contracts to raise the leg to position **(i)**?
 f Which muscle bends the knee as in position **(ii)**?
 g Is the muscle which bends the knee in **(ii)** a flexor or extensor? Explain your answer.
 h When the leg is drawn back as in position **(iii)**, which two muscles will contract?

Exercise

The natural way of life for humans is an active one. Our ancestors used their muscles and took exercise as they worked hard to provide food, warmth and shelter in order to keep alive. For example, they:

◆ hunted for meat,
◆ gathered nuts, berries and other fruits,
◆ collected firewood for cooking and warmth,
◆ carried water,
◆ travelled on foot or on the back of an animal,
◆ had to be fit enough to defend themselves against enemies and wild animals, or to flee from them.

Replacement of muscle power by machines

In our modern way of life, much of the work necessary to keep us alive is done by machines rather than muscles. For example:

◆ Animals are reared on farms with the aid of machinery.
◆ Food is prepared by machines.
◆ A flick of a switch turns on an electric or gas heater.
◆ Water comes from a tap after being treated and pumped.
◆ Travel is by car, bus, train or plane.
◆ Guns and other weapons are used for defence.

A sedentary (sitting) **way of life** As machines replace muscles, much more time is spent sitting down to use the machines, either at work or when travelling. In addition, there are machines to help with the housework. Most people have time for leisure.

Daily life may, therefore, not provide enough exercise to keep the body as healthy as it could be.

Benefits of exercise

The body needs a certain amount of exercise to keep it in good working order. Regular exercise helps to:

◆ keep muscles, including the heart muscle, strong and in good condition,
◆ keep joints mobile and supple,
◆ prevent excess body weight by burning up fat,
◆ induce sound sleep,
◆ maintain good health – people who exercise regularly usually feel fitter and have fewer days off sick,
◆ develop **stamina** – the power to keep going.

Suitable and unsuitable exercise The amount and type of exercise needs to be suitable for each individual and depends on age, physical fitness and state of training. Unsuitable exercise can lead to damage of muscles, joints and ligaments.

Muscle fatigue During gentle exercise, muscles are able to obtain sufficient energy **aerobically** – energy is released from glucose with the use of oxygen. When muscles are working hard, and not enough oxygen is available, energy is released from glucose **anaerobically**, and lactic acid is then produced as a by-product. As lactic acid builds up in muscles, it slows the muscles down, makes them ache, and may also cause cramp.

Lactic acid diffuses from muscles into the blood stream. On reaching the liver, some lactic acid is converted back to glucose, and the rest is oxidised to carbon dioxide and water. An **oxygen debt** arises if lactic acid is produced faster than it can be oxidised.

Stiffness Unaccustomed exercise may make muscles stiff and sore. The muscles become waterlogged because the tissue fluid which entered during muscle activity is unable to drain away through the lymph vessels.

Cramp Cramp is painful spasm of a muscle or group of muscles (**spasm** is a prolonged muscle contraction). Cramp can be relieved by gently stretching the muscle, for example, by bending the foot upwards at the ankle if the calf muscle is affected.

A 'stitch' This is a sharp pain in the side, generally below the ribs on the left side, which occurs in long-distance running. It is not known why it occurs or how to prevent it. It appears not to be dangerous and works off with continued exercise. Trained athletes are less prone to it.

Sports training

Training is necessary to become skilful at a particular sport, and has the following effects:

◆ It increases the size and power of the muscles which are used. The increase is due to enlargement of the individual muscle fibres.
◆ It opens up all the blood vessels in the muscles, so that they are well supplied with blood.
◆ It reduces the amount of lactic acid produced, thus reducing muscle ache and cramp.
◆ It improves the performance of the heart. A trained heart beats more slowly than an untrained heart to do the same amount of work, and it can more easily increase its output when more oxygen is required by the muscles.
◆ It improves co-ordination – for example, between hand and eye – to obtain a more skilful and smooth muscle action.
◆ It makes deep breathing easier, to obtain extra oxygen.

Warming-up exercises

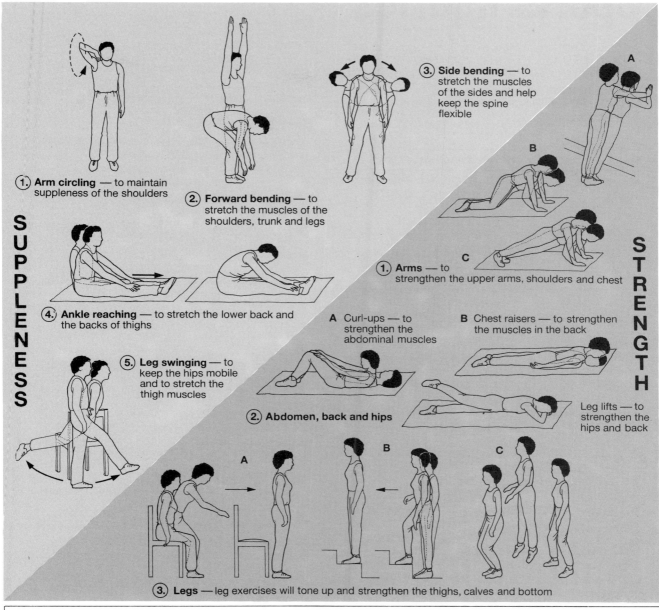

S
U
P
P
L
E
N
E
S
S

(1.) **Arm circling** — to maintain suppleness of the shoulders

(2.) **Forward bending** — to stretch the muscles of the shoulders, trunk and legs

(3.) **Side bending** — to stretch the muscles of the sides and help keep the spine flexible

(4.) **Ankle reaching** — to stretch the lower back and the backs of thighs

(5.) **Leg swinging** — to keep the hips mobile and to stretch the thigh muscles

S
T
R
E
N
G
T
H

(1.) **Arms** — to strengthen the upper arms, shoulders and chest

A Curl-ups — to strengthen the abdominal muscles

B Chest raisers — to strengthen the muscles in the back

Leg lifts — to strengthen the hips and back

(2.) **Abdomen, back and hips**

(3.) **Legs** — leg exercises will tone up and strengthen the thighs, calves and bottom

STAMINA

The best activities for stamina are fairly energetic, make people slightly out of breath, and keep them moving for 20 minutes or more. This type of exercise is often called 'aerobic' exercise because enough oxygen has to be breathed in to supply the working muscles.

Figure 1 Exercising to keep fit. Fitness is having suppleness, strength and stamina

QUESTIONS

1a Give examples of exercise undertaken by our ancestors.
 b Give examples of the replacement of muscle power by machines in our modern way of life.
 c What is meant by sedentary?
2a Why does the body need a certain amount of exercise?
 b Give six benefits of regular exercise.
 c How may the body be harmed by unsuitable exercise?
3a **(i)** What is an oxygen debt? **(ii)** Describe how energy can be produced

without oxygen. **(iii)** Name the acid produced and give its effects on muscles. **(iv)** Explain why breathing continues to be rapid and deep after muscle activity stops.
 b Explain stiffness.
 c What is cramp, and how can it be relieved?
 d What is a 'stitch', and is it dangerous?
4a Give six effects of sports training.
 b What is meant by fitness?

FURTHER WORK

1 Describe exercises for the **(i)** shoulders and arms, **(ii)** back, **(iii)** abdomen, **(iv)** thighs and legs.
2 Complete exercise 5, p. 32.

15

Sports injuries

It is inevitable that some injuries occur to some people who take part in sport. Most injuries to fit people will heal quickly and completely if given the proper attention.

Particular types of injury are often associated with particular sports:

Sport	Serious injuries
Soccer	Torn cartilage of the knee
Rugby	Neck fracture and spinal cord injury
Horse riding	Injuries to the skull
Athletics	Torn muscles and strained ligaments
Skiing	Fractured leg bones
Squash	Eye damage by squash ball

Fracture

A broken or cracked bone is called a **fracture**. A fractured bone is painful, swollen, has an unnatural shape, and a crunching feel and sound when the broken ends are moved against each other. An **X-ray** will show the position of the bones. If normal movement is possible, it is unlikely that any important bones have been broken. Fractures most commonly occur in the:

◆ radius and/or ulna near the wrist, caused by falls on the outstretched hand.
◆ tibia and/or fibula near the ankle.
◆ collar bone, from falls on the shoulder.
◆ femur, due to falling awkwardly on the hip.

First Aid If a bone is thought to be broken it should first be **immobilised** – stopped from moving.
Broken arm. An injured arm can be immobilised by binding it firmly to the side of the chest with a broad bandage and, if it can be bent without pain, by placing the forearm in a sling: **Fig 2A**.
Broken leg. To keep the leg immobile until help arrives, place padding between the legs and tie the injured leg to the other with strips of material such as scarf, tie or belt: **Fig 2B**. The uninjured leg acts as a splint.

A. Closed fracture - when the skin surface is not broken

B. Open fracture (compound fracture) - when there is an open wound near the fracture. The fractured bone may or may not be visible.

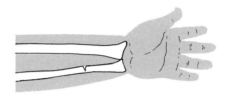

C. Greenstick fracture - the bone is cracked on one side only. This type of fracture only occurs in young bones which are still soft.

Figure 1 Types of fracture

Treatment Fractures require expert medical treatment to:
◆ restore the ends of the bones to their natural position, and
◆ hold them there while the bone heals.
Nearly all bones heal in time because they are living tissues, but the **rate of healing** depends on which bone is involved and the age and general health of the patient.

A. A broken leg

Broken leg

Leg used as splint

Rolled blanket

B. A broken arm

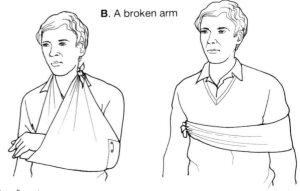

Figure 2 First Aid for fractures

Dislocation

A joint is **dislocated** when it is forced from its normal position. A dislocated joint is very painful, does not look normal, and no movement is possible immediately after it occurs.

The joint most frequently dislocated is the shoulder, because the socket into which the ball of the humerus fits is shallow. Sometimes the humerus slips back of its own accord, but usually it has to be put back in place under anaesthetic. The hip joint is much less likely to be dislocated because the socket is deeper and the muscles around it are stronger.

First Aid Do not try to put the bone back in place. Prevent movement with a sling or splint (as for a fracture) and seek medical aid.

Bruise (contusion)

A **bruise** is bleeding beneath unbroken skin, often due to the skin being hit hard. Small blood vessels are damaged and blood leaks from them into the surrounding tissues. The dark colour of this deoxygenated blood makes the bruised area look blueblack. Gradually, as the blood is removed, the colour of the bruise changes to green and then yellow, and finally disappears.

First Aid **Press hard** on the affected area immediately it has been knocked, and keep pressing for ten minutes. No bleeding into the skin will occur and there will be no bruise. Then apply a **cold compress** – material soaked in cold water – or an ice bag.

Torn Achilles tendon

The Achilles tendon anchors the calf muscles to the heel. Occasionally it becomes torn, either partly or completely. A complete tear results in weakness of the foot movements and inability to stand on tiptoe or run properly.

Treatment The leg is immobilised in plaster to allow the tendon to heal. Sometimes it is **sutured** – stitched together.

Sprain

A **sprain** is a torn ligament – usually only partly torn. It happens when a joint is forced beyond its normal range of movement and this results in swelling, bruising and severe pain around the joint. Sprains most commonly occur in ankles and they follow sudden and unexpected movements.

First Aid Support the joint with a firm bandage. The pain can be relieved by warmth and by pain-relieving drugs. The joint should be exercised as soon as the pain settles. If the pain persists, it is possible that there is also a fracture.

Cartilage damage to the knee

The bones of the upper and lower parts of the leg are separated at the knee joint by two small cartilages (menisci – each is a meniscus). They have a part to play in the complicated movements which take place at this joint, and they also act as shock-absorbers. If a cartilage is displaced or torn, the knee becomes locked in a bent position, cannot be straightened, and is very painful.

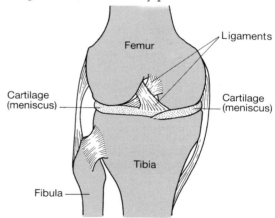

Figure 3 Front view of right knee joint with knee cap removed

Treatment The leg should be immobilised to allow the tissues to heal. Surgery may be necessary in some cases.

1a What is a fracture?
 b Where do fractures most commonly occur?
 c Describe, with the aid of diagrams, three types of fracture.
 d Describe First Aid for fractures in the arm and leg.
 e What treatment is given for fractures?
 f What does the rate of healing depend on?
2a How is a joint dislocated?
 b What are the signs of a dislocated joint?
 c Why is the shoulder joint more frequently dislocated than the hip joint?
 d Describe First Aid for a dislocated joint.

3a What is a sprain and when does it happen?
 b In which part of the body do sprains most commonly occur?
 c Describe First Aid for a sprain.
4a What is a bruise? Describe the colour changes of a bruise and the reasons for it.
 c Describe First Aid for a bruise.
5a Describe: (1) the position of the cartilages of the knee, (ii) their functions, (iii) what happens when they are displaced or torn.
 b What treatment is required for cartilage damage to the knee?
6 (i) In what way can the Achilles tendon be damaged? (iii) Describe the treatment.

FURTHER WORK

1 Draw diagrams to illustrate your answers to the questions.

2 List ten sports and for each, say what precautions are taken to lessen the possibility of injury.

Feet

The foot is a complex arrangement of interlocking bones, **Fig 1**, which are held in place by ligaments and muscles. The bones make an arch from heel to toe, and this structure allows the foot to carry out its two main functions:

◆ It **supports the weight of the body** in a standing position. To do this it must be able to spread the load to give stability. It can be held rigid but at the same time it has to be sufficiently flexible to adjust to uneven surfaces.

◆ It **acts as a lever** to propel the body forward when walking or running. To do this it must be strong, springy, and able to bend.

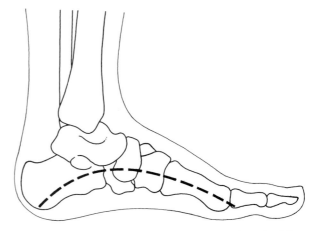

Figure 2 Side view of the foot to show the interlocking bones of the arch

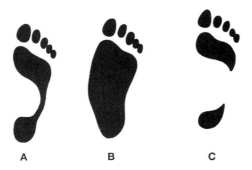

Figure 1 Footprints show the state of the arch of an adult:

A. Normal arch
B. Flat foot – weak ligaments and muscles allow the arch to collapse, and the foot has less 'spring'
C. High arch – makes the foot too rigid

Feet and footwear

Growth of feet Feet grow throughout the first eighteen years of life, and they grow particularly fast in early childhood and during puberty.

The bones in the feet of young children are rather soft and will be bent by shoes or socks which are not big enough. The child rarely feels any pain and therefore will not complain. If tight shoes are worn regularly, the bones will harden into an imperfect shape and the muscles will not be able to work properly.

Children do not need to wear shoes until they are walking. They then need them only when it is necessary to protect the feet against damage, or to keep them warm. **Going barefoot** as much as possible allows the bones and muscles to develop in the natural way to produce strong, healthy feet.

Shoes Well-fitting shoes help to prevent:
◆ **tired** and **painful** feet,
◆ **backache** caused by poor posture due to painful feet,
◆ **corns** and the other foot problems shown in **Fig 4** on the opposite page.

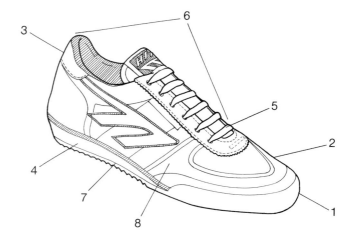

Figure 3 Well-fitting shoes
1. Long enough to allow the toes to move freely.
2. Wide enough for the toes to lie flat, and with no pressure on the bunion joint – the joint at the base of the big toe.
3. A firm-fitting heel – the heel of the shoe should not slip off when the foot bends.
4. A low heel so that the foot does not slide forwards.
5. An adjustable fastening.
6. Support and protection to the feet.
7. Non-slip soles.
8. Flexible uppers which bend as the foot bends.

High heels When high heels are worn, the weight of the body is almost all on the ball of the foot, which shortens the stride and makes for awkward walking. If worn for long periods, they may cause shortening of the calf muscles which will ache when flat shoes are worn.

Problems caused by ill-fitting footwear

A. Corns A corn is an area of thickened skin which develops in response to persistent friction (rubbing) or pressure. Any pain can be relieved by eliminating the cause – that is, by not wearing ill-fitting shoes.

Figure 4

B. Hammer toe Instead of lying flat, the toe is bent so that the end points downwards. It has become fixed in this 'pushed-up' position due to wearing shoes which are wrongly shaped or too small. If the pain is not relieved by wearing wider shoes, surgery may be necessary.

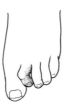

C. Ingrowing toe nail Toe nails become ingrowing when the soft flesh is pushed against a rough edge of the nail. Expert advice is required for this problem, and it may be necessary to remove the nail by surgery. Cutting the nails straight across may help to prevent this condition from developing.

D. Bunion A bunion is a painful swelling near the joint at the base of the big toe caused by long-term pressure on the joint. Wide fitting shoes, cushioning pads and, in extreme cases, surgery, can help the problem.

Chiropodists

Chiropodists are trained in foot care. Two aspects to their work are:
◆ Providing a foot-care service for people who are unable to look after their own feet, for example, some elderly people. Relieving pain and discomfort makes walking easier.
◆ Identifying and advising on common foot problems, a few examples of which are mentioned below and others are shown in **Fig 4**.

Verruca (Plantar wart) This is a wart on the sole of the foot and it can be very painful when pressed inwards during walking. It may clear up without treatment.

Athlete's foot This is the name given to ringworm, a fungus infection which grows on the feet. It develops quickly in the warm, damp conditions encouraged by shoes and socks, especially between the toes, where it makes the skin crack, turn white and peel off. The infected areas sometimes itch, and the cracks can be painful.

Sweaty feet Some people have feet which produce more sweat than is usual and their feet may give off a strong smell. Sweat itself has little smell; it is the action of bacteria which live in the moist conditions within the shoe which give off the strong odours. The smell is difficult to prevent, but the following action can help to reduce the problem:
◆ Wash feet daily and dry thoroughly.
◆ Avoid wearing nylon socks.
◆ Wear sandals when possible.
◆ Apply foot powder.
◆ Wear shoes with uppers made of leather or of fabric that allows air to move through to ventilate the shoe.
◆ Have two pairs of shoes and wear them alternately to allow those not in use to air and to dry out.

QUESTIONS

1a Describe the arrangement of the bones, ligaments and muscles in the foot.
 b Name the two functions of the foot.
 c Draw footprints to show three different states of the arch.
2a What happens to the bones of young children's feet when they wear shoes which are too small?
 b Give two reasons for wearing shoes.
 c What is the advantage of going barefoot?
3a Give three reasons for wearing well-fitting shoes.
 b List eight points of well-fitting shoes.
 c How do high heels affect walking?
4a Describe two aspects of the work of chiropodists.
 b Describe four foot problems caused by ill-fitting footwear.

 c Describe: (i) a verruca, (ii) athlete's foot.
 d (i) What produces the strong odour of sweaty feet? (ii) List six actions that can help to reduce the problem.

FURTHER WORK

1 Most people are born with perfect feet, but many develop some kind of foot problem in adult life. Suggest ways in which the problems can be reduced.
2 Carry out an investigation to find out whether it is usual for both feet to be the same length.
 a Devise a method by which you could measure the length of feet.
 b Using this method, measure the feet of a number of people and record the measurements on a chart.

 c Conclusion – did your investigation show that more than half the people you measured had feet of the same size?
 d Evaluate your investigation. What was the smallest difference you were able to measure between two feet? In your opinion, is it really necessary to measure more accurately than this? – say why? Did you measure enough pairs of feet to obtain a reliable result?
Suggestions for further investigations
(i) Is it desirable for shoe manufacturers to make shoes of different widths?
(ii) Does it matter if customers in shoe shops have their feet measured when in the sitting position or the standing position?

Posture

Figure 1 Good standing posture

1. The backbone is kept in its natural shape when:
   - the head is held up.
   - the shoulders are held back in a relaxed manner.
   - the lower part of the back is hollow.
   - the abdominal muscles are held in firmly and give support to the lumbar region of the backbone.
2. The weight is well balanced on the feet.

Figure 2 Poor standing posture

1. The natural shape of the backbone is changed by:
   - drooping head,
   - rounded shoulders,
   - deep hollow in the back,
   - weak abdominal muscles which give no support to the backbone.
2. Uneven distribution of weight on the feet makes them ache.

Posture is the position in which the body is held when standing, sitting, sleeping, walking or working. It depends on:
- flexibility of the joints,
- training to improve muscle power,
- state of health, weight and physical fitness,
- mood – whether happy, depressed, tired, angry, etc.

Poor posture puts the muscles out of balance. If it becomes a regular habit, those muscles and ligaments which are put under extra strain will tire more easily and begin to ache.

Figure 3 The right way to lift a heavy object:
- Keep the backbone in its natural shape.
- Hold the heaviest part of the object nearest to the body.
- Bend at the hips and knees.
- At the time of lifting, tighten the abdominal muscles. This reduces the strain on the back by 30%.
- Place the feet slightly apart and close to the object.

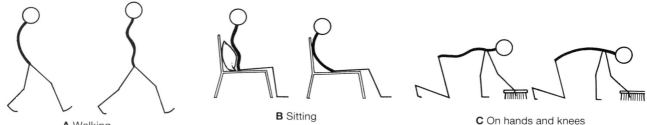

A Walking **B** Sitting **C** On hands and knees

D Pushing a car

E Using a computer

F Washing up

G Picking up an object

Figure 4 Posture. **S**-shaped backbone – good posture. **C**-shaped backbone – poor posture

Back pain (backache)

Back pain is a common problem in adults and, once it starts, often lasts on and off throughout life. It may begin suddenly when lifting or bending, or may develop gradually and get worse over months or years. The most likely cause is poor posture which puts a strain on the back and results in one or more of the following:

◆ over-stretching of the **muscles** of the back,
◆ tearing the **ligaments** which bind the vertebrae firmly together,
◆ a **slipped disc** (p. 7).

Treatment. The back should be rested to give the damaged tissues time to heal. When the pain is severe, pain-relievers will help, but it may be necessary to go to bed and stay in a flat position for a week or two – or longer for a slipped disc. If the pain has not lessened in 24–48 hours, medical advice should be sought.

Prevention of back pain The following should help to prevent back pain:

◆ Learn to keep your backbone in its natural shape as shown in **Fig 1**.
◆ Keep the back straight when lifting heavy objects **Fig 4**. People in jobs which demand much heavy lifting are liable to have back trouble, for example nurses and building workers.
◆ Avoid standing or sitting for hours at a time in the same position.
◆ Avoid sudden movements when the back is bent, for example, leaping out of bed or jumping up from sitting in a low chair.
◆ Ensure that the bed is comfortable and that the mattress is firm and does not have a hollow in it.

Figure 5 Back pain is less likely to occur, or recur, when correct posture is maintained in the many activities of daily living

A Kneel down to make the bed

B Balance the load – use 2 bags or cases

E Support your back well when reading in bed

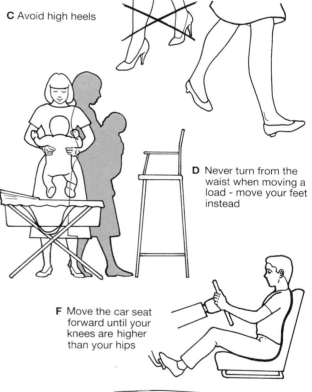

C Avoid high heels

D Never turn from the waist when moving a load – move your feet instead

F Move the car seat forward until your knees are higher than your hips

G When getting into a car - sit then turn with knees together. When getting out of a car - turn with knees together and then stand

QUESTIONS

1a What is meant by posture?
 b List the factors on which posture depends.
2 Draw and label diagrams to show: (i) Good standing posture, (ii) poor standing posture.
3a Name the most likely cause of back pain?
 b Give three ways in which poor posture can strain the back.
 c Describe treatment for back pain.
 d How is it possible to help prevent back pain? Make a list.
 e Draw and label a diagram to show the right way to lift a heavy load.
4 List seven ways of reducing the strain on the back caused by daily living activities.

FURTHER WORK

1 Study the pin-men diagrams in **Fig 4**. Copy them under the appropriate heading – *Good posture* or *Poor posture*.

2 Describe how posture can be affected by: (i) one leg being shorter than the other, (ii) an arthritic hip, (iii) feeling 'good', (iv) feeling depressed, (v) training for athletics.

3 (i) Sit on a variety of chairs, stools, benches, etc. Describe how each affects your posture. Describe the type of chair which you prefer, and give your reasons. (ii) Stand on 'heels' of various sizes and observe the change in spinal posture. (iii) Put increasing weight on an outstretched arm and observe changes in posture.

Cells

The human body is made up of millions and millions of cells which are microscopic, that is, they can only be seen through a microscope. Each cell consists of living matter called **protoplasm** which appears as transparent, granular jelly under the microscope.

Structure

Cells vary greatly in shape and size. Structures common to most types of cell are:
◆ an outer **cell membrane,**
◆ a **nucleus** which is often near the centre of the cell;
◆ **cytoplasm** containing a large number of organelles. An **organelle** is a specialised part of the cytoplasm with its own particular function.

Movement of substances into and out of the cell

The cell membrane is **selectively permeable** (semi-permeable), that is, it allows some substances to pass through it but not others, and this gives the cell some control over which substances can enter and leave.

Substances are continuously passing into and out of living cells. Oxygen and carbon dioxide move by diffusion (a form of passive transport). Other substances are actively transported across the membrane in various ways, eg amino acids.

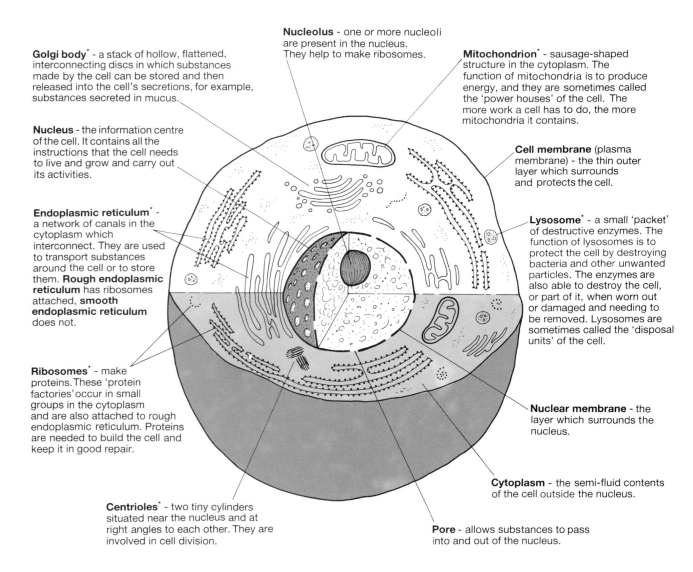

Golgi body[*] - a stack of hollow, flattened, interconnecting discs in which substances made by the cell can be stored and then released into the cell's secretions, for example, substances secreted in mucus.

Nucleus - the information centre of the cell. It contains all the instructions that the cell needs to live and grow and carry out its activities.

Endoplasmic reticulum[*] - a network of canals in the cytoplasm which interconnect. They are used to transport substances around the cell or to store them. **Rough endoplasmic reticulum** has ribosomes attached, **smooth endoplasmic reticulum** does not.

Ribosomes[*] - make proteins. These 'protein factories' occur in small groups in the cytoplasm and are also attached to rough endoplasmic reticulum. Proteins are needed to build the cell and keep it in good repair.

Centrioles[*] - two tiny cylinders situated near the nucleus and at right angles to each other. They are involved in cell division.

Nucleolus - one or more nucleoli are present in the nucleus. They help to make ribosomes.

Mitochondrion[*] - sausage-shaped structure in the cytoplasm. The function of mitochondria is to produce energy, and they are sometimes called the 'power houses' of the cell. The more work a cell has to do, the more mitochondria it contains.

Cell membrane (plasma membrane) - the thin outer layer which surrounds and protects the cell.

Lysosome[*] - a small 'packet' of destructive enzymes. The function of lysosomes is to protect the cell by destroying bacteria and other unwanted particles. The enzymes are also able to destroy the cell, or part of it, when worn out or damaged and needing to be removed. Lysosomes are sometimes called the 'disposal units' of the cell.

Nuclear membrane - the layer which surrounds the nucleus.

Cytoplasm - the semi-fluid contents of the cell outside the nucleus.

Pore - allows substances to pass into and out of the nucleus.

Figure 1 Diagram of a generalised animal cell, greatly magnified and cut open to show the many different parts, each with its own function. *indicates the organelles.

Different types of cell

There are at least twenty different types of cell in the body. They all have a similar basic structure, but their shape and contents vary according to the particular job which each type of cell has to do: **Fig 2**.

Size of cells

Cells, because they are so small, are measured in **micrometres (μm)**. A micrometre is 1 thousandth of a millimetre. (**Micron** is an older name for micrometre.) The diameter of cells varies widely from 7.5μm (red blood cells) to 300μm (egg cells). The length also varies as **Fig 2** shows: some cells are more or less spherical, others are elongated.

Figure 2 Different types of cell

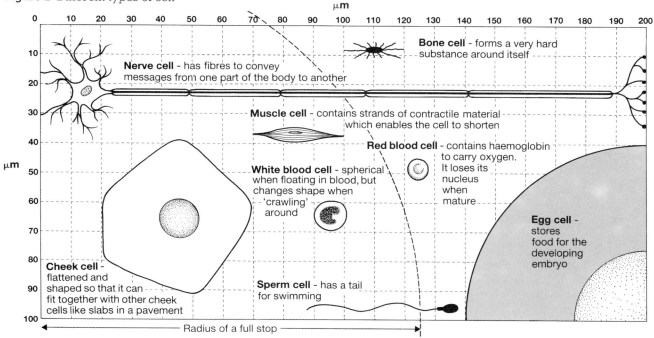

Radius of a full stop

QUESTIONS

1 Draw the diagram in **Fig 3** to show the main parts of the cell. Label the parts 1–12, using **Fig 1** as a guide.

2a Which part of the cell contains large numbers of organelles?

b What is an organelle?

c Name six types of organelle shown in Fig 1.

3 Match each of the parts of the cell in the following list with one of the following descriptions: mitochondria, nucleus, ribosomes, endoplasmic reticulum, lysosome.
   (i) the information centre of the cell
   (ii) produce energy
   (iii) make proteins
   (v) transports materials around the cell
   (v) disposal unit

4a What is the plural of: (i) mitochondrion, (ii) nucleolus?

b What is a micrometre? Give its abbreviation.

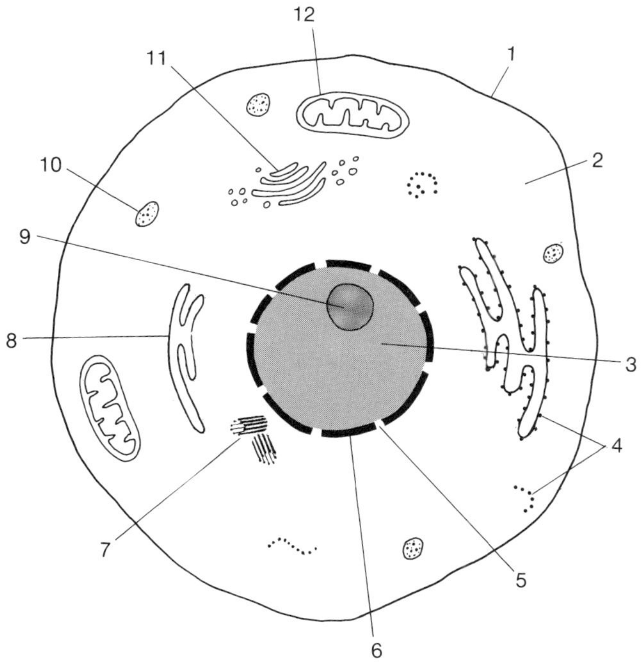

FURTHER WORK

1 For each of the cells shown in **Fig 2**:
(i) draw, label and describe briefly, (ii) find the length and width in μm.

2 **Examining epithelial cells**
(i) Obtain a pig's trachea from a butchers shop.
(ii) Gently scrape the inside of the trachea with a spatula to remove the ciliated epithelium.
(iii) Transfer the scrapings to a drop of water on a clean slide.
(iv) Add a drop of methylene blue to the scrapings. This stains the cells and makes them more visible.
(v) Place a coverslip on top and examine under a microscope. Nuclei should be clearly visible and it may be possible to see the cilia.

Figure 3 Diagram to show the main parts of a cell

Cell division

New cells are formed from existing cells by cell division – a process which takes about two hours to complete and involves the chromosomes.

Chromosomes

Most of the time chromosomes are invisible, even with an electron microscope. They exist in the nucleus as long, fine threads, and their presence is indicated by the granules of chromatin (DNA). Arranged along the chromosomes are the **genes** (p. 126).

A cell which is not in the process of dividing is said to be in the **resting stage: Fig 1**. This is the usual state of a cell – it is resting only from reproductive activity, for it is continuously active in all other respects.

Chromosomes become visible only during cell division, **Fig 2**. They appear as thin threads which gradually shorten and thicken.

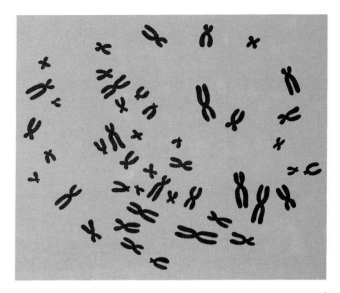

Figure 2 Human chromosomes just before the cell divides.

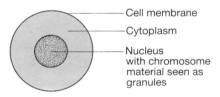

- Cell membrane
- Cytoplasm
- Nucleus with chromosome material seen as granules

Figure 1 Cell in the 'resting stage'

Why chromosomes are present in pairs Each person develops from a single cell – the fertilised egg (**zygote**, p. 140). This contains 46 chromosomes – 23 were already in the unfertilised egg and 23 were added from the sperm, and they match together in 23 homologous pairs: **Fig 3.**

The fertilised egg divides into two cells, and these divide again and again to produce the countless millions of cells which make up the human body. Every time a cell divides its chromosomes also divide, so the number of chromosomes in a cell remains the same, that is, 46 – or 23 pairs: **Fig 3**. In 22 of the 23 pairs, both chromosomes look alike. The 23rd pair are the sex chromosomes and they look alike only in females.

Sex chromosomes There are two sex chromosomes, one is called **X** and the other **Y**. All cells (except gametes) in a female contain two X chromosomes (**XX**). All cells (except gametes) in a male contain one X and one Y chromosome (**XY**).

The sex of an individual is determined at the moment of conception and depends on whether the egg, which has an X chromosome, was fertilised by a sperm containing an X or a Y chromosome: **Fig 4.**

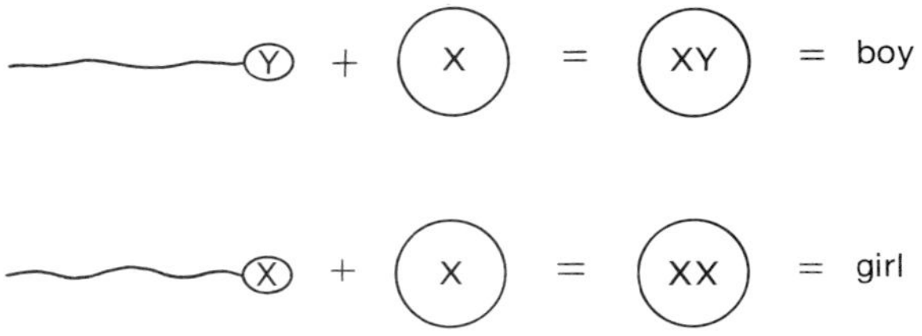

Figure 3 Karyotype of the chromosomes from the cell of a human male. It was made by cutting out the chromosomes from a photomicrograph (eg Fig 2) and arranging them in **homologous** (matching) pairs.

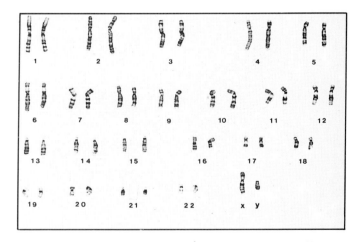

Figure 4 Boy or girl?

Cell division

There are two types of cell division:

1. Mitosis This type of cell division produces new cells for growth and for replacement of worn-out or damaged body cells. Cells produced by mitosis have the same number of chromosomes as the parent cell – 46 (the **diploid** number).

For simplicity, only two of the 46 chromosomes are shown in the diagrams below.

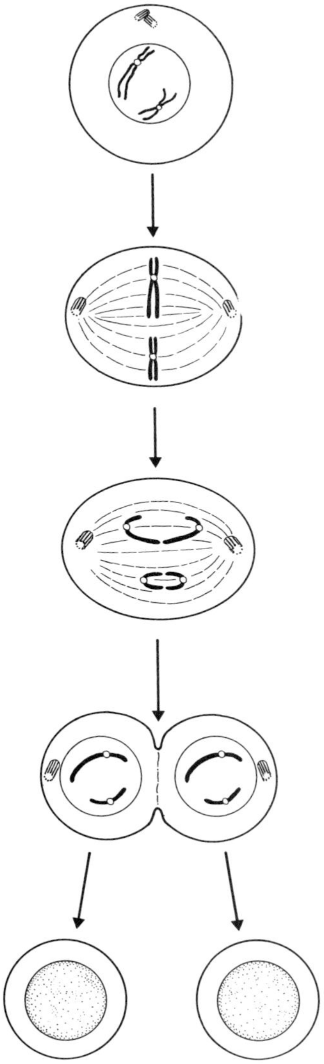

2. Meiosis (reduction division) Meiosis produces cells with half the number of chromosomes that are in the parent cell. This special type of cell division takes place only in the ovaries or testes to produce **gametes** – eggs or sperm containing 23 chromosomes each (the **haploid** number). Because of 'crossing-over', these chromosomes are not identical with those in the parent cell.

For simplicity, the behaviour of only two pairs of chromosomes is followed in the diagrams below. The chromosomes which originated from one parent are shown as thick lines; those from the other parent as thin lines.

1. **Chromosomes become visible:** each is seen to consist of two threads - chromatids - joined at the **centromere**

2. The **nuclear membrane** disappears.
The **chromosomes** shorten and thicken and move to the equator of the cell
The **centrioles** separate and go to opposite poles of the cell
Spindle fibres appear in the cytoplasm

3. The **chromatids** (now called **chromosomes**) separate and move to opposite poles.

4. A **nuclear membrane** forms around each group of chromosomes.
The **chromosomes** lengthen and become invisible.
The cell splits across the middle to form **2 daughter cells.**

5. These new cells will grow and then either divide again or develop into a particular type of cell, eg. neurone, blood cell

Figure 5 Cell division by mitosis

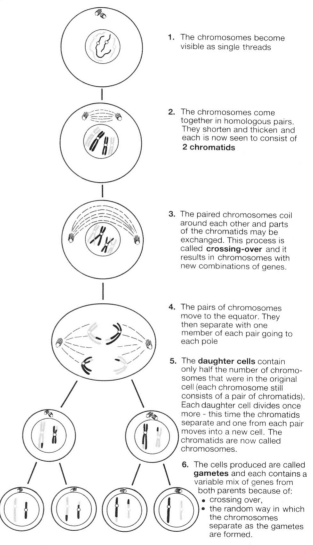

1. The chromosomes become visible as single threads

2. The chromosomes come together in homologous pairs. They shorten and thicken and each is now seen to consist of **2 chromatids**

3. The paired chromosomes coil around each other and parts of the chromatids may be exchanged. This process is called **crossing-over** and it results in chromosomes with new combinations of genes.

4. The pairs of chromosomes move to the equator. They then separate with one member of each pair going to each pole

5. The **daughter cells** contain only half the number of chromosomes that were in the original cell (each chromosome still consists of a pair of chromatids). Each daughter cell divides once more - this time the chromatids separate and one from each pair moves into a new cell. The chromatids are now called chromosomes.

6. The cells produced are called **gametes** and each contains a variable mix of genes from both parents because of:
• crossing over,
• the random way in which the chromosomes separate as the gametes are formed.

Figure 6 Cell division by meiosis

QUESTIONS

1a In what form do chromosomes exist while invisible?
b (i) What is meant by the 'resting stage' of a cell? (ii) Draw a diagram to show this stage.
c When do chromosomes become visible?
2a (i) Count the chromosomes shown in **Fig 2.** (ii) Is this the right number for human body cells?

b How is a karyotype made?
c (i) What are the sex chromosomes called (ii) How do they differ in males and females?
d When is the sex of an individual determined?
3 Describe briefly the differences between the two types of cell division.

FURTHER WORK

1 Girls and boys are born in approximately equal numbers. Explain with the aid of a diagram why this is likely to happen.

2 Draw labelled diagrams to show the process of (i) mitosis, (ii) meiosis.

Tissues

A **tissue** is a group of cells organised for a particular function. There is usually one main type of cell, and a matrix may be present. The **matrix** is usually a jelly-like substance between the cells:

◆ It aids the diffusion of food, gases, hormones, etc throughout the tissue.

◆ It allows other materials to be deposited to give particular qualities, for example, calcium deposited in the matrix between the bone cells gives bone its strength.

◆ It acts as a barrier against germs.

Different types of tissues

Lining or covering tissues Sheets of cells cover the outside of the body and line the tubes and spaces inside the body. Examples follow:

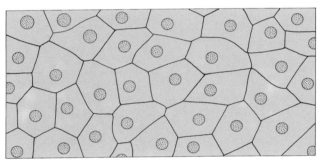

A. Simple epithelium – a single layer of flattened cells forming a smooth lining to the inside of the cheeks.

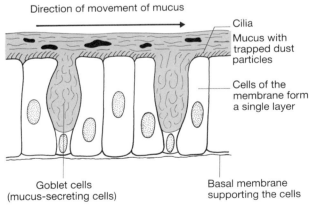

Direction of movement of mucus

Cilia

Mucus with trapped dust particles

Cells of the membrane form a single layer

Goblet cells (mucus-secreting cells)

Basal membrane supporting the cells

B. Mucous membrane (mucosa; columnar epithelium) – a layer of tall cells which lines the air passages and alimentary canal. The tissue is kept moist by **mucus** produced by the **goblet** cells. In some places, **cilia** are present which beat regularly and in the same direction to move the mucus along.

C. Epidermis – a layer several cells deep forming the outer part of the skin (p. 28).

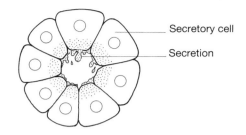

Secretory cell

Secretion

Glandular tissue It lines the spaces of glands and secretes (releases) substances into those spaces.

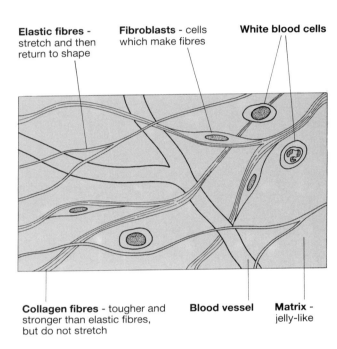

Elastic fibres - stretch and then return to shape

Fibroblasts - cells which make fibres

White blood cells

Collagen fibres - tougher and stronger than elastic fibres, but do not stretch

Blood vessel

Matrix - jelly-like

Connective tissue It holds other tissues and organs together and gives them support. It contains different types of cells and fibres.

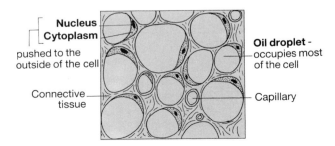

Nucleus
Cytoplasm
pushed to the outside of the cell

Connective tissue

Oil droplet - occupies most of the cell

Capillary

Adipose tissue Fat is stored in it. This tissue forms an insulating layer under the skin which retains heat inside the body. At body temperature (37°C), human fat is an oil.

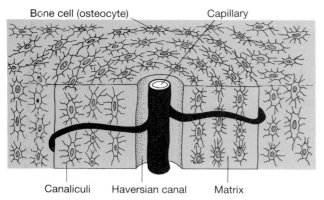

Bone cell (osteocyte) Capillary

Canaliculi Haversian canal Matrix

Bone tissue It strengthens the skeleton. Bone cells (osteocytes) are usually arranged in cylindrical layers around a central channel (**Haversian canal**) containing a blood vessel. **Canaliculi** – tiny channels – connect the cells with each other and with the central channel. Tissue fluid moves through the canaliculi, bringing food and oxygen to the bone cells.

The hard matrix takes up much more space than the bone cells and gives the tissue its strength. It is built from a framework of **collagen** fibres embedded in a cement-like substance containing calcium, mainly in the form of calcium phosphate and calcium carbonate.

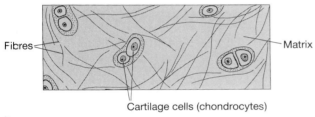

Fibres Matrix

Cartilage cells (chondrocytes)

Cartilage This is a tough but flexible tissue which (like bone) consists of far more matrix than cells. But, unlike bone:
◆ The cells occur singly or in small groups in a blueish-coloured matrix.
◆ The matrix is formed from a dense network of collagen fibres embedded in a firm gel. Sometimes elastic fibres are also present.
◆ There are no blood vessels.
Cartilage is found in those places in the body which require firm support (exercise 3, p. 32).

QUESTIONS

1a What is a tissue?

Type of tissue	Main function	Notes
Simple epithelium	Forms a smooth lining	
Mucous membrane	Secretes mucus	
Glandular tissue	Secretion	
Connective tissue	Connects and supports	
Adipose tissue	Stores fat	
Bone	Strengthens the skeleton	
Cartilage	Gives firm support	
Muscle	Brings about movement	
Nerve tissue	Conducts messages	
Blood	Transport of materials	

b Copy the chart above and complete the third column by adding the appropriate note from the following: Can contract. Lines the spaces of glands. Forms a network throughout the body. A liquid matrix. Lines air passages and alimentary canal. Contains different types of cells and fibres. Hard matrix. Lines the inside of the cheeks. Forms an insulating layer under the skin. Tough but flexible.

2 There are three types of muscle tissue. (i) Name them. (ii) Describe each type of tissue. (iii) How does each contract? (iv) Draw a diagram of each type.

Muscle tissue It consists of bundles of cells or fibres whose function is to contract and relax, and thus bring about movement. It is the most abundant tissue in the body and there are three types:

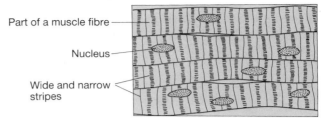

Part of a muscle fibre

Nucleus

Wide and narrow stripes

A. Skeletal muscle (striped muscle) is connected to the skeleton. It consists of bundles of parallel muscle fibres. Each fibre is a long, thin thread up to 40 mm in length made up of cells fused together and with their nuclei at the outside of the fibre. This type of muscle can contract and relax quickly, but tires after a while.

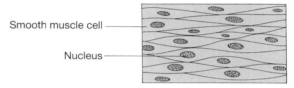

Smooth muscle cell

Nucleus

B. Smooth muscle is found in the walls of blood vessels, alimentary canal, bladder and other hollow organs. It consists of long, pointed cells which interlock. Smooth muscle contracts more slowly than skeletal muscle, but does not become tired.

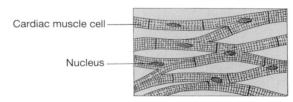

Cardiac muscle cell

Nucleus

C. Cardiac muscle is found only in the heart. It consists of cells which branch and join together to form a network. These cells contract and relax rhythmically throughout life.

Nerve tissue It forms a network throughout the body to conduct and co-ordinate messages. Nerve tissue contains **neurones** which are dealt with on p. 100. The spaces between neurones are filled with cells called **neuroglia** which form a type of connective tissue.

Blood This is a tissue with cells in a liquid matrix called plasma (p. 34).

FURTHER WORK

1 Compare bone tissue with cartilage as regards: (i) arrangement of the cells, (ii) description of the matrix, (iii) presence or absence of blood vessels.

2 Draw and label diagrams to show the differences between different types of tissue.

3 Find information about other types of tissue mentioned in this book, eg epidermis p. 28, lymphoid tissue p. 50.

Skin

The skin has many functions. It covers and protects the body, is a barrier against the entry of germs and, being almost waterproof, it prevents unregulated water loss. It is also sensitive to touch and pain, regulates body temperature and makes vitamin D and melanin.

Structure

There are two main layers – epidermis and dermis.

Epidermis The epidermis (epi = outer; dermis = skin) is the tough, outer layer of the skin which protects the more delicate tissues underneath. It is thickest on those parts which have the hardest wear – the palms and soles – and thinnest on the lips.

Continuous growth takes place in the innermost part of the epidermis – the **basal layer** (germinative layer) – to replace the dried, dead cells that are constantly being shed from the outer surface of the skin. The cells produced move outwards and are gradually filled with a tough substance called **keratin**. They die and, for a time, become part of the protective keratin layer before flaking off or being rubbed away. In this way, the epidermis is replaced every few weeks.

The basal layer contains **melanocytes** – cells which produce brown pigment **melanin**. Pigment granules pass from these cells to nearby epidermal cells, giving colour to skin and hair.

Dermis The dermis is the soft, inner layer of the skin. It is thicker than the epidermis and contains blood vessels, nerves, glands, hair roots and connective tissue.

Connective tissue occupies the spaces between the various structures in the dermis. It contains **collagen fibres** which prevent the skin from being over-stretched, and **elastic fibres** which pull the skin back into shape after it has been stretched. If the skin is over-stretched, for example by pregnancy, scars called **stretch marks** form. The elastic fibres gradually disappear as a person ages and, as a result, the skin becomes looser and more wrinkled.

The **sebaceous glands** produce a greasy liquid called **sebum** which spreads over the surface of the skin and keeps it supple. Too much sebum makes the skin greasy; too little makes it dry and rough.

The **sweat glands** produce a dilute salt solution called **sweat** (see p. 122).

Skin colour

The colour of the skin depends on a number of factors including the following:
- **The thickness of the epidermis.** A thin epidermis allows the colour of the blood in the capillaries close to the surface to show through, for example, lips look red.
- **Amount of blood.** When the capillaries in the skin are open, a large amount of bright red blood flows near the surface (due to oxyhaemoglobin). The skin has a blueish tinge when the circulation is sluggish (due to haemoglobin).
- **Melanin** – a dark-brown pigment. All races have about the same number of melanin-producing cells in the skin. The cells are much more active in people with naturally dark skins and in sunbathers. **Albinos** are unable to produce melanin; they have white hair, pink eyes, and also pink skin, because the thin, white epidermis does not modify the colour of the blood underneath.
- **Carotene** – the yellowish pigment in the skin of some Asians.

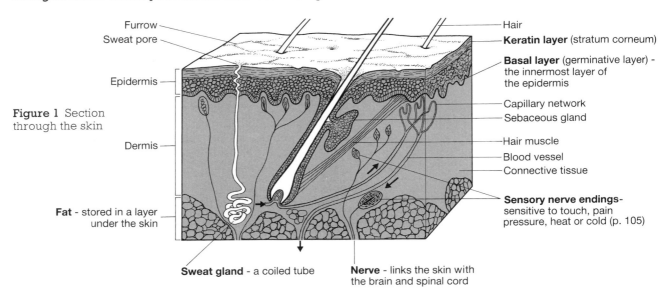

Figure 1 Section through the skin

Furrow
Sweat pore
Epidermis
Dermis
Fat - stored in a layer under the skin
Sweat gland - a coiled tube

Hair
Keratin layer (stratum corneum)
Basal layer (germinative layer) - the innermost layer of the epidermis
Capillary network
Sebaceous gland
Hair muscle
Blood vessel
Connective tissue
Sensory nerve endings - sensitive to touch, pain pressure, heat or cold (p. 105)

Nerve - links the skin with the brain and spinal cord

Effects of sun on the skin

Tanning. Pale skins produce melanin in response to ultraviolet rays in sunlight, turn brown, and are then protected against sunburn.

Freckles. These brown pigment spots become more obvious when the sun activates the melanin-producing cells.

Vitamin D. This vitamin is made in the skin when it is exposed to sunshine.

Ageing. Long-term exposure of skin to the sun accelerates the ageing process and wrinkling. It also increases the likelihood of skin cancer, which is more common in sunny climates, for example, Australia.

First Aid

Burns and scalds For a **small burn** (or scald), put the affected part under cold running water as soon as possible and keep it there for several minutes to remove the heat and reduce pain and tissue damage. Cover, if necessary, with a dry dressing, but not sticking plaster. For a **severe burn**, rush the patient to hospital without waiting to call a doctor.

Never put ointment, cream, oil or butter on a burn – they delay healing.

Sunburn The sun's rays can easily damage pale skin, so sunbathing should be a gradual process in order to give time for melanin to develop. The sun's rays are stronger at the seaside and in the snow because the reflected sun's rays increase the amount of ultraviolet light.

Prevention. Special sun-screening creams or oils rubbed into the skin before and during sun-bathing help to protect against sunburn.

Treatment. Severe sunburn is a dangerous condition and needs medical attention. In milder cases, cold water, calamine lotion or special creams sold for the purpose may help to soothe.

Acne

This common skin complaint develops at puberty in about 80% of teenagers. Acne is associated with the sebaceous glands. These glands produce the grease and are most numerous on the face, shoulders, back and chest. They become very active at puberty and the openings may become blocked and form blackheads – the first sign of acne. A **blackhead** is a plug of greasy material which blocks the pore and turns black at the skin surface where it is in contact with the air.

If the blockage persists, greasy material builds up under the skin and becomes infected with bacteria, and small abscesses form (pimples with pus). When the infection spreads, the surrounding skin becomes inflamed. Squeezing the spots can scar the skin.

Treatment. There is no reliable treatment that works in all cases, and acne normally disappears after a few years. In the meantime the following may be helpful:

◆ The skin should be kept scrupulously **clean** and make-up avoided.
◆ Sunlight is beneficial.
◆ Lotions and creams sold for the purpose could be tried.
◆ If simple remedies fail, small doses of an **antibiotic** such as tetracycline are sometimes given in a course lasting several weeks or months. They are often very effective but, as with all potent drugs, should be taken only with medical supervision.

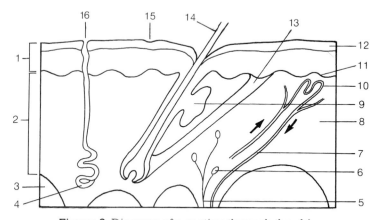

Figure 2 Diagram of a section through the skin

QUESTIONS

1 Draw a simple diagram of the skin, **Fig 2**, and label 1–16.

2 List **the functions of the skin** by adding one of these words to complete each sentence below correctly: sensitive regulates, barrier, protects, waterproof, vitamin D, melanin.
   1. It _____ the body.
   2. It forms a _____ against the entry of germs.
   3. It prevents unregulated water loss from the body because it is fairly _____.
   4. It _____ body temperature.
   5. It produces _____ to protect against sunburn.
   6. It is _____ to touch and pain.
   7. It makes _____ when exposed to sunlight.

3a What is the difference between the epidermis and the dermis?

b (i) Which part of the skin grows continuously and why (ii) What happens to the cells which are produced?

c (i) Where is connective tissue found? (ii) Describe the part played by the fibres.

4a Name four factors which affect skin colour.

b (i) Where is melanin produced? (ii) When are the melanin-producing cells more active?

c What is meant by 'albino'?

d Describe four effects of sun on the skin.

e What is the recommended treatment for: (i) a small burn, (ii) a severe burn, (iii) sunburn?

f What is a blackhead?

FURTHER WORK

1 Carry out the experiments on the skin described on p. 215.

2 Explain how the skin protects the body against each of the following: (i) water loss, (ii) entry of bacteria, (iii) ultra-violet light, (iv) rickets.

Hair and nails

Hair

Hairs are found on nearly every part of the skin and show considerable variation. The hairs on the head can be very long, curly or straight, and of various colours. The eyelashes, beard and pubic hairs are very thick. On many parts of the body the hairs are very small and fine – giving an appearance of hairlessness.

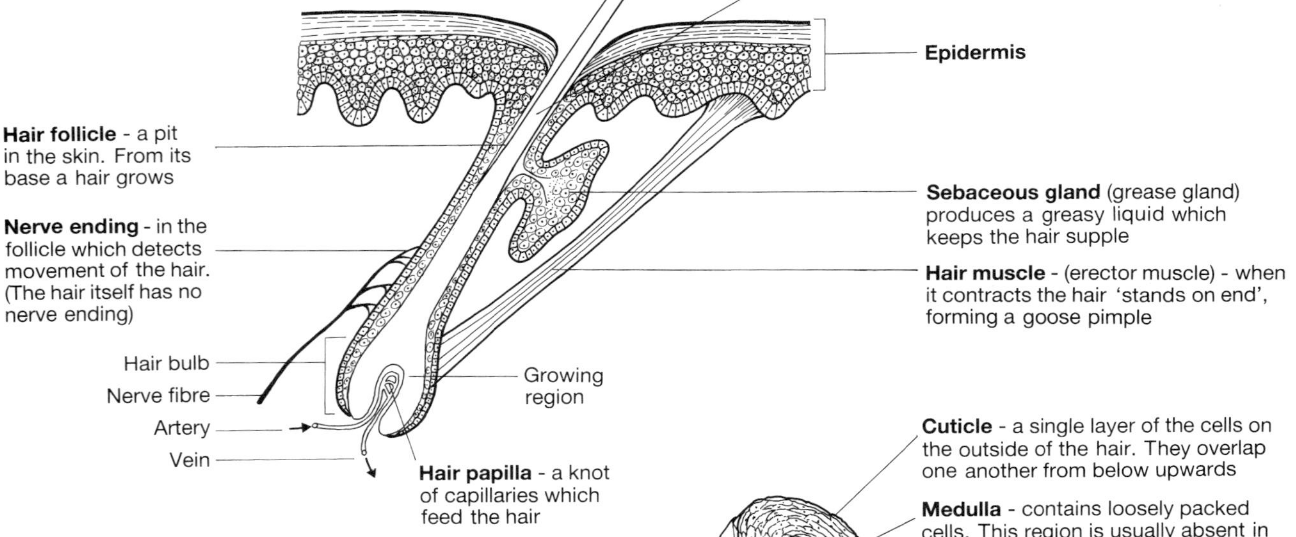

Shaft - part above the surface

Root - part below the surface

Hair

Epidermis

Hair follicle - a pit in the skin. From its base a hair grows

Nerve ending - in the follicle which detects movement of the hair. (The hair itself has no nerve ending)

Sebaceous gland (grease gland) produces a greasy liquid which keeps the hair supple

Hair muscle - (erector muscle) - when it contracts the hair 'stands on end', forming a goose pimple

Hair bulb
Nerve fibre
Artery
Vein

Growing region

Hair papilla - a knot of capillaries which feed the hair

Figure 1 Diagram of a hair in the skin

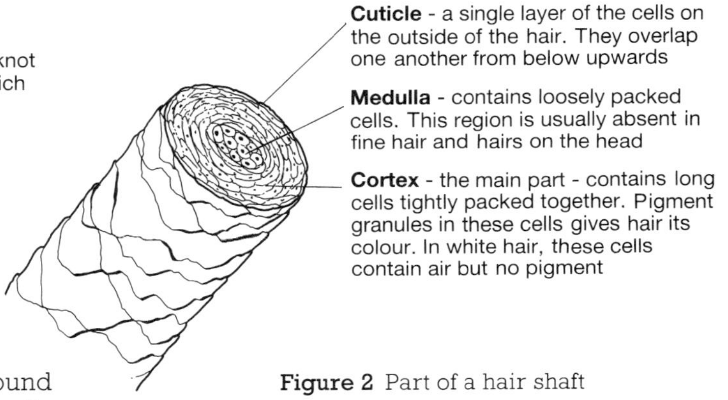

Cuticle - a single layer of the cells on the outside of the hair. They overlap one another from below upwards

Medulla - contains loosely packed cells. This region is usually absent in fine hair and hairs on the head

Cortex - the main part - contains long cells tightly packed together. Pigment granules in these cells gives hair its colour. In white hair, these cells contain air but no pigment

Figure 2 Part of a hair shaft

Hair growth

A hair grows from its root. A layer of cells around the hair papilla constantly produces new cells which become added to the base of the hair, making it grow. Pigment-producing cells add colour (melanin) to the new cells – brown or red. As the cells move away from the growing region they become filled with keratin and die.

Growth cycle Each hair follicle has its own growth cycle:
- ◆ **Active phase** during which the hair grows at a rate of about 1 cm per month and faster in hot weather. The length of this phase determines the length of the hair. It varies between 2 and 6 years for scalp hair.
- ◆ **Resting phase** when growth ceases but the hair remains in place for a while.
- ◆ **The hair falls out** at the end of the resting phase.
- ◆ **A new hair starts to grow** from the same follicle.

Hair growth is not synchronised, so the hairs do not all fall out at the same time (as happens with some animals when moulting).

Baldness (alopecia) The common type of baldness affects many men, often quite early in life. Normal hair recedes from the temples and crown and is replaced with very short, fine, pale hairs. The same type of baldness may affect women, but it starts later and causes thinning of the hair rather than complete baldness.

Dandruff Scales of dead skin which are continuously shed from the scalp (the skin on the head) collect as dandruff. This condition is more noticeable in people with greasy skins than dry skins. It is harmless but it may be considered unsightly.
Treatment Dandruff can be kept under control by washing hair frequently using a medicated shampoo.

Nails

Nails are outgrowths of the epidermis. They strengthen and protect the fingertips and enable the hands to pick up small objects more easily.

Nail growth

Special epidermal cells in the root of the nail divide and grow and become filled with a hard type of keratin. The nail is continuously being pushed forward as more cells are formed. Growth is quicker in summer than in winter but, on average, finger nails grow about 1 mm a week, and three times as fast as toe nails. Of the finger nails, the middle one grows the fastest, and that on the little finger the slowest.

Figure 3 Structure of a nail

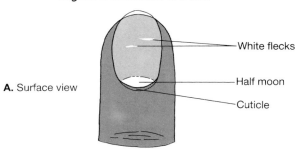

A. Surface view

White flecks
Half moon
Cuticle

White flecks - sometimes occur. They are due to the development of minute air bubbles in the substance of the nail

Half moon - region containing root cells. It is usually visible on the thumb nail and becomes progressively smaller to the little finger

Cuticle - a thin fold of skin which tends to cover the half moon

Root - where the nail grows in length. It lies under the half moon

Nail bed - the part beneath the rest of the nail to which it is attached. It provides a surface over which the growing nail glides

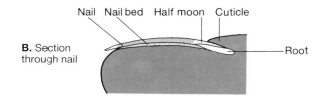

Nail Nail bed Half moon Cuticle

B. Section through nail

Root

Nail damage

Ridging. Any severe illness may slow the rate of growth and cause a ridge to form across the nail. This is pushed forward as health is restored and nail growth returns to normal.

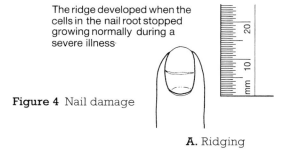

The ridge developed when the cells in the nail root stopped growing normally during a severe illness·

Figure 4 Nail damage

A. Ridging

Spooning of the nail. Severe anaemia causes the nail to develop a concave shape.

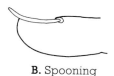

B. Spooning

Ringworm. The fungus which causes 'athlete's foot' may also infect the toe nails, making them thicken, discolour and crumble. It is not a harmful condition but is difficult to treat – requiring tablets to be taken for several months.

Splitting of the nails is not related to any known disease, and filing the nails short helps to prevent it. It is more common amongst those whose hands are frequently in contact with detergents or who use harsh nail varnish remover.

Hangnail – a piece of skin which has broken away from the side of the nail. This should be cut off, not torn off, to prevent the skin in this region from being opened and infected. Infection between the nail and its bed is very painful and may require a minor operation to release the pus and, perhaps, remove part of the nail. The nail then regrows normally.

Damage to the root of the nail. When the root is severely damaged, the nail comes away within a week or two. It takes several months for the new nail to grow. The new nail may be permanently misshapen as a result of the damage.

QUESTIONS

1a Draw a diagram of a hair, labelling: hair follicle, hair muscle, hair papilla, hair bulb, shaft, root, growing region, nerve ending, sebaceous gland.
 b Draw a diagram of a section through the shaft of a hair, labelling the three regions.
 c What gives hair its colour?
2a Describe how a hair grows.
 b List the stages in the growth cycle.
 c Why do all hairs not fall out at the same time?

 d Describe the common type of baldness.
 e (i) What is dandruff? (ii) How can it be treated?
3a Draw and label diagrams to show the structure of a nail.
 b Describe how a nail grows.
 c The person whose finger is shown in **Fig 4A** has recovered from a serious illness. About how long ago was she seriously ill?
4 Describe six types of nail damage.

FURTHER WORK

1 Look at a hair through a microscope. Compare it with hairs of other colour and from different parts of the body.

2 Assuming that the hair on your head grows at a rate of 1 cm per month. (i) How long has it taken the hair follicle to produce your longest hair? (ii) Estimate the length of the active phase of the hair follicles of someone whose hair reaches down to their waist.

Section 1 EXERCISES

1 For (a) and (b), match each of the terms in bold type with the correct statement in the list below.

(a) **abdomen**   **ligament**
    cartilage   **sinus**
    collagen   **spasm**
    diaphragm   **tendon**
    flexor   **thorax**

lower region of the trunk
separates abdomen and thorax
upper region of trunk
hollow cavity inside a bone
a protein
links bones at a joint
attaches muscle to bone
muscle which bends a joint
prolonged muscle contraction
a tough, flexible tissue   [10]

(b) **lumbago**   **nucleus**
    melanin   **organ**
    micrometre   **organelle**
    mitochondria   **ribosomes**
    mitosis   **tissue**

pain in the lower back
a specialised part of the cytoplasm
one thousandth part of a millimetre
a type of cell division
a group of cells with a particular function
dark brown pigment
part of the body with a specialised function
information centre of the cell
make proteins
produce energy   [10]

2 Draw a diagram and label it to show the following places where cartilage is found in an adult's body:
    the ends of the bones of a freely movable joint
    intervertebral discs
    the cartilage linking ribs to sternum (costal cartilage)
    cartilage in the walls of the larynx
    the C-shaped cartilages of the trachea
    the epiglottis
    the lobe of the ear
    the end of the nose   [20]

3 Devise and carry out an experiment to find out if it is possible to tie a knot in a bone as shown here.

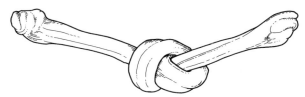

4 Copy the outline of the human body shown below. Then draw in the following organs to show their position and shape:
    brain
    thyroid gland
    diaphragm
    heart
    left lung
    right kidney
    stomach
    left ovary
    bladder
    appendix

Label the organs.   [20]

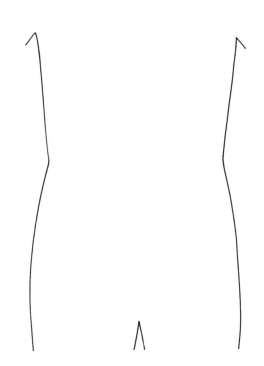

5 Study this histogram showing the rate of blood flow to various organs.

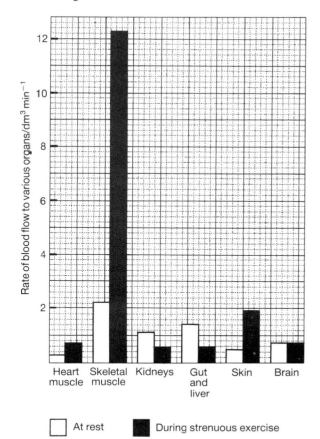

Rate of blood flow to various organs/dm³ min⁻¹

Heart muscle | Skeletal muscle | Kidneys | Gut and liver | Skin | Brain

☐ At rest   ■ During strenuous exercise

(a) Copy the table below and complete it to show the rate of blood flow per minute to each of the organs when the body is at rest and when the body is undergoing strenuous exercise.

Rate of blood flow/litres per minute (dm^3min^{-1})		
	at rest	**during strenuous exercise**
Skeletal muscle		
Heart muscle		
Kidneys		
Gut and liver		
Skin		
Brain		

[3]

(b) What is the total volume of blood per minute being pumped by the heart to all these organs when the body is:
  at rest? [1]
  undergoing strenuous exercise? [1]
(c) If the pulse rate when the body is at rest is 70 per minute, what volume of blood is pumped out by the heart to all these organs at each heart beat? [1]
(d) If the pulse rate during strenuous exercise is 160 per minute, what volume of blood is pumped out by the heart to all these organs at each heart beat? [1]

(MEG: GCSE Human Biology Specimen)

Blood

The amount of blood in the body depends on its size. For example, an average adult weighing 70 kg will have 5–6 litres, whereas a child weighing 12 kg will have about 1 litre.

Blood has a number of functions, one of which is to help keep all parts of the body at the right temperature by carrying heat from the warmer, central regions to the colder, outer regions – hands, feet and tip of nose.

Structure

Blood is a thick red liquid composed of four parts – plasma, red cells, white cells and platelets. When blood comes into contact with air or with damaged tissue within the body, it becomes sticky and clots.

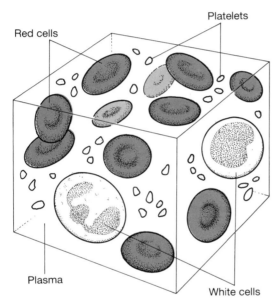

Figure 1 Components of blood

If blood which has been removed from the body is allowed to stand, with a chemical added to prevent clotting, it will separate into layers as shown in **Fig 2**. The red cells sink to the bottom. The white cells and platelets, looking rather like a layer of dust, settle on top of the red cells. The plasma forms a clear layer at the top.

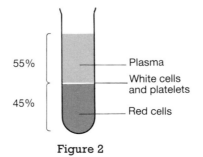

Figure 2

Plasma

Plasma is the liquid part of the blood. It is a clear, pale yellow fluid consisting of 90% water. The remaining 10% consists of a large number of substances including:

◆ **food** – glucose, amino acids, lipids – being carried from intestines to tissues,
◆ **carbon dioxide** (CO_2) – being carried from tissues to lungs,
◆ **waste products** – being carried from tissues to kidneys,
◆ **hormones** – being carried from glands to tissues or other glands,
◆ **minerals** – in the form of ions, eg sodium, calcium, hydrogen carbonate,
◆ **plasma proteins** –
  albumin helps maintain osmotic pressure,
  fibrinogen for clotting,
  globulins – some of the globulins are **antibodies**. The function of antibodies is to destroy germs.

Serum is the liquid which is left over after blood has clotted. As fibrinogen is used up in clotting, serum differs from plasma in having no fibrinogen.

Red cells

Red blood cells are also called **red corpuscles** or **erythrocytes** and their chief function is to carry oxygen (O_2) from the lungs to the tissues.

Red cells are all alike and they do not have a nucleus (the nucleus disappears as the red cells develop). They are made inside bones – in the bone marrow. Each is a disc which is thicker round the edge than in the middle, and is a pale red colour with the centre appearing lighter because it is thinner. These discs are able to fold and bend as they are squeezed through the smallest blood vessels.

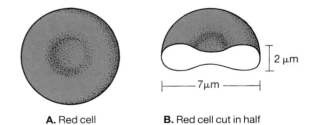

A. Red cell   **B.** Red cell cut in half

Figure 3 (The average diameter of a red cell is 7 μm.)

The life span of a red cell is about 100–120 days, after which it is destroyed in the liver or spleen. This means that about 1%, or 250 000 million red cells have to be replaced each day if the number is to remain constant.

The strong red colour of blood is due to the vast numbers of red cells. There are about 5 million red cells in 1 mm³ (cubic millimetre) of blood. Red cells contain **haemoglobin** and it is this substance which

gives them their red colour and enables them to carry oxygen. It also carries CO_2.
- ◆ **Haemoglobin** is a dark red colour (it appears blue through the skin). Haemoglobin is sometimes referred to as 'reduced haemoglobin'.
- ◆ **Oxyhaemoglobin** – haemoglobin linked with oxygen – is a bright red colour.

White cells

White blood cells are also called **white corpuscles** or **leucocytes** and their function is to protect the body against infection.

White cells are colourless and they have a nucleus. They are larger than red cells but there are fewer of them, with 1 mm³ of blood containing between 5000 and 7000. As can be seen from **Fig 1** and **Fig 4**, there are different types of white cell which vary in size, shape of nucleus, and whether or not they contain large granules in the cytoplasm. Many white cells are made in the bone marrow, others are made in the lymph nodes. They live from a few hours to ten years or more, depending on the type.

Many white cells are able to change their shape and to move by crawling. They are more or less spherical when being carried along in the blood stream, but they flatten and continuously change shape when crawling. They are able to crawl along the inside walls of blood vessels. Some can also leave the blood by squeezing between cells of the thin walls of tiny blood vessels, and then move around between the cells of the tissues.

Some white cells are able to engulf ('eat') germs and other small particles of unwanted matter. They surround and enclose germs as shown in **Fig 5**, and then destroy them. White cells able to do this are called **phagocytes**. Other white cells – **lymphocytes** – make antibodies to destroy germs or the poisons made by germs.

Platelets

Platelets, also called **thrombocytes**, are much smaller than red cells and, as can be seen from **Fig 1**, their shape is variable. They are made in the bone marrow and have a life span of 8–14 days. 1 mm³ of blood contains about a quarter of a million platelets and their function is to help the blood to clot. Clotting prevents loss of blood from wounds (p. 36).

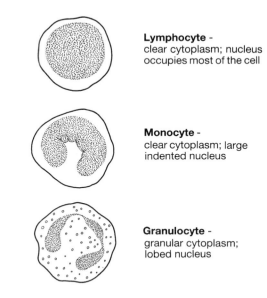

Lymphocyte -
clear cytoplasm; nucleus occupies most of the cell

Monocyte -
clear cytoplasm; large indented nucleus

Granulocyte -
granular cytoplasm; lobed nucleus

Figure 4 Different types of white cell

Bacteria

Figure 5 A white cell engulfing a group of bacteria

QUESTIONS

1a How much blood does the body contain: (i) in an adult, (ii) in a child?
  b Blood is composed of four parts. Name them.
  c Name the substance which gives blood its red colour.
2a Describe plasma.
  b Name five types of substance dissolved in plasma.
  c (i) What is serum? (ii) How does it differ from plasma?

Differences between red and white cells

	Red cells	White cells
Other names		
Nucleus present?		
Haemoglobin present?		
Where made		
Number per mm³ of blood		
Life span		
Function		

3a Copy and complete the table below.
  b Draw diagrams to show the structure of (i) red cells (ii) white cells.
4a (i) What are phagocytes? (ii) Illustrate your answer with a diagram.
  b (i) Describe platelets. (ii) Draw some platelets of varying shape.
5 Copy and complete these notes:
  Functions of blood
    A. Transport Blood carries:
    1. food from i_____ to t_____.
    2. oxygen from l_____ to t_____.
    3. carbon dioxide from t_____ to l_____.
    4. waste products from t_____ to k_____.
    5. hormones from g_____ to t_____ or other g_____.
    6. heat from w_____ to c_____ regions.
    B. Protection
    7. Germs are destroyed by w_____ cells and by a_____.
    8. Clotting prevents loss of b_____.

FURTHER WORK

1 Which of the eight functions listed in Question 5 are carried out by: (i) plasma, (ii) red cells, (iii) white cells, (iv) platelets?

2 Describe **Fig 2**. Demonstrate either by leaving a sample of blood to separate or by using a centrifuge.

More about blood

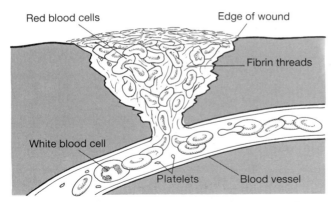

Figure 1 Formation of a blood clot. The blood vessel and blood cells are much smaller than shown here.

Clotting

Clotting takes place when blood vessels are damaged. The fibrinogen in blood plasma forms threads of fibrin. These are sticky and stick to each other and the damaged tissue and, at the same time, trap platelets and blood cells.

In wounds, this tangled mass of threads and platelets and blood cells forms a plug which covers the wound and stops the bleeding. At first the clot is soft and jelly-like. Gradually it shrinks and hardens into a scab. When the tissue underneath has been repaired, the scab drops off leaving a scar.

When a blood clot forms in a blood vessel it is called a thrombus (p. 48).

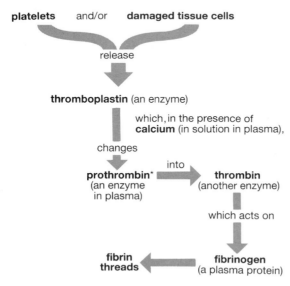

NOTES *Prothrombin** is made in the liver and requires **vitamin K** for its formation

Several other factors including **Factor VIII** are also involved in the clotting process

Figure 2 The series of chemical changes which take place to convert fibrinogen to fibrin

Blood defects

Anaemia Anaemia is due to lack of haemoglobin, the red pigment in the blood which carries oxygen. The blood cannot supply the tissues with enough oxygen, so an anaemic person often feels tired, weak and breathless. There are various causes of anaemia including:

A. Iron-deficiency anaemia. There is not enough iron to make the required amount of haemoglobin. This is the usual reason for anaemia and it can result from any of the following:

◆ **Insufficient intake of iron:**
    on a low-iron diet without meat, eggs, vegetables.
    in babies who are fed entirely on milk for longer than a few months.

◆ **Increased need** during:
    rapid growth at puberty.
    pregnancy, because of the baby's need to make blood.

◆ **Excess loss** caused, for example, by:
    heavy periods.
    piles.
    peptic ulcers.

Treatment. Iron taken in the form of tablets or liquid will quickly enable the bone marrow to increase its output of red blood cells. The reason for iron deficiency must also be identified and the cause treated.

B. Pernicious anaemia. A shortage of vitamin B_{12} prevents the bone marrow from making enough red cells. This type of anaemia develops when the stomach fails to make a substance called **intrinsic factor** which enables vitamin B_{12} to be absorbed from the small intestine.
Treatment. Injection of B_{12} every 1–2 months.

C. Hereditary anaemia. Genes inherited from the parents cause an abnormal type of haemoglobin to be made, for example:

◆ **Sickle-cell anaemia.** This inherited disease has been given its name because the red cells change to a sickle shape when there is a shortage of oxygen. These red cells contain an abnormal type of haemoglobin – haemoglobin S – and do not last as long as normal red cells.

◆ **Thalassaemia.** This type of inherited anaemia is found mainly in countries bordering the eastern Mediterranean, in the Middle East, India and Asia, or in people who have originated from these areas.

D. Anaemia due to malaria. The malaria parasite destroys red cells.

Leukaemia This disease occurs when abnormal white cells are produced in enormous numbers. It is a form of cancer. Some leukaemias respond well to treatment by drugs, radiation or marrow transplant.

Blood tests

Blood can be tested for:

1. **Cells and platelets**
   amount of haemoglobin
   number, size and shape of red cells
   number and types of white cells
   number of platelets

2. **Blood group**
   ABO system
   rhesus factor

3. **Chemicals in the plasma**
   hormones
   enzymes; levels are raised after heart attacks
   the amounts of the various clotting factors
   liver function tests
   urea for kidney function

4. **Microbes** – to identify germs
   causing disease

5. **Antibodies**, for example:
   hepatitis
   AIDS

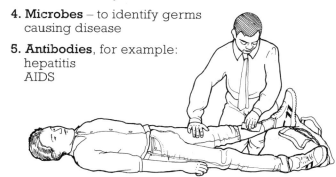

Figure 4 Nose bleed. Sit with the head held slightly forward, and pinch the soft part of the nose. Breathe quietly through the mouth and continue pinching the nose for up to ten minutes if necessary.

Loss of blood (haemorrhage) from wounds

Surface wounds Bleeding from small cuts, grazes and pin-pricks soon stops because:

1. the surrounding blood vessels constrict and cut off the blood supply.
2. a blood clot forms over the wound: **Fig 1**.

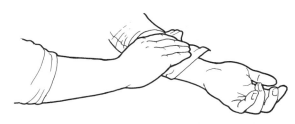

Figure 3A. Light bleeding. Press firmly on the wound with a clean pad until the bleeding stops.

Deep wounds If a large blood vessel is cut, particularly an artery, the pressure of the blood flowing from the wound may be too great to allow a clot to form.

Figure 3B. Loss of blood from wounds: severe bleeding. Lay the casualty down. Raise the injured part. Press firmly on the wound while at the same time holding the sides together. Apply pressure on the appropriate pressure point. Obtain medical help urgently.

Figure 5 The two main pressure points.
A pressure point is a place where an artery comes near the surface and can be pressed against firm tissue underneath. Pressure applied at a pressure point prevents blood from reaching the tissues served by the artery and therefore should not be applied for more than a few minutes.

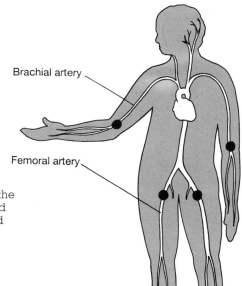

Brachial artery

Femoral artery

QUESTIONS

1a Describe the process of clotting.
 b Draw a diagram to show the formation of a blood clot.

2a What does haemorrhage mean?
 b Give two reasons why bleeding from surface wounds soon stops.
 c Why may a blood clot be unable to form over a deep wound?
 d What is a pressure point?
 e Why should pressure not be applied to a pressure point for more than a few minutes?

 f Describe First Aid for: (i) a surface wound, (ii) a deep wound, (iii) a nose bleed.

3a Describe anaemia.
 b (i) What is meant by iron-deficiency anaemia? (ii) Give three causes with examples of each. (iii) Describe the treatment given for this type of anaemia.
 c Describe three other reasons for anaemia.
 d When does leukaemia occur?

4a Give three reasons for carrying out a blood test.
 b What can blood be tested for?

FURTHER WORK

1 Draw diagrams to illustrate First Aid for loss of blood from wounds.

2 Describe the series of chemical changes which take place to convert fibrinogen to fibrin.

Blood groups and transfusion

Figure 1 The four ABO blood groups

		GROUP A contains	GROUP B contains	GROUP AB contains	GROUP O contains
	On the cells	A	B	A and B	nil
	In the plasma	Anti-B	Anti-A	nil	Anti-A and Anti-B

Key
A   •
Anti-A   ◡
B   —
Anti-B   ⌐

If A mixes with Anti-A, the red cells clump together
If B mixes with Anti-B, the red cells clump together

Every person has an individual blood group which depends on:
◆ one of the four groups in the ABO system,
◆ whether the rhesus factor is present or not,
◆ other blood factors – which are usually of little importance, apart from their use in blood identification.

The blood group is inherited (p. 129) and does not change through life.

ABO system

The four groups in this system – A, B, AB and O – depend on the presence or absence of:

two **proteins** called **A** and **B** found on red cells;
two **antibodies** in plasma – **Anti-A** and **Anti-B**.

Anti-A causes red cells containing **A** to clump together (agglutinate). The same happens when **Anti-B** mixes with **B**. So people with blood type A only have Anti-B, and those in blood type B only have Anti-A. AB people have neither.

To test for blood group

Put a drop of serum containing Anti-A and a drop containing Anti-B separately on a white tile. Add to each, a drop of the blood to be tested. Note whether or not the red cells clump together. (See **Fig 2**.)

Rhesus system

Another substance which occurs in blood is the rhesus factor. People who have this substance are rhesus positive (**Rh pos**). Those who do not are rhesus negative (**Rh neg**).

The rhesus factor and pregnancy The rhesus factor is important during pregnancy if the mother is Rh negative and the father Rh positive. The rhesus factor is inherited, and if the baby is Rh negative like its mother there will be no problem. But if the baby is Rh positive like its father then a dangerous situation can arise:

During labour a small amount of the baby's blood can become mixed with the mother's blood. The mother will then develop antibodies against Rh positive blood, but the baby is unlikely to be affected by them. However, if the mother has another Rh positive baby she will produce large numbers of these harmful antibodies. They will get into the unborn child's blood and destroy its red cells, causing anaemia, jaundice and, possibly, stillbirth.

Prevention During antenatal care, the mother's blood is tested to find out if she is Rh positive or Rh negative. If she is Rh negative, a blood sample is taken from the baby before or during birth (from the umbilical cord) to find out if it is Rh positive or Rh negative. If the baby is Rh positive, the mother will be immunised to prevent harmful antibodies from forming in her blood.

Blood identification

Because of the great variety of factors to be found in the blood, it is possible to identify a person from a blood sample in the same way as with fingerprints. Using this knowledge:
◆ Blood found at the scene of a crime can be used to identify the criminal.
◆ Blood samples can also be used in paternity cases to show with almost complete certainty whether the man is or is not the father.

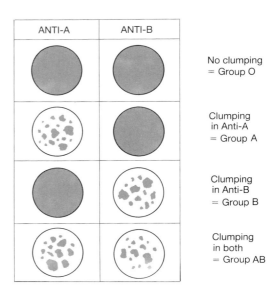

Figure 2 Testing for blood group – Results Chart

Blood transfusion

In a blood transfusion, blood taken from one person is put into another person. The person who gives the blood is called the **donor**. The person who receives the blood is called the **recipient**.

When a great deal of blood is lost suddenly, eg haemorrhage from severe wounds or a stomach ulcer, there is the danger that not enough blood will be left to maintain the circulation. When this happens the blood pressure falls and the patient may lose consciousness. Blood transfusion is then urgent to:

◆ **restore the blood volume** so that the heart can keep the blood circulating through the tissues, particularly the brain and kidneys – to keep the cells alive and functioning.
◆ **provide more red cells** so that enough oxygen can be carried to the tissues.

Points about blood transfusion

◆ Rh negative blood can be given to either Rh positive or Rh negative people.
◆ Rh positive blood should only be given to Rh positive people. If Rh− people receive Rh+ blood they will form anti-rhesus antibodies. They will then react against future transfusions of Rh positive blood and, when pregnant, against a Rh+ baby.

In an emergency:

◆ Blood group O Rh negative can be given to any other group. People with this group are therefore called **universal donors**.
◆ People with blood group AB Rh positive can receive blood of any group. They are called **universal recipients**.

Cross-matching Before a blood transfusion is given, a drop of the patient's blood is tested with the blood to be transfused. The test ensures that the patient receives **compatible** blood, that is, blood which can mix with his own. The transfused blood must be compatible in ABO type, rhesus type and, where necessary, other uncommon factors.

If the wrong blood is given, the patient's blood will make the red cells of the transfused blood stick together in clumps (**agglutinate**). This causes a severe reaction in the patient and may lead to collapse, kidney failure and death.

Other types of transfusion Sometimes, transfusion of whole blood is unnecessary because the patient requires only one particular part of the blood. For example:

◆ **Plasma** transfusion is given in cases of severe burns to replace the liquid and protein parts of the blood which have been lost through the skin.
◆ **Red cells** may be given to patients with severe anaemia but who have normal blood volume.
◆ **Fibrinogen** may be given to stop haemorrhage.
◆ **Factor VIII** is given regularly to haemophiliacs (see p. 131).

Other rare factors A patient who requires 'rare blood' is usually someone who has received many blood transfusions, and who has acquired a number of different antibodies from the transfused blood. Such a person needs blood which lacks those factors to which the patient's antibodies will now react – and a suitable donor may be hard to find.

Blood donors

Many donors give blood regularly twice a year. About 500 cm³ – half a litre – is taken each time. It is immediately mixed with a chemical to prevent it from clotting and to provide food for the living cells. The blood is then stored in a refrigerator, called a **blood bank**, until required. It will keep fresh at 4°C for about a month. Blood is often separated into its different parts for other medical uses (see above).

The loss of half a litre of blood does not weaken a healthy donor. The blood volume can be quickly restored to normal by drinking a glass of water or a cup of tea.

Blood is not accepted for donation from people who have had infectious hepatitis (jaundice), syphilis or AIDS, or who have had their ears pierced within the previous month. There is the risk that germs may still be in the blood and the recipient would then be likely to develop the disease.

QUESTIONS

1a Name the four ABO blood groups.
 b Draw diagrams of the four blood groups showing the red cells and antibodies.
 c (i) Describe the test for blood group. (ii) Draw the Results Chart.

2a What is meant by Rh positive and Rh negative?
 b (i) Describe the dangerous situation that can arise when the mother is Rh negative and the baby Rh positive. (ii) How can this situation be prevented?

3a What is the difference between a blood donor and a recipient?
 b (i) Describe the effect on the patient of suddenly losing a great deal of

blood. (ii) Why is blood transfusion then urgent?
 c Describe other types of transfusion.

4a (i) What is meant by cross-matching? (ii) What would happen if the wrong blood is given?
 b Who are: (i) universal donors, (ii) universal recipients?

5a (i) How often do donors give blood? (ii) How much do they give? (iii) How is blood prevented from clotting? (iv) Where is it stored? (v) For how long does it keep fresh? (vi) What happens to blood if not used within that time?
 b Name three diseases which can be passed on by blood transfusion.

FURTHER WORK

1 When were blood groups first discovered? Why was blood transfusion often unsuccessful before then? Who discovered the rhesus factor and where does it get its name from?

2 Where and when do blood donor sessions take place in your area? Describe the procedure.

Heart

The function of the heart is to pump blood around the body. The size of a person's heart is about the size of the fist, and the heart walls are composed almost entirely of a special type of muscle called **cardiac muscle** (p. 27).

Position

The heart is situated in the thorax between and in front of the lungs. It is centrally placed, but tilted so that most of the heart muscle is to the left of centre, and this causes the heartbeat to be felt on the left side.

The **pericardium** is a thin, tough membrane which surrounds and encloses the heart and holds it in position. The membrane has a slippery surface inside which allows the heart to move easily as it beats.

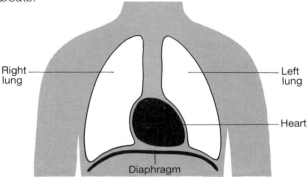

Figure 1 Diagram of the thorax to show the position of the heart

Structure

The heart is composed of four chambers – right atrium, right ventricle, left atrium and left ventricle. The right side of the heart is completely separate from the left side, and blood flowing through one side does not mix with the blood flowing through the other side.

A section through the heart, **Fig 3**, shows that the atria have thin walls and the ventricles have thick walls. The left ventricle has a thicker wall than the right one – it needs more muscle power as it has to pump blood to all parts of the body. The right ventricle pumps blood only to the lungs.

Valves There are four valves in the heart each consisting of two or three small flaps of tissue (**cusps**) which surround an opening. The valves are:

◆ **tricuspid valve** – has three cusps.
◆ **mitral valve** (bicuspid valve) – has two cusps and is shaped like a bishop's mitre (hat) but upside down.

◆ **pulmonary valve** ⎫ have three cusps each. They
◆ **aortic valve** ⎬ are called semi-lunar valves
⎭ because their cusps are
half-moon shaped.

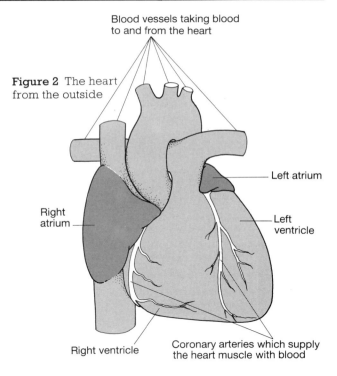

Figure 2 The heart from the outside

Blood vessels taking blood to and from the heart

Left atrium
Left ventricle
Right atrium
Right ventricle
Coronary arteries which supply the heart muscle with blood

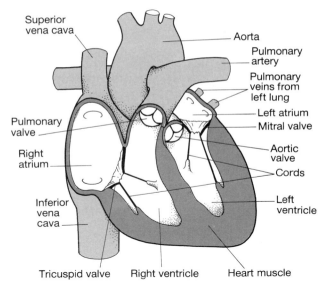

Figure 3 Section through the heart

Superior vena cava
Aorta
Pulmonary artery
Pulmonary veins from left lung
Left atrium
Mitral valve
Pulmonary valve
Right atrium
Aortic valve
Cords
Inferior vena cava
Left ventricle
Tricuspid valve
Right ventricle
Heart muscle

The function of heart valves is to ensure a one-way flow of blood through the heart. When blood flows in the correct direction, the cusps are pressed out of the way to allow the blood to pass. When the blood tries to flow backwards, the backward flow of the blood catches the cusps and pushes them together so that the valve opening is blocked.

Cords (chordae tendineae, heart strings) The tricuspid and mitral valves are connected to the ventricle walls by thin, strong cords. These cords prevent the valves from being turned inside out – like a blown umbrella – during heartbeat. If this happened, the blood would be able to flow backwards.

Heartbeat

Heartbeat is caused by the alternate contraction and relaxation of the muscular walls of the ventricles. There are two phases to each heartbeat – **systole** and **diastole** (pronounced *siss*-toe-ly and die-*ass*-toe-ly).

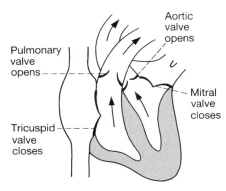

A. Systole — the ventricles contract and blood is pumped into the arteries

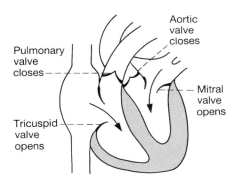

B. Diastole — the ventricles relax and fill up again with blood from the veins

Figure 4 Heartbeat

Heart rate (rate of heartbeat) When resting, the heartbeat of an adult is about 70 times a minute, faster in a child and slower in an athlete. The rate can increase up to 200 times a minute when exercise is being taken in order to supply the muscles with extra oxygen and food (the increase will be less in the fit than the unfit). Heart rate is also increased by excitement, fear, and by some diseases.

Heart sounds As the heart beats it makes rhythmical sounds described as LUB—DUP. LUB is a soft sound made when the tricuspid and mitral valves close. DUP is a shorter, sharper sound made when the pulmonary and aortic valves close. The rhythm of sound goes:

$\xrightarrow{\text{pause}}$ LUB—DUP $\xrightarrow{\text{pause}}$ LUB—DUP $\xrightarrow{\text{pause}}$ LUB—DUP $\xrightarrow{\text{pause}}$ . . .

Heart murmurs are other sounds made by the heart. They are the result of eddy currents within the blood as it flows through the heart, and they indicate that this flow is not smooth, as may be the case when a valve within the heart is damaged.

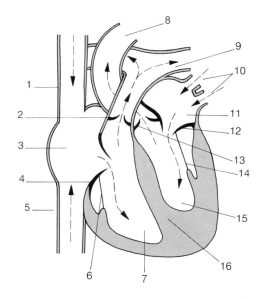

Figure 5 Diagram of a section through the heart. Arrows indicate direction of blood flow

QUESTIONS

1a Describe, with the aid of a diagram, the position of the heart in the body.
  b Why is the heartbeat felt more on the left side?
  c What is the pericardium?
  d Name the four chambers of the heart.
2a Give the function of the valves of the heart.
  b Name the valve between the: **(i)** right atrium and right ventricle, **(ii)** right ventricle and pulmonary artery, **(iii)** left atrium and left ventricle, **(iv)** left ventricle and aorta.
  c **(i)** To which valves are tendons attached? **(ii)** What is their function?
3a Describe the sounds made by the heart.
  b What are heart murmurs?

4a What causes heartbeat?
  b What is the name given to: **(i)** contraction of the ventricles, **(ii)** relaxation of the ventricles?
  c Use the following words to complete the chart below to show the differences between the two phases of heartbeat:
  close; close; contract; flows in; is forced out; open; open; relax.

	Systole	Diastole
Ventricles		
Mitral and tricuspid valves		
Aortic and pulmonary valves		
Blood in the ventricles		

FURTHER WORK

1 Draw the diagram of a section through the heart in **Fig 5**. Label 1–16 using **Fig 3** as a guide. Colour the right side of the heart blue to indicate deoxygenated blood; colour the left side red to indicate oxygenated blood.

2 Listen to the heart sounds through a stethoscope and identify the two sounds. (The cardboard roll from the centre of a kitchen towel roll makes a simple stethoscope.)

More about the heart

'Hole in the heart'

Normally the right and left sides of the heart are completely separate. Occasionally a baby is born with a hole between the right and left atria or between the right and left ventricles. As the pressure in the left side of the heart is normally greater than in the right side, blood will flow through the hole from left side to right side. When the hole is small, little blood can cross, and no surgery is required.

'Blue' babies In a few cases, the pressure in the right side of the heart is higher than the left side, and blood then flows through the hole from right to left. The blood in the right side of the heart is 'blue' because it has not been through the lungs and therefore lacks oxygen. This 'blue' blood goes into the left side of the heart and is pumped round the body, making the baby look 'blue' – especially its tongue, lips and cheeks.

If the 'hole in the heart' is serious, it must be repaired by surgery so that the child will grow and develop normally, although this may be delayed for some years after birth until the child and the heart are larger and stronger.

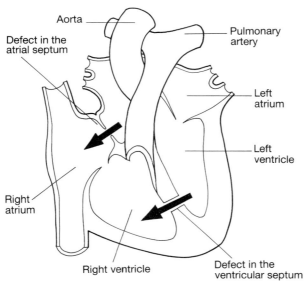

Figure 1 Hole in the heart

Defective valves

Valves in the heart are defective when they are unable to open or to shut completely. The blood cannot then circulate properly and it collects in the lungs – causing breathlessness, or in the legs – making the ankles swell.

A few babies are born with defective valves. In other cases, the valves become damaged by infections such as rheumatic fever. 'Open heart' surgery is performed to replace the damaged valves with artificial heart valves, and the results are usually excellent.

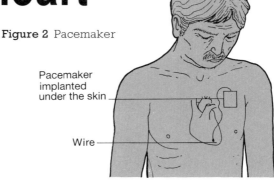

Figure 2 Pacemaker

Pacemaker implanted under the skin

Wire

Pacemaker

The heart has a natural pacemaker in the wall of the right atrium which controls the rate of heartbeat. This small mass of tissue transmits regular electrical impulses which make the heart muscle contract. The rate at which the pacemaker works is partly under the control of the brain, but it is also affected by hormones such as adrenaline, and by some drugs.

If the heart's own pacemaker fails to make it beat satisfactorily, an artificial pacemaker powered by a battery may be fitted. This will send regular electrical impulses to the heart at the rate of about 70 per minute.

ECG (electrocardiogram)

When the heart beats, there is a wave of electrical activity which passes through it from top to bottom. Electrodes placed on the skin can detect electrical activity which can be recorded as a trace on a screen or strip of paper. This trace is called an ECG.

A normal healthy heart produces a particular pattern of electrical activity. The trace differs when the heart is not working normally or if it has been damaged, for example by a heart attack which gives the trace shown in **Fig 3**.

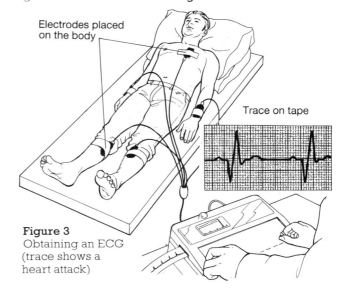

Electrodes placed on the body

Trace on tape

Figure 3
Obtaining an ECG
(trace shows a
heart attack)

Angina and heart attacks

(Coronary Artery Disease – CAD; Coronary Heart Disease – CHD)

When the coronary arteries are narrowed by disease (p. 48), less blood is able to get through to them to supply the heart muscle with oxygen. Shortage of oxygen supply to the heart muscle causes a cramp-like pain to develop in the centre of the chest which often spreads to the shoulder neck and arms. This can be due to either angina or a heart attack.

Prevention The following advice is given to those who wish to reduce the chance of suffering from angina or a heart attack.

◆ Do not smoke.
◆ Have the blood pressure checked regularly.
◆ Keep physically fit with sensible exercise.
◆ Eat food low in fat and cholesterol.
◆ Slim if necessary.

Angina Angina is pain due to cramp in the heart muscle. The pain is brought on gradually by factors which increase the heart's work load, such as exercise, emotion, heavy meals, and cold weather. There is only a temporary shortage of oxygen and the heart muscle is not damaged, and the pain disappears with rest.

Treatment of angina Various kinds of medicines help to reduce the occurrence of heart pain. If medicines are unsuccessful, a **coronary artery bypass** operation may be carried out. A healthy vein from a leg is grafted on to the heart to bypass a part of the coronary artery which is dangerously narrow.

1. One or two thumps to the centre of the chest with a clenched fist may start the heart beating again. If not:

2. Press with the heel of open hand, covering it with the other, on the lower end of the breast bone, **Fig 4.** Rock yourself forwards and backwards to apply and release pressure to the patient's chest 50–60 times a minute.

   If this fails to start the heart beating again,

3. Give **mouth-to-mouth ventilation** (p. 55).

4. Alternate cardiac massage with mouth-to-mouth ventilation by pumping the heart 15 times, then blowing twice into the patient's lung.

   Repeat until the patient shows signs of life or until professional help arrives.

Heart attack When heart pain happens without any obvious cause, it may be due to a blockage in a coronary artery or one of its branches – this is called a **heart attack** (a **'coronary'**). Part of the heart muscle has lost its blood supply, stops working and dies. Other signs of a heart attack may include a cold sweat, nausea, shortness of breath and a feeling of weakness.

Whether a heart attack is mild or severe depends on where the blockage takes place and, consequently, how much of the heart muscle is deprived of oxygen and damaged. Usually, only a small part is affected and the rest of the heart continues to beat normally.

Heart attack – What to do

When a heart attack is suspected, the patient should rest in a reclining half-sitting position to reduce the strain on the heart. A doctor or ambulance should be called immediately.

Cardiac arrest If the heart stops beating – **a cardiac arrest** – as noted by loss of consciousness, stillness, pallor and the absence of wrist or neck pulse, **cardiac massage** should be started (see below).

Figure 4 Cardiac massage (heart massage)

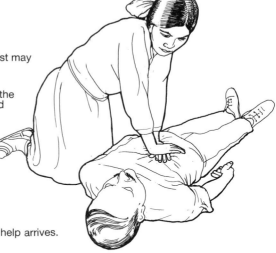

QUESTIONS

1a Whereabouts may there be a 'hole in the heart'?
  b Describe the pattern of blood flow which causes 'blue' babies.
  c What treatment is given for a 'hole in the heart'?

2 (i) Describe defective heart valves.
   (ii) What effect do they have on circulation?
   (iii) When do they occur?
   (iv) How may they be treated?

3a (i) Describe the heart's natural pacemaker.
   (ii) What controls the rate at which it works?
  b When may an artificial pacemaker be fitted?

4a What effect does a shortage of oxygen have on the heart muscle?
  b Describe angina.
  c Describe a heart attack.

d List five pieces of advice for those who wish to reduce the chance of angina or a heart attack.

5a What should be done when a heart attack is suspected?
  b (i) What is meant by cardiac arrest?
   (ii) Give four signs.
  c Describe how to give cardiac massage.

FURTHER WORK

1 Describe an ECG. Whereabouts on the skin are the electrodes placed? What use can be made of the information obtained?

2 Dissect a sheep's heart, or examine the model of a heart. Note: the shape; right and left ventricles; right and left atria; coronary arteries and veins; position of any fat; pulmonary artery; pulmonary veins; aorta; superior vena cava; inferior vena cava.

Cut the sheep's heart open to show: the thicker heart muscle of the left ventricle; the thin walls of the atria; mitral valve and tendons; aortic valve; tricuspid valve and tendons; pulmonary valve.

3 Arrange for a demonstration of First Aid for heart attacks.

Blood vessels

MAIN VEINS   **MAIN ARTERIES**

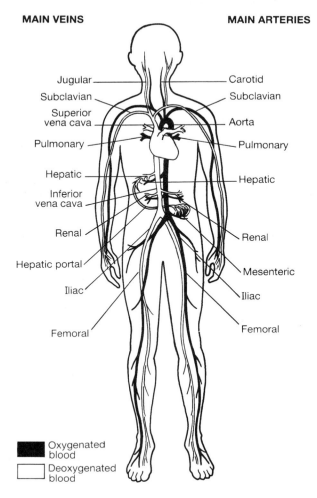

- Jugular
- Subclavian
- Superior vena cava
- Pulmonary
- Hepatic
- Inferior vena cava
- Renal
- Hepatic portal
- Iliac
- Femoral

- Carotid
- Subclavian
- Aorta
- Pulmonary
- Hepatic
- Renal
- Mesenteric
- Iliac
- Femoral

■ Oxygenated blood
□ Deoxygenated blood

Figure 1   Main arteries and veins in the body

Structure of the wall   The walls of all blood vessels have a thin lining of a single layer of cells. Capillary walls consist only of this layer: **Fig 2A**. Arteries and veins have walls with three layers:

- a thin lining of a single layer of cells;
- a middle layer of elastic fibres and muscle;
- a tough outer layer of connective tissue.

Capillaries

These minute blood vessels interconnect to form a network of fine tubes: **Fig 2B**. The network penetrates throughout the tissues so that few cells are more than 2 or 3 cells away from a capillary.

Not all the capillaries are open at the same time – there would not be enough blood to fill them if they were. The capillaries open when the tissue is active, but when the tissue is resting many are closed. For example, the capillaries in the stomach wall are open when food is being digested, but most of them are closed when the stomach is empty. The capillaries are opened and closed by **pre-capillary sphincters** in the arterioles: a **sphincter** is a ring of muscle fibres.

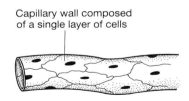

Capillary wall composed of a single layer of cells

A. Structure of a capillary

Blood travels around the body through blood vessels. There are three different types:

- **Arteries** carry blood from the heart.
- **Veins** return blood to the heart.
- **Capillaries** link arteries to veins.

The heart pumps blood into the main **arteries**. These branch into narrower and narrower tubes and carry blood to all parts of the body. The thinnest arteries are called **arterioles** and they link with even smaller blood vessels – the **capillaries**. The blood flows through the capillaries into small veins called **venules**. These link up to form larger and larger **veins** which return the blood to the heart.

Size   Blood vessels vary in size from the largest, the **aorta** with a diameter of about 2.5 cm, to the smallest capillaries with a diameter of about 8 μm.

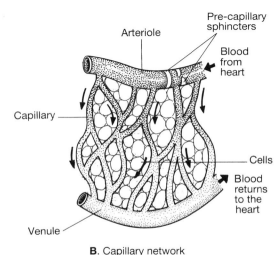

- Arteriole
- Pre-capillary sphincters
- Blood from heart
- Capillary
- Cells
- Blood returns to the heart
- Venule

B. Capillary network

Figure 2

Comparing arteries with veins

When arteries and veins of similar size are compared:

Arteries have thicker walls and smaller passageways due to a larger elastic and muscle layer. Blood flows through arteries rapidly and at high pressure, and the elastic tissue in the middle layer allows the artery wall to expand and contract with each heartbeat. Also, the extra muscle in this layer enables the arteries to control the blood supply to particular organs or tissues – when the muscle in the artery wall contracts, the blood supply is reduced.

Veins have wider passageways and thinner walls. Blood moves slowly through veins so, in order to return the same amount of blood to the heart as leaves it, there are more veins and they have larger cavities.

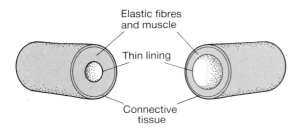

A. Structure of an artery   B. Structure of a vein

Elastic fibres and muscle

Thin lining

Connective tissue

Figure 3

In cross section arteries tend to appear round and veins oval or flattened.

Many veins have valves which prevent the blood from flowing backwards. A valve remains open only so long as the blood flows towards the heart: Fig 4.

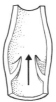 

The pressure of blood pushes open the valve and allows the blood to flow through

When the pressure is relaxed, the valve closes and stops blood flowing back

Figure 4 Section through a vein to show how a valve works

Bleeding When an artery is cut, bright red blood spurts out with each heartbeat. When a vein is cut, darker blood oozes out (sometimes fast) but never spurts. The blood from veins is darker because much of the oxygen has been removed.

QUESTIONS

1a Name the three types of blood vessel and say how they differ.
 b What are: (i) arterioles, (ii) venules?
 c Name the largest blood vessel and give its diameter.
 d Which are the smallest blood vessels and what is their diameter?

2a Describe walls of (i) capillaries, (ii) arteries and veins.
 b Draw a diagram to show the structure of: (i) a capillary, (ii) capillary network.
 c (i) When are capillaries open? (ii) When are many closed? (iii) Why are they not all open at the same time?

3a Draw diagrams to show: (i) the structure of an artery, (ii) the structure of a vein.
 b Describe, with the aid of diagrams, how the valves in veins work.

4a **Differences between arteries and veins.** Copy the chart on the right, then complete by placing a tick in the appropriate column.

FURTHER WORK

1 Complete exercise 2, page 60.
2 Complete exercise 3, page 60.

	Arteries	Veins
1. Carry blood away from the heart		
2. Have thicker walls		
3. Round in cross-section		
4. Return blood to the heart		
5. Have wider passageways		
6. More elastic in the wall		
7. More muscle tissue in the wall		
8. Oval in cross-section		
9. Twice as many of them		
10. Blood spurts out when cut		
11. Blood moves more slowly		
12. Have valves		
13. Blood is bright red		
14. Blood contains less oxygen		

Circulation

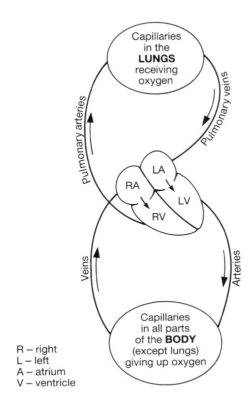

R – right
L – left
A – atrium
V – ventricle

Blood continuously circulates in this way:

$$\rightarrow \text{HEART} \rightarrow \text{LUNGS} \rightarrow \text{HEART} \rightarrow \text{BODY}$$

It takes about half a minute to complete the full circuit each time.

The heart is a double pump

The heart is in fact not one pump but two. With every heartbeat:

◆ the **right side** of the heart pumps **deoxygenated** blood to the lungs to collect oxygen. At the same time –
◆ the **left side** of the heart pumps **oxygenated** blood from the lungs to other parts of the body, where oxygen is released

Figure 1 Simple diagram of circulation. *Points to note:* The right side of the heart is separate from the left side, so
◆ blood can only get from the right side to the left side by passing through the lungs,
◆ blood can only get from the left side to the right side by passing through blood vessels in various parts of the body.

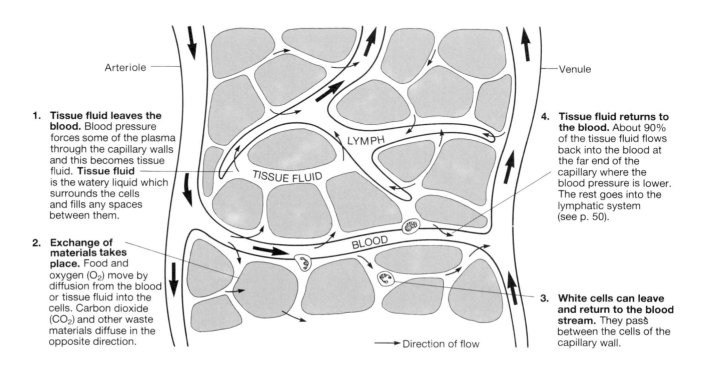

1. **Tissue fluid leaves the blood.** Blood pressure forces some of the plasma through the capillary walls and this becomes tissue fluid. **Tissue fluid** is the watery liquid which surrounds the cells and fills any spaces between them.

2. **Exchange of materials takes place.** Food and oxygen (O_2) move by diffusion from the blood or tissue fluid into the cells. Carbon dioxide (CO_2) and other waste materials diffuse in the opposite direction.

4. **Tissue fluid returns to the blood.** About 90% of the tissue fluid flows back into the blood at the far end of the capillary where the blood pressure is lower. The rest goes into the lymphatic system (see p. 50).

3. **White cells can leave and return to the blood stream.** They pass between the cells of the capillary wall.

Figure 2 What happens in the capillaries as blood flows through them

How the blood keeps moving

A. Through arteries and capillaries The continuous pumping action of the heart drives blood through the arteries. Every time the heart beats, a pressure wave of blood moves rapidly through the arteries, and it can be felt as the **pulse** wherever a main artery comes near to the surface of the body.

B. Through capillaries The pressure from behind keeps blood moving through the capillaries.

C. Through veins Movement of blood through veins is caused by:

◆ the squeezing action of the surrounding muscles. This squeezing tends to press the blood in both directions but the valves prevent backward flow.

◆ the pressure in arteries. This is higher than the pressure in the veins, and pushes the blood on-ward from the arteries through the capillaries and veins.

◆ the suction action of the heart, which draws blood towards it.

Pulse The pulse is the rhythmic expansion of the artery wall as it is stretched by the wave of blood which is pumped through with each heartbeat. It is most easily felt at places where a main artery comes close to the surface of the body.

To take the carotid pulse Place the fingertips on the neck in the hollow between the voice box and the angle of the jaw

To take the radial pulse Rest the forearm on the table with the hand slightly closed and resting on the little finger. Place the fingertips just below the bone (radial bone) at the bend of the wrist.

Figure 3 Taking the pulse – it is easily felt at the wrist (radial pulse)

Figure 4 General plan of circulation

■ Oxygenated blood
□ Deoxygenated blood

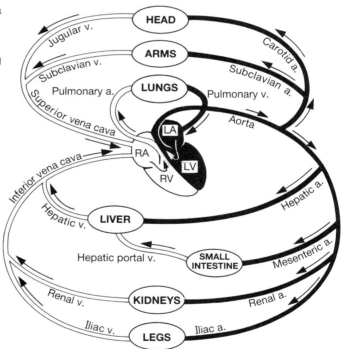

QUESTIONS

1a Where is blood pumped: **(i)** from the right side of the heart, **(ii)** from the left side of the heart. In each case, state whether the blood is oxygenated or deoxygenated.

 b Because the blood flow of the right side of the heart is completely sep-arate from that of the left side, how does blood get: **(i)** from right side to left side, **(ii)** from left side to right side?

2a Blood circulates continuously. Des-cribe how it is kept moving through: **(i)** arteries, **(ii)** capillaries, **(iii)** veins.

 b Describe: **(i)** the pulse, **(ii)** how to take the pulse rate.

3a What is tissue fluid?

 b (i) List four activities that take place as blood flows through the capillaries. **(ii)** Draw a diagram to illustrate your answer.

4 On **Fig 4**, follow the pathway of the blood as it circulates from the arms to the kidneys. Then complete the list below of the blood vessels and cham-bers of the heart through which the blood flows:

 a _____ vein
 b Superior _____ _____
 c _____ atrium
 d Right _____
 e _____ artery
 f Pulmonary _____
 g _____ atrium
 h Left _____
 i A_____
 j Renal _____

FURTHER WORK

1 Sit quietly for about ten minutes, then take your pulse for one minute and make a note of the rate. Spend a few minutes running or taking some other form of vigorous exercise. Immediately you stop, take your pulse rate for one minute and note the rate. Continue to take the pulse each minute until it has returned to what it was before the exercise was taken.

Draw a graph to show the effect of exercise and rest on your pulse rate.

Does the pulse rate of fit people return to normal more quickly than that of the unfit?

2 To demonstrate the return of blood to the heart through the veins:
Lightly grip the arm just above the wrist for 30 seconds. Note how the veins in the wrist fill with blood. Release the pressure and they empty.

3 Copy **Fig 2**, colouring oxygenated blood red and deoxygenated blood blue. Using question 4 as a guide, make a list of the blood vessels and chambers of the heart through which blood passes as it circulates from: **(i)** legs to arms, **(ii)** intest-ines to head.

More about circulation

Arterial disease

The two main conditions which affect artery walls tend to occur together and worsen with age. They are:

Atheroma – narrowing of the arteries. The lining of an artery wall is normally smooth, but rough patches containing cholesterol may form. The patches slowly enlarge and the passageway inside the artery gradually becomes narrower. Less and less blood can flow through, and eventually the flow may be blocked completely.

Arteriosclerosis – 'hardening' of the arteries. With this condition the artery walls become thicker and less elastic. This occurs in everyone to some degree as they get older. It only causes disease if severe.

Atherosclerosis is a term often used to include both arteriosclerosis and atheroma because they usually occur together.

Prevention Advice given to people who wish to reduce the likelihood of arterial disease is the same as is given to those who wish to reduce the chance of a heart attack (p. 43).

Blocking blood vessels

Thrombosis This is the formation of a blood clot (**thrombus**) inside a blood vessel. It can happen when the lining of the blood vessel becomes damaged or when the blood flow becomes very slow or stops. The clot blocks circulation in that area partly or completely.
- If the clot is in an artery, the tissue served by the artery gets no oxygen from it and may die. When this happens in the heart it causes **coronary thrombosis** (a heart attack), and in the brain it causes **cerebral thrombosis** (a stroke).
- If the clot is in a vein, the blood cannot get back to the heart and the tissues become swollen behind the blockage. When this happens in the legs it may cause **deep vein thrombosis (DVT)**.

Embolism An **embolus** is a blood clot which breaks away from where it was formed and travels in the blood stream until it becomes trapped in an artery small enough to prevent it moving any further. It causes
- **pulmonary embolism** in the lungs.
- **stroke** in the brain.
- **heart attack** in the coronary arteries.
- **gangrene** in the legs (sometimes).

Strokes Brain cells depend on a continuous supply of oxygen and if it is cut off for more than four minutes they die. The oxygen supply becomes cut off if one of the brain's arteries becomes blocked by a blood clot, or by bleeding into the brain (**cerebral haemorrhage**). The result is a **stroke**. The affected area is destroyed and the functions controlled by that part of the brain cease. Commonly, this results in paralysis, or partial paralysis, of the other side of the body. The ability to speak may also be lost, although the patient often understands what is being said. Being unable to communicate causes great frustration.

Recovery from strokes is variable, and can be aided by physiotherapy and occupational therapy.

Circulation problems in the legs

Deep vein thrombosis The main reason why blood clots form in the veins of the leg is slow circulation. Circulation slows down in the legs of people who sit still for long stretches of time as this kinks the veins in the knees. It also slows in patients kept in bed after an operation, and this is why they are encouraged to get out of bed and move around, even after major surgery.

Varicose veins When the valves in the veins near the surface of the leg fail, blood collects in the veins and stretches them. This causes aching and swelling around the ankles, and ulcers may form on the lower part of the leg.

A tendency to varicose veins often runs in families, and their development is encouraged by standing for long periods, lack of exercise, overweight and pregnancy. If the veins are painful or unsightly, they can be removed by surgery or closed up by injections. The blood finds other veins in the legs through which to reach the heart.

Blood pressure

The heart pumps blood into the arteries in sharp bursts at every beat. The blood pressure rises and falls in time with this, being greatest just after the heart contracts (**systolic pressure**) and least at the end of the relaxation phase (**diastolic pressure**). These two pressures are measured in millimetres of mercury (mmHg). The figure for systolic pressure is placed above that for diastolic pressure.

Blood pressure varies with age, sex and weight. Generally, blood pressure of about $\frac{120}{80}$ mmHg is considered to be normal for a young man; it is slightly less in young women, and tends to increase with age.

Blood pressure can alter from minute to minute according to activity and also to feelings. For example, strenuous activity, anger or nervousness raise the blood pressure; rest and contentment lower it.

Measuring blood pressure Blood pressure can be measured by an instrument called a sphygmomanometer (pronounced sfig-mo-man-ommeter). A column of mercury is linked to an inflatable cuff which is wound around the upper arm. A stethoscope is then used to listen to the sounds of the blood in the main artery (brachial artery) at the bend of the elbow. The sounds start at systolic pressure and finish at diastolic pressure.

Figure 1 Measuring blood pressure

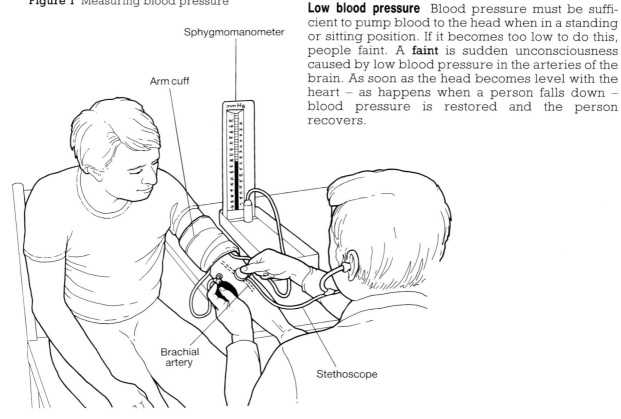

Sphygmomanometer

Arm cuff

mm Hg

Brachial artery

Stethoscope

High blood pressure (hypertension) People whose blood pressure is continuously at a high level have a greater risk of suffering from strokes, heart attacks, kidney disease or eye trouble. High blood pressure need not be a cause for worry as it can be kept under control by medicines which are both safe and effective.

The cause of high blood pressure in most people who suffer from it is unknown. It does have a slight tendency to run in families so some factor is likely to be inherited.

Low blood pressure Blood pressure must be sufficient to pump blood to the head when in a standing or sitting position. If it becomes too low to do this, people faint. A **faint** is sudden unconsciousness caused by low blood pressure in the arteries of the brain. As soon as the head becomes level with the heart – as happens when a person falls down – blood pressure is restored and the person recovers.

QUESTIONS

1 Name and describe the two main conditions which affect arteries.

2a (i) What is thrombosis?
   (ii) when can it happen?
 b What happens when a blood clot forms in:
   (i) an artery, (ii) a vein?
 c What is an embolism? (ii) What does it cause?
 d (i) What is the cause of a stroke?
   (ii) What are the effects of a stroke?

3a What is the main reason for the formation of blood clots in the leg?

 b Describe varicose veins.
 c What encourages the development of varicose veins?

4a What is normal blood pressure?
 b Give examples of how this alters according to activity and feelings.
 c Describe how to measure blood pressure.
 d Continuously high blood pressure increases the risk of certain diseases; name four of them.

3 (i) What is the cause of a faint?
   (ii) What aids recovery?

FURTHER WORK

1 Consider the pathway of circulating blood and work out why: (i) embolism only happens in arteries, (ii) pulmonary embolism is usually due to a clot from the legs, (iii) cerebral embolism is usually due to a clot from the heart.

2 What advice would you give to a person who wished to reduce the likelihood of arterial disease?

Lymphatic system

The **lymphatic system** consists of lymph glands linked together by a system of tubes – **lymph vessels** (lymphatics) – which penetrate throughout all tissues of the body and contain a clear fluid called **lymph**.

Functions of the lymphatic system

The lymphatic system:
- filters lymph to remove unwanted matter from it.
- produces lymphocytes } to destroy germs (bacteria and viruses).
- produces antibodies
- removes excess fluid from the tissues.
- lacteals absorb digested fat.

How the lymphatic system works

The system starts as blind-ended tubes – **lymph capillaries** – situated between the cells. Lymph capillaries are like blood capillaries in having walls one cell thick, but they differ in allowing much larger particles to pass through, eg bacteria and large proteins. Lymph capillaries in the small intestine are called **lacteals** and they have a specialised function (p. 82).

About 10% of tissue fluid flows into the lymph capillaries instead of back into the blood stream. As it does so, many bacteria, viruses, protein molecules and other particles from the tissue spaces flow with it. Fluid in the lymphatic system is called **lymph** and is similar to tissue fluid except that it contains more protein: **Fig 2**.

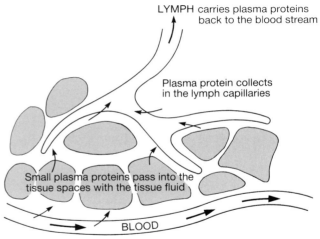

LYMPH carries plasma proteins back to the blood stream

Plasma protein collects in the lymph capillaries

Small plasma proteins pass into the tissue spaces with the tissue fluid

BLOOD

Figure 2 Protein in lymph: Although most plasma protein molecules in the blood are too large to pass through the capillary wall, the smallest ones manage to do so. If they accumulated in the tissue spaces they would exert an osmotic pressure and thus hinder the return of tissue fluid to the blood. The result would be **oedema** – swelling due to excess tissue fluid. This does not occur because the walls of lymph capillaries allows the plasma proteins to pass easily through

Lymph capillaries unite to form **lymph vessels** and these join up to form a system of increasingly larger tubes which branch and join up freely. As lymph travels through the lymph vessels it has to pass through **lymph nodes** where it is filtered and unwanted matter removed.

The main lymph vessel is the **thoracic duct** which lies in front of the vertebral column. This duct collects lymph from all parts of the body except the upper right side; the lymph from this region collects into the **right lymphatic duct**. These two ducts open into the **subclavian veins** and return lymph to the blood system at the base of the neck.

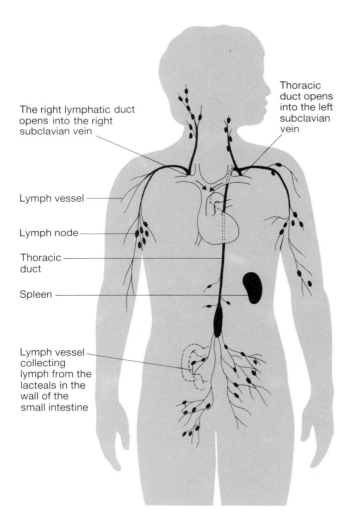

The right lymphatic duct opens into the right subclavian vein

Thoracic duct opens into the left subclavian vein

Lymph vessel

Lymph node

Thoracic duct

Spleen

Lymph vessel collecting lymph from the lacteals in the wall of the small intestine

Figure 1 Lymphatic system. Note the groups of lymph nodes in the neck, armpits, elbows, abdomen and groin

Lymph nodes (lymph glands)

These are small bean-shaped bodies situated along the course of the lymph vessels, rather like beads on a string. They vary in size from 1 to 20 mm in diameter. Their function is to protect the body by:
◆ filtering lymph,
◆ making lymphocytes,
◆ making antibodies.

Lymphoid tissue Lymphoid tissue is formed of white cells **(lymphocytes)** which detect antigens and make antibodies. It is the main tissue in lymph nodes and it also occurs in tonsils and adenoids, thymus, spleen, digestive tract and lungs.

How lymph is filtered Inside, the node contains a network of tiny passageways lined with **phagocytes** – white cells which engulf (eat) bacteria, viruses and other small particles as they flow slowly by in the lymph. (Antibodies are made in response to the antigens trapped by the phagocytes: p. 35.)

'Swollen glands' When the body has an infection, the lymph glands (nodes) become very active and often swell. The infection may be in the gland itself, or it may be at some distance from the gland. For example, when a hand is infected, germs from the infection are carried along the lymph vessels and become trapped in the glands at the elbow or armpit, causing the nodes there to swell.

Glandular fever (Infectious mononucleosis) Glandular fever is an infectious disease caused by a virus and is spread by droplets (it is sometimes known as the 'kissing disease'). It starts as a sore throat, the lymph glands usually swell, particularly those in the neck, and abnormal lymphocytes are seen in the blood.

Tonsils and adenoids The tonsils in the throat and the adenoids at the back of the nose are patches of lymphoid tissue which help to protect the body against infection. Germs from inhaled air which fall on this tissue cause it to produce antibodies. The tonsils and adenoids are very active in childhood, normally enlarging at 5–6 years of age and shrinking after the age of 10. If they become chronically infected, they may need to be removed, because they are then a source of infection and not a protection against it.

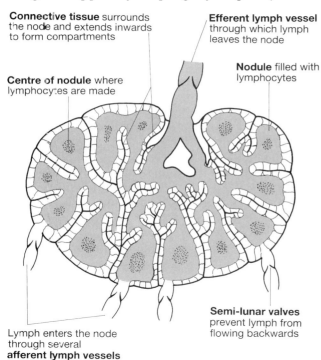

Connective tissue surrounds the node and extends inwards to form compartments

Efferent lymph vessel through which lymph leaves the node

Nodule filled with lymphocytes

Centre of nodule where lymphocytes are made

Semi-lunar valves prevent lymph from flowing backwards

Lymph enters the node through several **afferent lymph vessels**

Figure 3 Section through a lymph node

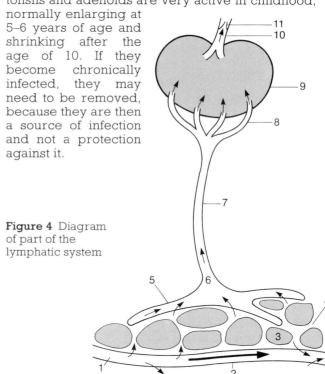

Figure 4 Diagram of part of the lymphatic system

QUESTIONS

1a Briefly describe the lymphatic system.
 b Name five functions of the lymphatic system.
2 Name the following parts of the lymphatic system:
a the blind-ended tubes,
b the fluid inside the lymphatic system,
c lymph capillaries in the small intestine,
d the tubes which branch and join up,
e the main lymph vessel,
f the vessel which collects lymph from the upper right side of the body,
g lymph glands,
h cells made in the lymph nodes,
i tissue which makes antibodies.

3a Describe a lymph node.
 b Give three functions of lymph nodes.
 c Describe how lymph is filtered.
 d Draw a diagram to show the structure of a lymph node and label the parts.
 e Why does lymph leaving a node contain more lymphocytes than when it entered?

4a Explain why, when the hand is infected, the lymph nodes in the elbow or armpit may swell.
 b (i) Give the technical name for glandular fever. (ii) What is its cause? (iii) How are the lymph glands and lymphocytes affected?

FURTHER WORK

1 Draw **Fig 4** and label 1–11.

2 Using **Fig 1** as a guide, draw an outline of the body and shade in that part in which lymph is drained by the right lymphatic duct.

3 Use the following words to complete the chart: blood; yes, open-ended; towards the heart; lymph vessels; around the body; blind-ended; no; lymph; veins.

	Lymphatic system	Blood system
Name of fluid		
Capillaries		
Tubes with valves		
Direction of flow		
Nodes present		

Respiratory system

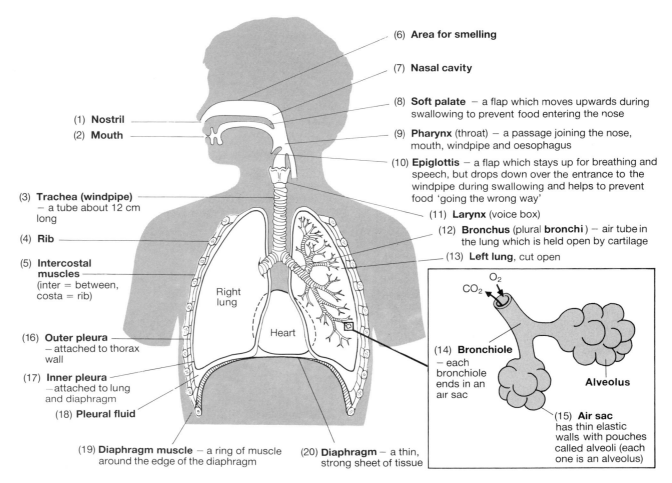

Figure 1 Respiratory system

(6) **Area for smelling**

(7) **Nasal cavity**

(8) **Soft palate** – a flap which moves upwards during swallowing to prevent food entering the nose

(9) **Pharynx** (throat) – a passage joining the nose, mouth, windpipe and oesophagus

(10) **Epiglottis** – a flap which stays up for breathing and speech, but drops down over the entrance to the windpipe during swallowing and helps to prevent food 'going the wrong way'

(11) **Larynx** (voice box)

(12) **Bronchus** (plural **bronchi**) – air tube in the lung which is held open by cartilage

(13) **Left lung**, cut open

(1) **Nostril**

(2) **Mouth**

(3) **Trachea (windpipe)** – a tube about 12 cm long

(4) **Rib**

(5) **Intercostal muscles** (inter = between, costa = rib)

(16) **Outer pleura** – attached to thorax wall

(17) **Inner pleura** – attached to lung and diaphragm

(18) **Pleural fluid**

(19) **Diaphragm muscle** – a ring of muscle around the edge of the diaphragm

(20) **Diaphragm** – a thin, strong sheet of tissue

Right lung

Heart

O_2

CO_2

(14) **Bronchiole** – each bronchiole ends in an air sac

Alveolus

(15) **Air sac** has thin elastic walls with pouches called alveoli (each one is an alveolus)

The **respiratory system** consists of lungs and air tubes and is used for breathing.

Respiratory tract

The respiratory tract is the passageway along which air flows during breathing: **Fig 1**. From the larynx onwards, the walls of the larger air tubes are strengthened by **cartilage** to keep them open and allow the air to flow freely through. The cartilage forms plates in the larynx and complete rings in the bronchi. It forms incomplete C-shaped rings in the trachea where cartilage is missing on the side adjacent to the oesophagus, and this allows the oesophagus to expand as food passes down to the stomach.

Muscle fibres in the walls of the bronchi can alter the size of the air tubes. When they contract, the tubes become narrower and the rate at which air which can be breathed out and in is reduced.

Lungs

The two lungs occupy the greater part of the thorax with the heart situated between them. Each lung is divided into lobes – three lobes in the right lung and two in the left.

The main **bronchus** of each lung, **Fig 1**, gives rise to a number of branches and these divide and sub-divide into smaller and smaller tubes. The smallest tubes – **bronchioles** – lack cartilage and each ends in an air sac. The millions and millions of tiny air sacs, together with the air tubes and blood vessels, make up the tissue of the lungs.

A thin, tough membrane – the **pleura** – forms a double layer around each lung and between the lobes, with the **inner pleura** being attached to the lung and the **outer pleura** attached to the thorax wall. In the thin space between the two pleurae is the **pleural fluid** which acts as a lubricant and allows the lungs to slide easily during breathing.

Ciliated mucous membrane (mucosa)

This membrane (see **Fig 2**, p. 26), lines most of the air passages and consists of two types of cell:

◆ **Cells of mucus glands** secrete a clear sticky substance, **mucus**, which:

keeps the surface moist and prevents it drying out, shrinking and cracking,

traps dust, smoke and other matter harmful to the lungs.

◆ **Ciliated cells.**

Cilia are fine hairs which produce a velvet-like cover over the surface of the mucous membrane. They beat continuously, pushing the mucus along like a moving carpet and taking the dust and dirt with it. The cilia in the nose push mucus towards the nostrils where it is removed by **sneezing** or 'blowing the nose'. The cilia in the lungs push the mucus towards the windpipe so that it can be removed – normally by swallowing, although we are not aware of this. Excess mucus is called **sputum** or **phlegm** and is removed by **coughing**.

Nose

Four functions of the nose are:

◆ **warming** the air entering the body,
◆ **moistening** the air so that it does not have a drying effect on the air passages,
◆ **trapping** inhaled dust and dirt,
◆ **smelling** odours in the inhaled air (see p. 105).

QUESTIONS

1 Copy the diagram of the respiratory system, **Fig 2**, and label 1–20 using the information in **Fig 1**.
2 Complete the following sentences:
The respiratory system consists of l ____ and air t ___ and is used for b _____ . Air enters the n ___ or m ___, then passes through the p _____, l ____ , t _____ , b _____ , b _____ , and into the a _ s ___ to reach the a ____ .
3a Describe how the air tubes are kept open.
b How can the size of the air tubes be altered?
c Name two other types of structure besides air sacs which make up lung tissue.
d (i) Describe the pleurae. (ii) What is the function of the pleural fluid?
4a Name the membrane which lines the air passages.
b Describe mucus and name two functions.
c What are cilia and how are they able to move mucus?
d What is sputum and how is it removed?
5 Give four functions of the nose.

FURTHER WORK

1 Examine the lungs and windpipe of a pig.
a Note the sponginess, colour, smoothness of the pleura covering the lung, and mucus in the air passages.
b Cut off a piece of lung tissue. Note the open air tubes, their size and branching.
c Remove a cartilage from the trachea and from a bronchus and compare.
d Note the cartilage of the larynx wall and the vocal cords inside.
2 Describe First Aid treatment for choking in adults and in children.

Diseases of the respiratory system

Asthma Breathing is difficult and wheezy. This happens when the airways in the lungs become narrower because:

◆ the muscles in the walls go into **spasm** (tighten), and
◆ the mucosa lining the tubes swells and secretes extra mucus.

Factors which bring on an asthma attack include lung infections, allergy, emotion, cold air, exercise and smoke.

Bronchitis Bacterial or viral infection of the air passages in the lungs causes fever, coughing and much sputum, which is yellow or green when it contains pus.

Pneumonia Infection of lung tissue (alveoli and small bronchioles) by bacteria such as pneumococcus and legionella, or by viruses. Legionnaires' disease is a form of pneumonia.

Pleurisy Inflammation of the pleura causes jabbing pain on taking a deep breath or coughing.

Laryngitis An infection of the larynx. It results in a painful throat and larynx, and a hoarse voice. It may also be painful to speak.

Emphysema A disease of the lungs in which the alveolar walls are destroyed, leaving large air spaces. This reduces the internal surface of the lungs available for gas exchange.

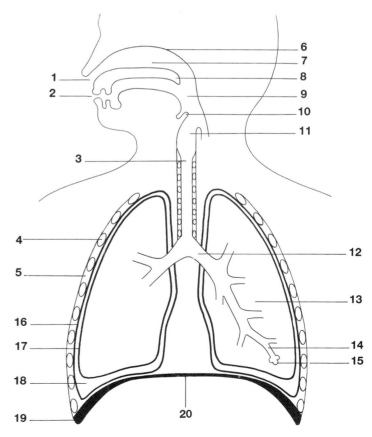

Figure 2 Diagram of the respiratory system

Breathing

Breathing in (Inhaling; Inspiration) –

(a) Intercostal muscles contract pulling the rib cage upwards and outwards

(b) The diaphragm muscle contracts pulling the diaphragm downwards, making it flatter

(c) The thorax enlarges and the lungs expand as they are drawn outwards

(d) Air is sucked in to the lungs as they enlarge

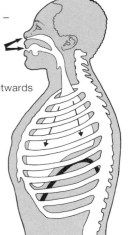

Breathing out (Exhaling; Expiration) –

(a) Intercostal muscles relax and the rib cage moves downwards and inwards

(b) The diaphragm muscle relaxes and the diaphragm moves upwards to become more dome-shaped

(c) The thorax becomes smaller and the lungs recoil because they are elastic

(d) Air goes out as the space inside the lungs is reduced

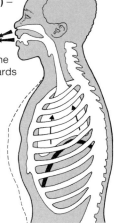

Figure 1 Breathing

Breathing is achieved by the combined movements of the thorax wall, the diaphragm and the abdomen. These movements are brought about by the **intercostal muscles** and the **diaphragm muscle**. With each breath the lungs, being elastic, **expand** and **recoil** (spring back).

Ways of breathing

Although breathing usually involves both sets of muscles, the amount each is used varies with individuals, with training, and with the demands made upon the lungs at any particular time.

Thoracic breathing uses the intercostal muscles – the chest can be seen to rise and fall.

Abdominal breathing uses the diaphragm – and the abdomen moves in and out.

Quiet breathing is mainly abdominal with most of the work being done by the diaphragm muscle.

Control of the rate and depth of breathing

Breathing is a regular and mainly automatic process under the control of the nervous system. The amount of carbon dioxide in the blood flowing through the brain is an important factor in this process. An increase above the usual level stimulates the brain to send messages to the muscles to increase the rate and depth of breathing. The faster and deeper breathing removes the extra carbon dioxide from the blood. As the level falls, the brain readjusts breathing to its usual pattern.

Volume of air in the lungs

When a person is resting and breathing quietly, the lungs (of an adult) hold about three litres of air and a little of this, about half a litre, is exchanged with each breath. When the lungs are fully expanded in deep breathing, they can hold up to seven litres – depending on body size.

No matter how much effort is put into exhaling, it is impossible to squeeze all the air out of the lungs.

Tidal air is the amount of air that passes in and out during quiet breathing—about $\frac{1}{2}$ litre.

Residual air is the amount of air that always remains in the lungs and cannot be squeezed out—1–$1\frac{1}{2}$ litres.

The **vital capacity** of the lungs is the maximum amount of air that can be breathed out after taking one deep breath—4–6 litres in most healthy young adults.

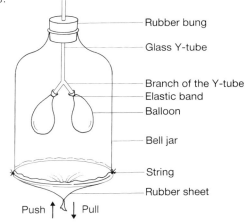

Figure 2 Model of the thorax to demonstrate breathing
   'Breathing in': When the rubber sheet is pulled downwards, extra space is created in the bell jar. Air is sucked into the balloons to fill up the space.
   'Breathing out': When the rubber sheet is 'let go', the space inside the bell jar is reduced, and air goes out of the balloons.

Composition of air

Inhaled air Air taken into the lungs comes from the room or the 'open air' and its composition remains remarkably constant. The approximate amounts of gases in inhaled air are:

nitrogen	78%
oxygen	21%
carbon dioxide	0.03%
other gases	1%

The air will also contain water vapour (moisture) but the amount varies: dry air contains a little and damp air a great deal especially if warm. Dust, pollen, smoke etc may also be present.

Exhaled air Air which comes from the lungs has the following composition:

Nitrogen – the same amount comes out as goes in because the body cannot use nitrogen gas.
Oxygen – exhaled air contains about 17% oxygen. (Note that only $\frac{1}{5}$ of the oxygen is removed by breathing.)
Carbon dioxide – is added to the air in the lungs, and exhaled air contains about 4%.
Water vapour – exhaled air is always saturated. The water comes from the layer of moisture which lines the alveoli.
Temperature – air is warmed while in the body, so exhaled air is warmer than inhaled air (unless of course, the outside air is exceedingly hot).
Other gases – the several other gases in air (xenon, neon etc) are, like nitrogen, unchanged by breathing.

Mouth-to-mouth ventilation (resuscitation)

The mouth-to-mouth method is by far the best way to try to revive a person who has stopped breathing as a result of drowning, electric shock, heart attack, suffocation etc. It is most important to **act quickly** as damage to brain cells occurs if they are deprived of oxygen for more than four minutes.

A. Lay the patient flat on a firm surface. Remove any obstruction from the mouth such as food or loose dentures.

B. Tilt the head well back to open up the airway, using one hand either to support the neck or keep the jaw open. Close the patient's nose by pinching the nostrils with your other hand.

C. Take a deep breath, then blow into the patient's mouth to inflate the lungs – if you are doing it properly the patient's chest will rise. The air you exhale contains about 17% oxygen—much more than the air in the patients lungs. Inflate the patient's lungs about every four seconds. If the patient's heart has stopped, it is also necessary to perform cardiac massage as well (p. 43).

(p. 43)

QUESTIONS

1a Breathing is achieved by the combined movements of three parts of the body. (i) Name them. (ii) Name the muscles involved in breathing. (iii) How do the lungs behave with each breath?
 b Describe: (i) thoracic breathing, (ii) abdominal breathing, (iii) quiet breathing.
2a Give two words which mean: (i) 'breathing in', (ii) 'breathing out'.
 b Copy Fig 3. Add the labels a–d, using **Fig 1** as a guide.
 c Describe how the rate and depth of breathing is controlled.

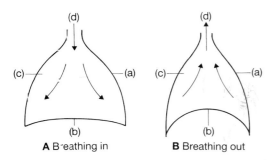

A Breathing in   **B** Breathing out

Figure 3 Movements during breathing

3a How much air do the lungs hold?
 b What is meant by: (i) tidal air, (ii) residual air, (iii) vital capacity?
4 Copy and complete the table.

Differences in composition of inhaled and exhaled air

	Inhaled air	Exhaled air
Nitrogen	%	%
Oxygen	%	%
Carbon dioxide	%	%
Water vapour	v − − − −	s − − − −

5a (i) When, and (ii) why is it important to start giving mouth-to-mouth ventilation as quickly as possible?
 b Describe mouth-to-mouth ventilation.

FURTHER WORK

1 Use a model of the thorax (or copy the diagram) and describe how it can be used to demonstrate breathing. List the ways in which a model such as the one shown in **Fig 2** differs from the human thorax.

2 Think about your breathing. Describe the different breathing movements you can make and name the muscles which are used. Find out how breathing is used: (i) for singing, (ii) by athletes. Listen to the air entering and leaving the lungs through a simple stethoscope such as a cardboard tube.

3 Obtain First Aid instruction on mouth-to-mouth ventilation.

Investigating breathing

Experiment 1 To show that breathing removes oxygen from the air

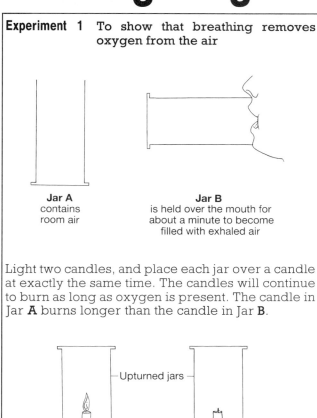

Jar A
contains
room air

Jar B
is held over the mouth for
about a minute to become
filled with exhaled air

Light two candles, and place each jar over a candle at exactly the same time. The candles will continue to burn as long as oxygen is present. The candle in Jar **A** burns longer than the candle in Jar **B**.

Upturned jars

Jar A   **Jar B**

Experiment 2 To show that breathing adds carbon dioxide to the air

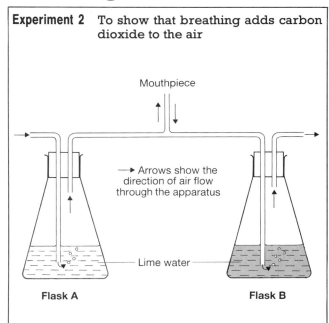

Mouthpiece

→ Arrows show the
direction of air flow
through the apparatus

Lime water

Flask A   **Flask B**

The tubes are arranged so that the air passes through flask **A** before being inhaled in gentle breathing at the mouthpiece. Then, the exhaled air passes through flask **B**. In both flasks the air has to bubble through limewater (a solution of calcium hydroxide in water), which turns cloudy as it absorbs carbon dioxide and produces calcium carbonate.

After a person has breathed through the apparatus for a short while, the limewater in **B** is obviously much more cloudy than in **A**.

Experiment 3 To show that exhaled air contains moisture

Mouthpiece

One way valves

Cobalt chloride
paper

Tube A   **Tube B**

This apparatus works in a similar way to that in Experiment 2, except that one-way valves are needed (in place of limewater) to ensure that inhaled air passes through **A** and exhaled air through **B**. Dry cobalt chloride paper, which is blue, is placed in both **A** and **B**. When cobalt chloride combines with water it turns from blue to pink.

After some gentle breathing through the mouthpiece, the cobalt chloride in **B** turns pink. The speed at which the cobalt chloride in **A** turns pink depends on the amount of moisture in the air in the room.

Experiment 4   To show that air is warmed by breathing

Take the temperature of the air in the room (inhaled air). Then take the temperature of exhaled air by holding the thermometer in the open mouth while breathing in through the nose and out through the mouth. Wait until the reading is steady, then compare the temperature with that of inhaled air. Any rise will be due to warming of the air while in the body. Repeat this experiment in the open air.

Experiment 5   To find the volume of air breathed

Glass jar with litre measurements

Breathe here

Tubing

Large container

Water

One or two blocks to support the jar

Apparatus to measure the volume of exhaled air.
(The volume of exhaled air equals the volume of inhaled air)

Fill the jar with water by turning it on its side in the container, then place in position on supporting blocks. Use the apparatus to find the volume of (i) a shallow breath (quiet breathing), (ii) a deep breath. Use this information to find out how much air was breathed in one minute:

Volume of air breathed per minute in quiet breathing
Number of breaths per minute (Rate) $= ?$
Volume of one breath (Depth) $= ?$ litres
Volume of air breathed in one minute
$$= Rate \times Depth$$

Take some vigorous exercise, counting the number of breaths per minute. Then calculate the **volume of air breathed per minute in deep breathing**.

FURTHER WORK

Experiment 1
a Name the experiment.
b Describe the experiment.
c Draw the apparatus at the end of the experiment.
d (i) Did both jars contain oxygen? How do you know? (ii) Which jar contained less oxygen? Why?

Experiment 2
a Name the experiment.
b Draw the apparatus.
c Describe the experiment.
d (i) Did the inhaled or the exhaled air contain more carbon dioxide? Why do you know? (ii) Why do you know that inhaled air contains a little carbon dioxide?

Experiment 3
a Name the experiment.
b Draw the apparatus.
c Describe the experiment.

d (i) Carry out the experiment to find which showed a quicker colour change, the cobalt chloride in **A** or **B**. What does this indicate?
(ii) Where has the extra water come from to cause a quicker colour change?
(iii) Under what circumstances would both A and B change colour at the same rate?
e When exhaled air is breathed on to a mirror, how could you show that the moisture which condenses on the mirror is water?

Experiment 4
a Name the experiment.
b Describe the experiment.
c Carry out the experiment indoors. (i) By how much did the temperature rise?
(ii) Where did the heat come from to warm the air?

(iii) Does this mean that the body is continuously losing heat by breathing?
(iv) Under what unusual circumstances would inhaled air be warmer than exhaled air?
d Carry out the experiment in the open air and compare with the result obtained indoors.

Experiment 5
a Name the experiment.
b Draw the apparatus.
c Describe the experiment.
d How much do you breathe out: (i) in a shallow breath, (ii) in a deep breath, (iii) in one minute of quiet breathing, (iv) in one minute of vigorous exercise?
e Use this apparatus to find out if the volume of air breathed differs between: (i) people different size, (ii) those who take a great deal of exercise and those who do not.

Respiration

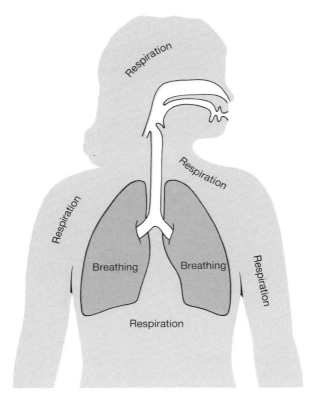

Figure 1 The difference between respiration and breathing

Respiration is the process of releasing energy from food and it takes place in all living cells throughout the body. For respiration to occur, the cells must have a constant supply of oxygen brought to them from the lungs in the blood stream.

The following events all have a part to play in respiration:

◆ **Breathing** – which is the moving of air into and out of the lungs.
◆ **Exchange of gases** in the lungs between air and blood.
◆ **Transport of gases** in the blood stream.
◆ **Exchange of gases** between blood and cells.
◆ **Energy release** in the cells – a process called **cell respiration** or **tissue respiration**.

Exchange of gases in the lungs

The structure of the lungs enables gases to move rapidly between air and blood. The lungs have:

◆ **a large surface area.** The total surface area of the walls of all these air spaces is about $85\,m^2$ – the size of a tennis court – because:
  the lungs are composed of millions of tiny air sacs;
  each air sac is divided into compartments – alveoli (singular: alveolus).

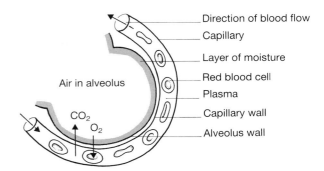

Figure 2 Exchange of gases in the lungs: Oxygen and carbon dioxide move in opposite directions in the lungs because each moves along its own concentration gradient, high→low.

◆ **thin walls.** The air in the alveoli comes very close to the blood, being separated by only two layers of cells – the alveolus wall and the capillary wall.
◆ **an excellent blood supply.** A dense network of capillaries surrounds the alveoli (**Fig. 3**).

Movement of oxygen There is more oxygen in the air in the alveoli than in the blood in the capillaries, so oxygen moves from air to blood by diffusion ((high→low). To do this, the oxygen:
  dissolves in the layer of moisture lining the alveolus wall,
  passes through the alveolus wall,
  passes through the capillary wall,
  enters the plasma,
  passes through the red cell membrane,
  then joins with the haemoglobin in the red cells to form oxyhaemoglobin.

Oxygen supply to the cells

The oxygenated blood from the lungs goes into the pulmonary vein and returns to the heart, which then pumps it through the arteries to all the tissues of the body. The arteries sub-divide many times to form capillaries, which penetrate between the cells of the tissues. Where there is an oxygen shortage, oxygen moves from the blood into the cells (high→ low). It goes:
  through the membrane of the red cells,
  into the plasma,
  through the capillary wall,
  into the tissue fluid,
  through the cell walls,
  into the cells.

Elimination of carbon dioxide

Carbon dioxide is a waste product of cell respiration and needs to be excreted from the body. It moves by diffusion from the cell through the capillary wall and into the plasma (high→low), then travels in the blood stream to the lungs. Carbon dioxide in the blood is mainly in the form of hydrogencarbonate ions (bicarbonates), most of which are dissolved in the plasma.

When carbon dioxide reaches the lungs, its concentration in the blood is greater than in the air. Therefore carbon dioxide diffuses from the blood, through the capillary wall, through the alveolus wall and its layer of moisture, and into the air in the air sac (high→low). It is then excreted from the body when the air is exhaled.

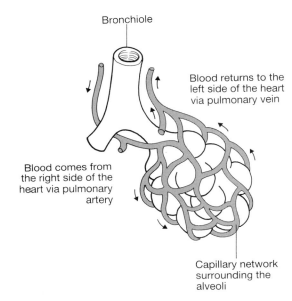

Figure 3 Movement of blood in the capillary network surrounding the alveoli.

Release of energy

Energy is released inside a cell when glucose and oxygen are converted to carbon dioxide and water. Respiration can be summed up in the following chemical equation:

$$C_6H_{12}O_6 + 6O_2 \xrightarrow{\text{enzyme action}} 6CO_2 + 6H_2O + \text{energy}$$

glucose containing stored energy; oxygen; carbon dioxide; water

This process of cell respiration is controlled by enzymes and takes place in the mitochondria (p. 22). As the energy is released, it is used to build molecules of ATP (adenosine triphosphate) from ADP (adenosine diphosphate) and phosphate:

ADP + phosphate + energy → ATP

An ATP molecule contains energy that can be used by any part of the cell which requires it, or the ATP can store the energy until it is needed.

After releasing its energy, ATP changes back to ADP and phosphate, which are then ready to be used to make more ATP.

ATP → ADP + phosphate + energy

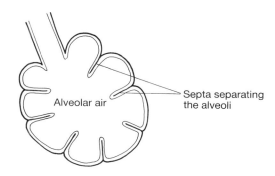

Figure 4 Section through Fig. 3 showing how the surface area for gas exchange is increased by the alveoli.

QUESTIONS

1a What is the difference between respiration and breathing?
b List five events which all have a part to play in respiration.
c Give two names used for the process of energy release in cells.
2a Name three features of lungs which enable gases to move rapidly between air and blood.
b Draw a diagram to show how the internal surface area of the lungs is increased by the alveoli.
3a (i) What process causes oxygen in the lungs to move from air to blood?
(ii) Describe the route it takes.
(iii) Describe the route oxygen takes as it then moves from the blood to the cells.
b Describe the route taken by carbon dioxide as it goes from: (i) cells to blood, (ii) blood to air.

c Draw a diagram to show the exchange of gases in the lungs.
4a Give the chemical equation for respiration.
b (i) What controls cell respiration?
(ii) Whereabouts does it take place?
c What is the meaning of: (i) ATP, (ii) ADP?
d Describe how ATP is formed and how it changes back to ADP and phosphate.

FURTHER WORK

Differences between Respiration and Breathing

1 Use the following to complete the table below:
given off as a waste product; lungs; air exchange; cells; release of energy; released into the air; combines with glucose; absorbed into the blood.

	Respiration	Breathing
Function		
Takes place in		
Oxygen		
Carbon dioxide		

2. Using a piece of thread, measure the difference between the inner surface of an air sac, **Fig. 4**, (i) with and (ii) without the septa.

Section 2 EXERCISES

1 For (a) and (b), match each of the terms with the correct statement in the list below.

(a) **arteries   bone marrow   haemoglobin   veins lymphocyte   phagocyte   plasma   platelets systole   universal donors**

  the liquid part of the blood
  makes blood cells
  links up with oxygen
  carry blood to the heart
  engulfs germs
  makes antibodies
  help blood to clot
  blood group O Rh negative
  contraction of ventricles
  carry blood from the heart   [10]

(b) **bronchioles   lymph   mucous membrane resuscitation   respiration   right ventricle sphincter   haemorrhage   tissue fluid   vital capacity**

  release of energy from food
  watery liquid surrounding the cells
  a ring of muscle
  pumps deoxygenated blood
  fluid in the lymphatic system
  small air tubes in the lungs
  lines the air passages
  mouth-to-mouth ventilation
  maximum amount of air in one breath
  loss of blood   [10]

2 (a) Copy the figure below showing the main arteries in the human body and label parts 1 to 8.
(b) Colour red the side of the heart and the arteries through which oxygenated blood flows. Colour blue the side of the heart and the arteries through which deoxygenated blood flows.

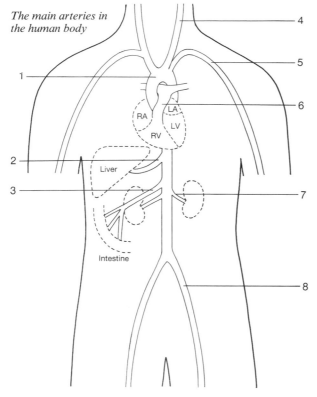

The main arteries in the human body

3 (a) Copy the figure below showing the main viens in the human body and label parts 1 to 9.
(b) Colour red the side of the heart and the veins through which oxgenated blood flows. Colour blue the side of the heart and the veins through which deoxygenated blood flows.

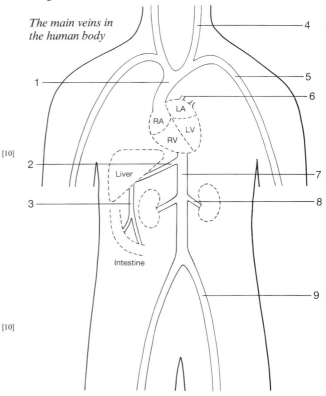

The main veins in the human body

4 (a) Distinguish between respiration and breathing. [4]
(b) Describe, with the aid of simple diagrams the processes occurring during inspiration. [10]
(c) Name two diseases or conditions which adversely affect the efficiency of the lungs, and explain why in each case. [6]

5 Below is a CT scan through the thorax. It is the view as seen from the feet end of the patient lying on her back. Identify the parts labelled 1 to 8, giving a reason for each identification. [10]

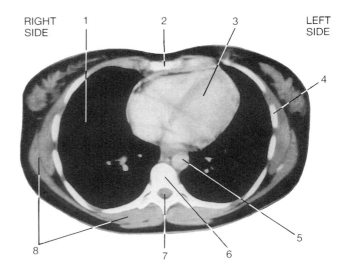

6 The diagrams below show two phases of a heartbeat, labelled **I** and **II**.

(a) Does **I** represent systole or diastole? Give a reason. [1]

(b) Name the structures **A, B, C** and **D**. [4]

(c) With reference to **I** and **II**, list in the correct sequence, the events which will occur during one heartbeat. [8]

(d) The sounds of the heartbeat are often referred to as 'lub-dup'. To which parts in the figure do these sounds relate? [2]

(Figures courtesy of the Microelectrics Education Unit, WJEC)

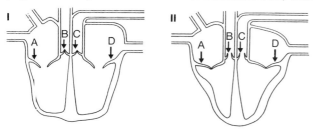

7 The diagram below represents a spirometer which can be used to measure breathing. As the person breathes in and out through the mouthpiece the upper box moves up and down so that differences in the volume of air breathed are recorded by the pen on the paper of the moving drum.

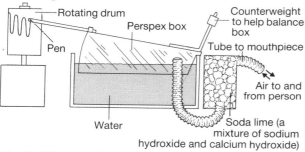

(a) (i) Why does the apparatus contain water? [1]

(ii) What is the purpose of the soda-lime? [1]

The apparatus was used before and for a short time after a period of exercise. The diagram below shows the two results.

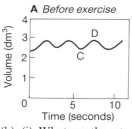
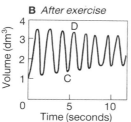

(b) (i) What was the rate of breathing (as breaths per minute) when the person was at rest before the exercise? [1]

(ii) Was the person breathing in or breathing out to cause the change between points C and D? Very briefly explain your answer. [1]

(iii) What was the maximum volume of one breath following exercise? [1]

(iv) What two things do these results tell you about the effect of exercise on breathing? [2]

(SEG: GCSE Human Biology Specimen)

8 Explain the significance of the following observations made on a person undertaking strenuous exercise:

(i) the blood flow to the skin is increased,

(ii) there is a very large increase in the blood flow to the skeletal muscles,

(iii) there is no change in the blood flow to the brain,

(iv) the blood flow to the alimentary canal is reduced. [12]

(AEB: O-level Biology)

SECTION 3
Food, Digestion and Excretion

Carbohydrates and fats

Carbohydrates are a large group of foodstuffs which include sugars, starches and fibre. Chemically, they contain only the elements carbon, hydrogen and oxygen, with the hydrogen and oxygen in the same proportion as in water – 2:1.

Types of carbohydrate

All types of carbohydrate are called saccharides. This means they consist of sugar units. There are different types of sugar unit, eg **Fig 1, A, B, C**, but they all have a ring structure.

Simple sugars (monosaccharides) contain only one sugar unit, eg:

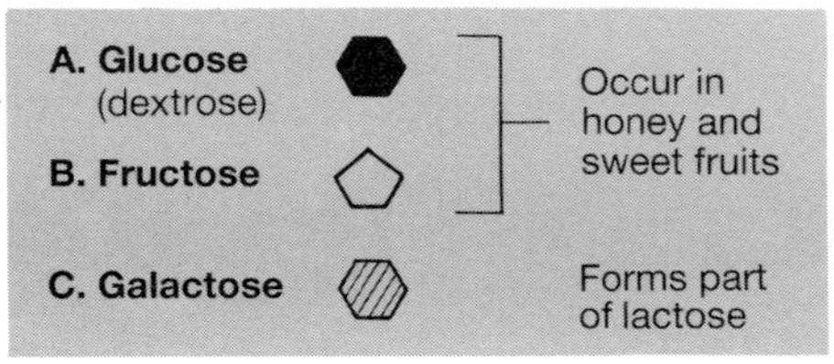

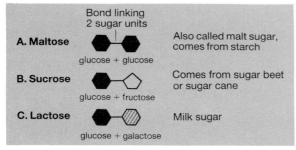

Figure 1
Simple sugars

Double sugars (disaccharides) contain two sugar units linked together chemically:

Figure 2 Double sugars

Starch, glycogen and cellulose (polysaccharides) contain hundreds or thousands of linked sugar units.

A **Starch** is made in plants. The sugar units are linked together in long chains. Starch forms the largest part of the diet of most humans.

B **Glycogen** (animal starch) is made in animals, chiefly in the liver and muscles. The sugar units are linked to form a branching chain.

C **Cellulose** is made in plants from long chains of sugar units which are grouped together into fibres. The fibres cannot be digested (broken down) in the small intestine and therefore cellulose cannot be used to supply energy.

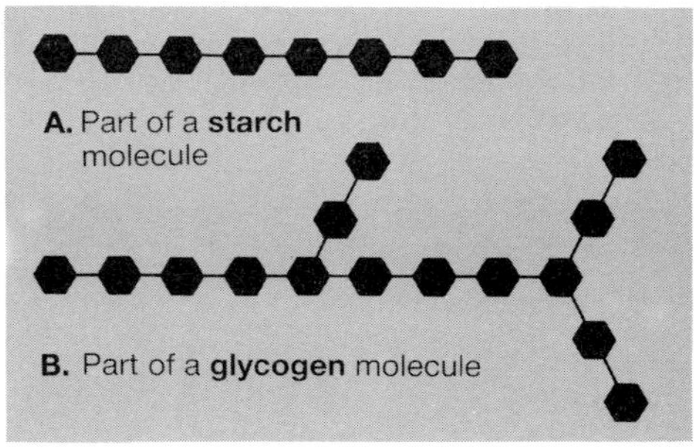

Figure 3
Polysaccharides

A. Part of a **starch** molecule

B. Part of a **glycogen** molecule

Dietary fibre is a mixture of cellulose and other plant polysaccharides such as pectin. When eaten, fibre absorbs water, swells, and makes the faeces bulkier and softer. The increased bulk stimulates the bowel muscles to become active and move the contents along, and the increased softness enables them to be moved more easily.

Fibre in food is sometimes described as either insoluble or soluble:

◆ **insoluble fibre** absorbs water (like a sponge), eg wheat bran.

◆ **soluble fibre** forms a gel with water, eg oat bran.

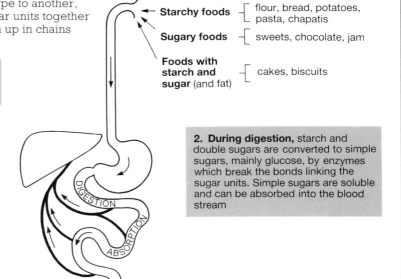

Figure 4 Carbohydrate conversion: Within the body, most carbohydrates can be converted from one type to another, either by breaking the bonds which link sugar units together – as happens in digestion, or by joining them up in chains – as when glycogen is formed from glucose.

1. Carbohydrates are eaten in:

Starchy foods — flour, bread, potatoes, pasta, chapatis

Sugary foods — sweets, chocolate, jam

Foods with starch and sugar (and fat) — cakes, biscuits

4. The level of blood sugar is kept constant by the conversion of glycogen back into glucose as necessary

3. Glucose goes to the liver, then:

A little circulates in the blood to provide the cells with energy

Some goes to the muscles to be stored as glycogen

Most is stored in the liver as glycogen

Any excess is converted into fat for storage

2. During digestion, starch and double sugars are converted to simple sugars, mainly glucose, by enzymes which break the bonds linking the sugar units. Simple sugars are soluble and can be absorbed into the blood stream

Lipids (fats and oils; cholesterol)

Fats and oils

Fats and oils are the same type of substance – they change from fats to oils, and vice versa, depending on the temperature. They are called **fats** if they are normally solid like butter, margarine and lard, and **oils** if normally liquid like olive oil, corn oil etc.

Chemically, they contain the elements carbon, hydrogen and oxygen but in different proportions to carbohydrates, and with a **higher energy value**, that is, weight for weight, fats provide more chemical energy (joules; calories). The energy ratio for 'fats and oils: carbohydrates' is 9:4.

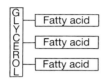

Figure 5 A molecule of fat (triacylglycerol).

Structure of fat Fats in food are mainly **triacylglycerols** (triglycerides) – so called because each molecule consists of three (tri) fatty acid (acyl) units combined with one glycerol unit. There are dozens of different fatty acids and they are combined together in various ways to form the many kinds of fat. Fats in food contain both saturated and unsaturated fatty acids, but in differing proportions:

> **Saturated fatty acids** Nearly all fatty acids in animal fats are saturated.
> **Unsaturated fatty acids** They are found in larger amounts in plant oils.

Most fatty acids can be converted from one type to another in the body as needed. But a few – the **essential fatty acids** – cannot be produced and, as they are essential to the body, they must be obtained from fat in the food.

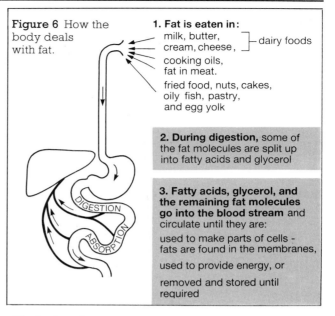

Figure 6 How the body deals with fat.

1. **Fat is eaten in:** milk, butter, cream, cheese, cooking oils, fat in meat. } dairy foods
fried food, nuts, cakes, oily fish, pastry, and egg yolk

2. **During digestion,** some of the fat molecules are split up into fatty acids and glycerol

3. **Fatty acids, glycerol, and the remaining fat molecules go into the blood stream** and circulate until they are:
used to make parts of cells - fats are found in the membranes,
used to provide energy, or
removed and stored until required

Cholesterol

It is an essential substance in the body. It circulates in the blood stream and is used in the formation of cell membranes and of some hormones. It is stored together with fat in the fatty tissues.

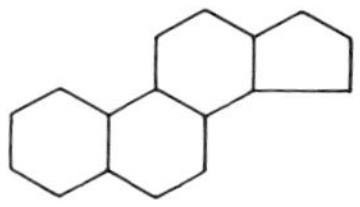

Figure 7 A cholesterol molecule.

Sources of cholesterol:

◆ Most is made in the body, mainly in the liver.
◆ A smaller amount comes from the diet – on average about 15%. It is found in the fat of animal foods – dairy produce, meat, lard and egg yolk, but not in plant foods – sunflower oil, corn oil etc.

Cholesterol and heart attacks Cholesterol is the main ingredient in the waxy substance deposited on the inside walls of arteries. This tends to block them and lead to heart attack (coronary thrombosis) – which is common in the Western World, where many people tend to eat too much of everything, especially foods containing cholesterol such as animal fats and dairy foods.

QUESTIONS

1a To which group of foodstuffs do sugar and starch belong?
b Name the three elements in carbohydrates.
c (i) What is the difference between a simple sugar and a double sugar? (ii) Draw and label diagrams to show three examples of each.
d (i) Name three types of polysaccharide. (ii) Draw two examples and describe how they differ.
2a Name some: (i) starchy foods, (ii) sugary foods, (iii) foods containing both starch and sugar.
b What happens to starch and double sugars during digestion?
c What happens to glucose when it reaches the liver?
d How is the level of blood sugar kept constant?
e (i) What is dietary fibre, (ii) What happens to it when it is eaten?

3a What is the difference between a fat and an oil?
b (i) What elements are contained in fats? (ii) How do fats differ from carbohydrates?
c Describe a molecule of fat. Illustrate your answer with a diagram.
d Why is it possible to have many kinds of fat?
e What is an essential fatty acid?
4a Name some foods containing fat.
b What happens to fat during digestion?
c What happens to fat when it goes into the blood stream?
5a Draw a diagram to show the chemical structure of a cholesterol molecule.
b Give two uses of cholesterol in the body.
c Name the two sources of cholesterol.

FURTHER WORK

Test a variety of foods for the presence of simple sugars, double sugars, starch and fat. Instructions are given on p. 216.

Protein

Protein is an essential ingredient of living matter and it forms part of the basic structure of cells. Protein contains the elements carbon, hydrogen, oxygen, nitrogen, and sometimes sulphur, phosphorus and iron. The molecules of protein can be in an insoluble form, eg collagen, keratin, or in solution, eg enzymes, plasma proteins.

Amino acids Protein molecules come in various shapes and sizes but they are all giants compared to molecules such as water and sugar. They are built up from hundreds or thousands of small units called **amino acids** which are linked together by **peptide bonds** in very long chains. Twenty-one different amino acids can occur in the proteins in the human body.

Figure 1 Part of a protein molecule built from five different types of amino acid. The rearrangement of even one amino acid, or a small change in cross-linking, would produce a different protein.

Types of protein There are a vast number of different types of protein because:

◆ of the **sequence of arrangement** of the amino acids – the number of different ways in which 21 amino acids can be arranged in a protein molecule is enormous,
◆ the chain of amino acids which make a protein molecule becomes **folded**, **coiled** and **cross-linked** in a way which is specific to each different kind of protein.

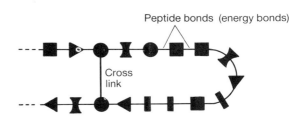

Peptide bonds (energy bonds)

Cross link

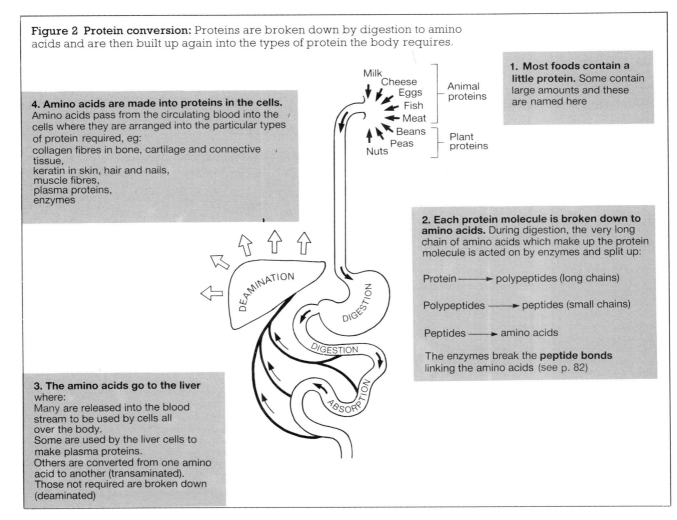

Figure 2 Protein conversion: Proteins are broken down by digestion to amino acids and are then built up again into the types of protein the body requires.

Milk
Cheese
Eggs
Fish
Meat
} Animal proteins

Beans
Peas
Nuts
} Plant proteins

1. Most foods contain a little protein. Some contain large amounts and these are named here

4. Amino acids are made into proteins in the cells. Amino acids pass from the circulating blood into the cells where they are arranged into the particular types of protein required, eg:
collagen fibres in bone, cartilage and connective tissue,
keratin in skin, hair and nails,
muscle fibres,
plasma proteins,
enzymes

DEAMINATION

DIGESTION

DIGESTION

ABSORPTION

2. Each protein molecule is broken down to amino acids. During digestion, the very long chain of amino acids which make up the protein molecule is acted on by enzymes and split up:

Protein ⟶ polypeptides (long chains)

Polypeptides ⟶ peptides (small chains)

Peptides ⟶ amino acids

The enzymes break the **peptide bonds** linking the amino acids (see p. 82)

3. The amino acids go to the liver where:
Many are released into the blood stream to be used by cells all over the body.
Some are used by the liver cells to make plasma proteins.
Others are converted from one amino acid to another (transaminated)
Those not required are broken down (deaminated)

Protein in the diet

In the average UK diet, about one-third of the protein comes from plant sources and two-thirds from animal sources. The amount of protein in nuts and dried peas and beans is very high – about the same as in meat, fish and cheese. Cereals, eg wheat, maize and rice, also contain protein, and for many people in the world cereals are the main source of protein.

Essential and non-essential amino acids Amino acids can be divided into two types:

Essential amino acids. These cannot be made in the body, so it is essential that they are present in the food which is eaten. A mixed diet normally supplies sufficient essential amino acids.

Non-essential amino acids. These can be made in the body if they are not present in the food. They are converted from other types of amino acids of which there is an excess.

The advantage of eating a mixture of foods containing protein at each meal – bread and cheese, beans on toast, cereals with milk, etc – is that a complete assortment of amino acids is likely to be present.

Deamination Amino acids cannot be stored in the body and those which are not immediately required for the body's tissues undergo the process of deamination in the liver – the nitrogen is removed from the amino acids and is converted into **urea**. The urea is carried in the blood stream from the liver to the kidneys and is excreted. The remains of the amino acids are used for energy or stored as glycogen or fat.

Personal and foreign proteins

Personal proteins ('Self' proteins) Genes control the formation of protein and, because every individual (except identical twins) has a different set of genes, then everyone will make their own slightly different range of proteins.

Foreign proteins ('Non-self' proteins) These are proteins of types different from those that the body builds for itself. Foreign proteins may get into the body in the form of:

◆ viruses,
◆ bacteria,
◆ toxins produced by bacteria,
◆ food proteins absorbed into the gut, eg those which cause food allergies,
◆ incompatible red cells when the wrong blood is transfused,
◆ transplanted tissue, eg heart, kidney, skin.

Rejection of foreign protein The body is able to recognise proteins which it does not make, and the white blood cells and antibodies set about trying to destroy and remove the 'foreign' protein. It is in this way that germs are destroyed because they contain foreign protein.

Transplants Transplanted tissue contains protein which is foreign to the person who receives the transplant, and the new owner's body will try to reject it. The patient has to be given anti-rejection drugs to suppress the rejection reaction.

Tissue typing This procedure is carried out before an organ is transplanted from one person to another to discover how closely their proteins match – the closer they are, the less the likelihood of rejection. Rejection does not happen in the case of identical twins and is less likely when the two people involved are closely related.

QUESTIONS

1a Name the units from which protein molecules are built.
 b Why is it possible for there to be so many different types of protein? Give two reasons.
 c Give two examples of: (i) insoluble proteins, (ii) soluble proteins.
2a Name eight foods which provide large amounts of protein, saying which are from animals and which from plants.
 b Describe how protein is broken down into amino acids during digestion.
 c What happens to amino acids in the liver?
 d Give examples of proteins which are made in the cells.

3a What is the difference between essential and non-essential amino acids?
 b Describe deamination.
4a What is foreign protein?
 b Name six forms of foreign proteins which may get into the body.
 c Describe the rejection of foreign protein.
 d (i) Why does the new owner's body try to reject transplanted tissue? (ii) What treatment has to be given?
 e When is tissue typing carried out and why?

FURTHER WORK

1 Draw **Fig 1**. Count the different types of amino acid. Suggest four alterations in the arrangement of the amino acids which would produce four different proteins.

2 Test a variety of foods for the presence of protein. Instructions are given on p. 216.

Vitamins and minerals

The difference between vitamins and minerals is that **vitamins** are complex organic compounds which can be made by some plants and animals, but not by humans, whereas **minerals** are inorganic substances which are not made by plants or animals or any living thing. Therefore, the vitamins and minerals the human body needs have to be taken in as food. They all have an essential part in the body's biochemistry, and they interact in a complicated manner.

A **varied diet** provides all the vitamins and minerals needed to keep healthy. They can all be stored for weeks or months in the body, so a healthy person on an average diet is very unlikely to develop a **deficiency disease** – a disease which develops when items in the diet are in short supply, **Figs** 1 and 2.

Figure 1 Some of the vitamins required by the human body.
  M – Main source in the United Kingdom
  N – Notes
  D – Deficiency disease/s

Vitamins

The chief functions of vitamins are to assist enzyme activity and to assist absorption.

When vitamins were first discovered, each was named by a letter – A, B and so on. Several of these letters are now known to include two or more vitamins and these are often referred to by their chemical names.

Vitamins A, D, E and K can be stored in the fat tissue in the body – they are fat-soluble. Vitamins B and C are water-soluble.

A few vitamins – A, B and D – are known to be poisonous when taken in excess (vitamin D can be used as a rat poison).

Minerals

Most foods contain a variety of minerals. People who have a balanced diet take in more than are needed and the surplus is either not absorbed or is excreted in the urine. About fifteen minerals are known to be required by the human body. These are shown in **Fig 2**.

VITAMINS

Vitamin A (retinol)
M Foods containing fat, eg dairy foods, margarine fish liver oils, liver.
N Can be obtained from carotene which occurs in carrots and some other vegetables and fruit.
D Night blindness; blindness in children; unhealthy skin.

The B Vitamins
A large group of vitamins which are chemically unrelated. The group includes:

Vitamin B_1 (thiamine)
M Bread, milk, vegetables and fruit.
N Added to fortified cereals such as cornflakes.
D Beri-beri – nervous disorders, muscle weakness and heart failure.

Vitamin B_2 (riboflavine)
M Milk, meat, fortified cereals, eggs.
N Destroyed by ultra-violet light.
D Skin problems.

Niacin (nicotinic acid)
M Meat, potatoes, bread, fortified cereals.
N Niacin is not the same as nicotine in tobacco.
D Pellagra – skin becomes dark and scaly.

Vitamin B_6 (pyridoxine)
M Potatoes and other vegetables, milk, meat.
N Sometimes taken for pre-menstrual tension (PMT). Excessive doses are poisonous.
D Anaemia.

The B Vitamins (contd.)

Vitamin B_{12} (cobalamine)
M Most animal products, especially liver.
N Absent in plants, therefore will be absent in a vegan diet – one which contains no animal products.
D Pernicious anaemia; weakens nerves of the legs.

Folic acid (folate)
M Green vegetables, liver, kidney, yeast, milk.
N Slightly increased amounts are required in pregnancy. Destroyed by prolonged cooking.
D Anaemia.

Vitamin C (ascorbic acid)
M Fresh fruit and vegetables.
N Disappears from food during storage and cooking.
D Scurvy – bleeding under the skin and from the gums; wounds which do not heal.

Vitamin D (calciferol)
M Foods containing fat, eg butter, margarine, herrings, egg yolk.
N With good exposure to sunlight, enough can be produced in skin for health.
D Soft bones and muscle weakness in adults; rickets in children, **Fig 3A**.

Vitamin E (tocopherol)
M Many foods.
N Never in short supply.

Vitamin K
M Green vegetables.
N Made by bacteria in the large intestine and never in short supply in a healthy person.
D Blood is slow to clot.

Figure 2 Some of the minerals required by the human body
M – Main source in the United Kingdom   **D** – Deficiency disease/s

MINERALS

Iron
M Meat, bread*, potatoes.
D Anaemia (p. 36).

Calcium
M Dairy foods, bread*, hard water.
D Weak bones. (p. 162).

*Added to white flour by Government Regulations.

Sodium and chloride (sodium chloride = common salt)
M Table salt, prepared foods.
D Salt deficiency – low blood pressure causing fainting.
   Salt deficiency can result from excessive sweating,
   vomiting or diarrhoea.

Phosphate ⎫ together with calcium, are constituents
Magnesium ⎭ of bones and teeth
Potassium – required by cells.
M Vegetables, meat, milk.
D Muscular weakness.

Trace elements
These minerals are only required in very small quantities:

Iodine – for thyroid hormone.
M Iodised table salt, milk, sea food.
D Goitre.

Cobalt – required for vitamin B_{12}.
Fluoride – hardens teeth and bones.
Zinc – present in some enzymes.
Selenium, copper, chromium and manganese are
other trace elements.

Figure 3 Some deficiency diseases

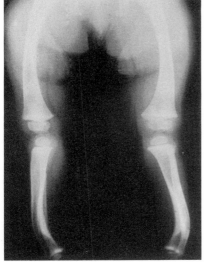

James Paget Hospital, Gorleston, Gt Yarmouth

A.Rickets. Children's bones do not form properly,
are soft and weak and bend under pressure, due to
lack of vitamin D.

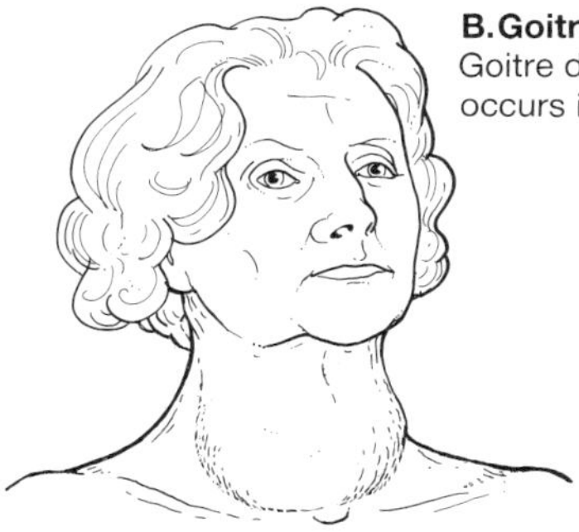

B.Goitre. Swollen thyroid gland.
Goitre due to lack of iodine rarely
occurs in the UK nowadays

C.Kwashiorkor (pronounced
quosh-ee-or-kor) — Children have
pot-bellies which are swollen
with water, their hair becomes
frizzy and reddish, and muscles
waste away, due to **starvation**
— deficiency of protein, calories,
vitamins and minerals.

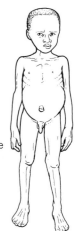

Table 1   Vitamins

Vitamin	Main sources	Notes	Deficiency disease/s

Table 2   Minerals

Mineral	Main sources	Deficiency disease/s

QUESTIONS

1a Describe the difference between
   vitamins and minerals.
 b Name four fat-soluble vitamins.
 c Which vitamins are water soluble?
 d Which vitamins are known to be
   poisonous when taken in excess?

2 Copy and complete Table 1 with information about the vitamins named
   in **Fig 1**.

3a How many minerals are essential for
   humans?
 b What are trace elements?
 c Use information in **Fig 2** to complete
   Table 2 for iron, calcium, sodium,
   chloride, iodine.

4a When do deficiency diseases
   develop?
 b Describe the deficiency diseases in
   Fig 3.

FURTHER WORK

1 When were vitamins discovered? Why
is the name Gowland Hopkins linked with
vitamins? How did they get the name
vitamin? How many vitamins are there?

2 a Compare the amount of vitamin C
in different types of fruit juice, squash,
milk, carrot juice and liquid extracted from
other vegetables. Instructions are given
on p. 215.

 b How can you make the experiment
more accurate?

 c Devise an experiment to find out if
vitamin C is affected by (i) boiling,
(ii) storage.

Metabolism

Metabolism is the term used to sum up all the chemical reactions which occur in living cells – activities which depend on **energy** and on **enzymes**. Metabolism involves two processes:

◆ **catabolism** – food molecules are broken down into smaller molecules, at the same time releasing energy: **Fig 1A**.

◆ **anabolism** – small molecules derived from food are built up into larger molecules, at the same time using up energy: **Fig 1B**.

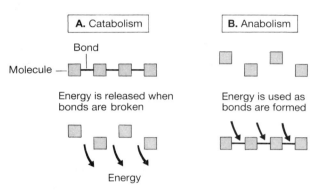

Figure 1 **A** Catabolism **B** Anabolism

Energy

At any one time enormous numbers of chemical reactions are taking place inside a living cell which either release energy or require it.

Release of energy Energy is present in food (e.g. glucose) in the form of chemical energy, and oxygen is usually required for its release. The two processes involved in energy release inside a cell are:

◆ **Respiration** – glucose is broken down to carbon dioxide and water. The energy released is in two forms:

  Heat. Heat is needed to maintain the body temperature at 37°C, the temperature at which enzymes in the human body work best.
  Chemical energy. Energy released by respiration is stored in ATP (p. 59).

◆ **Conversion of ATP** stored in the cell to ADP and phosphate: **Fig 2**.

Need for energy Energy is required for:

◆ **Building** larger molecules from smaller ones (synthesis), eg to make proteins and other materials to build and maintain the cells.

◆ **Transport** of substances within the cell.

◆ **Special uses** in different types of cell, eg for:
  contraction by muscle cells.
  transmission of impulses by nerve cells.
  movement of cilia by ciliated cells.
  secretion by gland cells.

◆ **Heat**, to replace the heat energy being continuously lost.

Energy release from food

Glucose is the main food substance used for energy. If this is in short supply, glycogen stored in the cell will be converted into glucose and used. Fats are used later if required, and protein from the muscles is used last.

The conversion of glucose to carbon dioxide involves nearly 30 different steps, and in several steps energy is released. A living cell requires a continuous supply of energy. There is not enough ATP in the cell to store large amounts of energy, so when cells require an increased amount of energy, more ATP is produced by cell respiration (p. 59) using glucose reaching the cells from the blood stream.

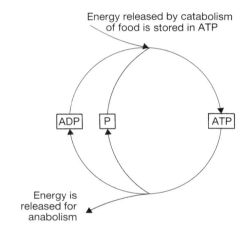

Figure 2 ATP⇌ADP

Enzyme control of metabolism

Enzymes are made inside cells and they speed up the chemical reactions on which life itself depends. Most enzymes – the **intracellular enzymes** – speed up the many different chemical reactions which take place within cells. **Extracellular enzymes** are secreted from the cells in which they are made and have an effect elsewhere, eg digestive enzymes (p. 80).

Properties of enzymes

Enzymes are proteins.

Enzymes are catalysts, that is, they speed up chemical reactions but are not themselves altered or consumed. Only a small quantity of an enzyme is required as it can be used over and over again.

Enzymes are specific, that is, an enzyme acts on only one substance and will not normally act on another substance. Therefore a very large number of enzymes are required for all the different chemical reactions that take place in the body.

Enzymes are affected by temperature. They work best at about 37°C – body temperature – and are destroyed by heat above 50°C.

Enzymes are sensitive to pH. Most intracellular enzymes work best in neutral conditions – pH 7. The digestive enzymes in the stomach require an acid medium and work best at pH 2.

Metabolic rate

The **metabolic rate** is the amount of energy used by the body in a set time. It is expressed in either:
  joules per second, or
  calories per second.
The faster the cells work, the greater is the demand for energy and the higher the metabolic rate. This results in an increase in both the rate and depth of breathing and the speed of circulation in order to:
  supply more oxygen,
  supply more glucose,
  remove extra carbon dioxide,
  remove excess heat.

Factors which affect the metabolic rate: Fig 3

The metabolic rate is influenced by a number of factors:

◆ **Resting metabolic rate (RMR)** – Fig 4.
◆ **Muscle activity** – The energy required by muscles for all the many activities of daily life as well as for strenuous physical exercise.
◆ **Digestion.** The energy used for digestion increases the metabolic rate for several hours after a meal. More energy is required to digest protein than carbohydrates or fats.
◆ **Environmental temperature.** Exposure to cold increases the metabolic rate and the extra heat produced helps to maintain body temperature. This is why more food is required in winter than in summer.

Resting metabolic rate: RMR
(Basal metabolic rate: BMR)

The RMR varies between individuals. It is influenced by a number of factors:

◆ **Surface area.** A small person has a relatively higher RMR than a large person because, proportionally, there is a greater surface area through which heat can be lost.
◆ **Age.** RMR decreases with age.
◆ **Sex.** Men have a higher RMR than women because they have a higher proportion of muscle tissue and less fat.
◆ **Thyroid hormones.** These control the rate of metabolism. Too much hormone speeds up metabolism. Too little hormone has the opposite effect.
◆ **Body temperature.** This affects the rate of RMR. It increases when the body temperature rises above normal due to fever.

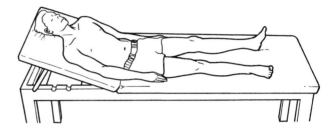

Figure 4 Resting metabolic rate (RMR) is the amount of energy required to maintain life when the body is at complete mental and physical rest. It is measured: lying down and at complete rest in a comfortably warm, quiet room 12–18 hours after the last meal.

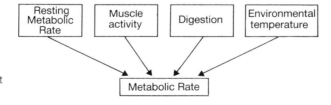

Figure 3 Factors which affect the metabolic rate

Food and diet

Food is any solid or liquid which can supply the body with substances for:
◆ growth,
◆ repair and replacement of tissues,
◆ energy.

Composition of food

All foods are composed of one or more of the following types of substance:

Main use in the body

1. **Carbohydrates**⎫
⎬ for energy
2. **Fats**⎭

3. **Proteins**————— for growth and repair of the tissues

4. **Minerals**⎫ to keep the body working
⎬ normally and to prevent
5. **Vitamins**⎭ deficiency diseases

6. **Fibre**————— for healthy functioning of the digestive system

7. **Water**————— for all chemical activities

These are called **nutrients**.

Diet

Diet means the kind and amount of food which is regularly consumed by eating and drinking. A person's diet depends on:
◆ the type of food which is available,
◆ cultural differences – affected by the place where, and the people with whom the person was brought up,
◆ personal preference,
◆ the level of physical activity,
◆ the money available for food.

Balanced diet A balanced diet is one which contains suitable amounts of carbohydrates, fats, proteins, vitamins, minerals and fibre to stay healthy.

The diet of babies

Babies are fed entirely on milk for the first few months of life, either from the breast or bottle. Milk is about 90% water and 10% nutrients, and it contains all the substances that a young baby needs.

Breast milk It is the natural food for babies:
◆ It contains all the necessary food ingredients for healthy growth and in the right amounts.
◆ It is easy for the baby to digest and absorb.
◆ It contains antibodies from the mother which help to protect the baby against infections.
◆ It is clean – fully breast-fed babies are much less likely to get gastro-enteritis.
◆ It is safe – it cannot be prepared incorrectly and does not cause allergies.

Bottle-fed babies Babies who are bottle-fed are usually given 'Infant formula'. This is a type of dried milk made from cow's milk which has been altered to make it more like breast milk.

Table 1 Nutrients in milk per 100 cm³

Nutrient	Breast milk	Cow's milk
Sugar	6.6 g	4.4 g
Protein	1.2 g	3.0 g
Fat	3.8 g	3.8 g
Minerals	0.4 g	0.8 g
Vitamins	traces	traces

Substances not present in milk Milk does not contain:
◆ **Iron** – the baby is born with several months' supply stored in the liver.
◆ **starch** – a new baby does not possess the right enzymes to digest starch.
◆ **fibre** – the digestive system has no need for fibre in the first few months.

Weaning Weaning is the gradual change of diet from milk to a mixture of foods, and it usually begins at 3–4 months. By the age of one year, the child will be eating a mixed diet similar to the rest of the family.

Energy in food

The energy in food is locked up in the bonds which hold the molecules together (p. 68). It is released when the food is split up by enzymes into its small parts.

Calories and joules Energy in food is measured in either **kilocalories** (kcal = 1000 calories) or in **kilojoules** (kJ = 1000 joules).
    1 kcal = 4.184 kJ (4.2 kJ approx.)
    1000 kJ = 1 MJ (megajoule).
In everyday usage, a kilocalorie is often just called a calorie.

Energy requirements

The energy a person requires, in terms of calories (or joules), varies greatly from one person to another, and from day to day, depending on:
◆ age,
◆ physical activity,
◆ whether the person is male or female.

Table 2 Examples of typical daily energy requirements

Age		kcal	MJ
At 1 year		about 800	about 3
At 2 years		1100–1300	4.5–5.5
At 8 years		1800–2000	7.5–8.5
Boys 12–18		2600–3600	11–15
Men 18–40	inactive	2500–2800	10.5–12
	very active	3500–3800	14.5–16
40–60	inactive	2400–2600	10–11
	very active	3500–3800	14.5–16
60–80		2100–2500	9–10.5
Girls 12–18		2400–3400	10–14
Women 18–40	inactive	2000–2200	8.5–9
	very active	2400–2600	10–11
40–60	inactive	1900–2100	8–9
	very active	2300–2500	9.5–10.5
60–80		1800–2100	7.5–9

Note. The energy requirements for women are slightly higher during pregnancy and lactation.

Appetite

The **appetite** – the desire to eat – is controlled by the **appetite centre** in the hypothalamus of the brain. **Hunger** – a feeling of emptiness – is one of a number of factors which can stimulate the appetite centre and result in a desire to eat, **Fig 1**.

Loss of appetite can be due to:
◆ illness,
◆ depression,
◆ tension
◆ anorexia nervosa.

Dieting

If a person **goes on a diet** it means making deliberate changes in the kinds and/or the amounts of foods which are regularly eaten. This is normally done in order to slim or for medical reasons.

Slimming   Weight is lost when fewer calories are eaten than are used up by the body's activities. Two rules for slimmers are:
◆ reduce calorie intake – **eat less**.
◆ increase calorie output – **exercise more**.

Anorexia nervosa

Anorexia nervosa means nervous loss of appetite, and it usually occurs in teenage girls. These girls consider themselves to be too fat even though they are very thin, so they refuse to eat. Occasionally they may gorge and then either make themselves vomit or take laxatives in excess.

This condition is sometimes called 'slimmer's disease' because the sufferers lose so much weight that it makes them ill. They become very thin, their bones stick out, their periods stop, they may become too weak to stand up and in need of hospital care.

Treatment is variable, but will include skilled counselling of both the patient and the parents in order to try to understand the reasons for the problem. In many patients it appears to be due to their failure to accept adult sexuality.

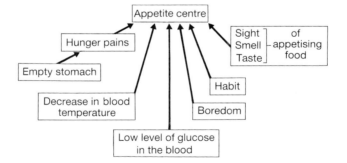

Figure 1 Factors which stimulate the appetite centre

QUESTIONS

1a What is food?
 b List the five nutrients in food and, for each, give the main use in the body.
 c Two other substances besides the nutrients are present in food. Name them and give their main function.

2a Give the meaning of:
 (i) diet, (ii) a balanced diet.
 b What does a person's diet depend on?

3a List three substances that milk does not contain, and say why each is not important in the diet of young babies.
 b Give five reasons why breast milk is the natural food for babies.

 c Name two ways in which the nutrients in breast milk and cow's milk differ.
 d What is meant by weaning?

4a Name the units in which energy in food is measured.
 b What does a person's energy requirements depend on?
 c Give the average daily energy requirement for a child aged: (i) 1 year, (ii) 2 years, (iii) 8 years.
 d From **Table 2**, compare the typical energy requirements of an inactive man of 20 with: (i) a very active man of the same age, (ii) a very active woman of the same age.

5a Whereabouts in the body is the appetite controlled?
 b List the factors which stimulate the appetite centre.
 c Give four reasons for loss of appetite.

FURTHER WORK

1 Use the information in **Table 2** to draw a bar chart showing differences between the average daily energy requirements of males and females.
2 Complete exercise 2, p. 94.

More about food

Variety of foods

A great variety of plant and animal materials can be used as food for humans. Some can be eaten raw, others have to be cooked to make them:
- edible (can be eaten);
- palatable (pleasant to eat);
- digestible (able to be broken down and used by the body).

Cooking

- enables a much wider range of plant and animals material to be used as food.
- can soften food and make it more digestible.
- changes the flavour, thus providing more variety.
- may improve the keeping quality by destroying microbes and enzymes in it.
- may destroy some of the nutrients, eg vitamins, or they may be lost, eg when the water in which vegetables are cooked is thrown away.

Figure 1 Average servings of popular foods

Pork chop 150g
Carrots 100g
Cabbage 100g
Boiled potatoes 100g
Gravy 50g

Chicken 150g
Jacket potato 150g
Tomato 40g
Lettuce 10g
Cucumber 15g
Salad cream 15g

Chocolate gateau 100g
Cream 30g

Crispbread, per slice 15g
Cottage cheese 75g
Apple 100g

Yoghurt, fruit, 150g

Spaghetti 100g
Meat sauce 120g

Biscuit 10g

Fish fingers 30g each
Chips 100g
Peas 75g

Treacle tart 100g
Custard 150g

Apple pie 60g
Ice-cream 50g

Fruit cake 50g

Chocolate bar 60g

Cheese and bacon flan 150g
Coleslaw 40g

Crisps 30g

Peanuts 50g

Beefburger 120g
White bread roll 50g
Tomato ketchup 10g

Wholemeal bread 50g
Cheese, cheddar 50g
Butter 7g
Pickle 15g

Milk, glass 200g
in tea or coffee 20g

Rice 100g
Curry, chicken or vegetable 200g

Pizza 150g

Egg 50g
White bread, per slice 25g
Margarine 7g
Jam/marmalade 10g

Wholemeal bread
Ham 50g
Butter 14g

Beer 285g (285 ml, ½ pint)

Orange juice 100g

Bacon 40g
Sausage 60g
Baked beans 75g

Cornflakes 20g
Milk 100g

Sugar 5g per spoonful

Wine 120g (120 ml)

Meat pie 200g

Fizzy drinks 200g

Figure 2 Food consumed by one person in a day

White bread, margarine, jam

Tea with milk and 1 spoonful of sugar

Cornflakes and milk

Ice-cream and apple pie

Coffee with milk

Pork chops with fat, carrots, peas and boiled potatoes

Milk

Apple and Pizza

Chocolate bar

Figure 3 Table showing the composition of some popular foods per 100 g. **Note**: The values given above are typical for the foods named. When foods are fried, they lose water and gain fat, and therefore will have a higher calorific value.

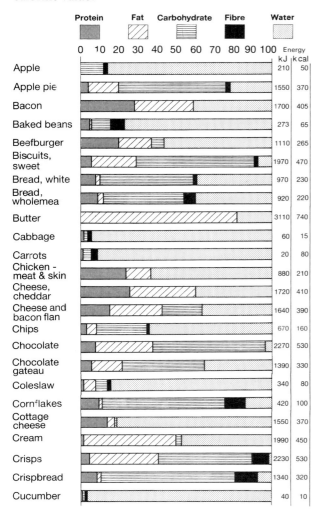

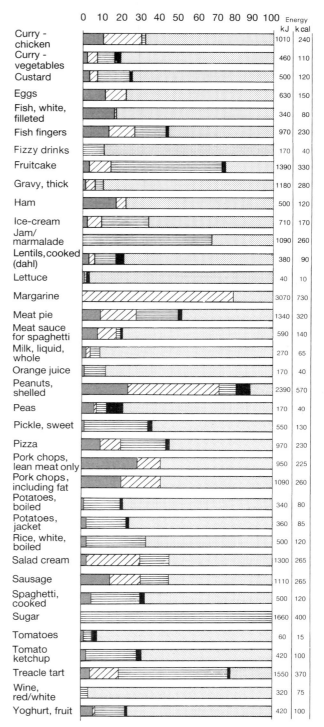

QUESTIONS

1 Give five effects of cooking on food.

2 Study **Fig 3**, then select: (i) five foods with the most protein, (ii) two foods containing large amounts of protein and carbohydrate, (iii) two foods containing large amounts of protein and fat, (iv) two foods containing large amounts of protein, carbohydrate and fat, (v) five foods with the most fibre.

3 Foods with a **high energy value** are those which contain a high proportion of fat or carbohydrate and little water. Foods with a **low energy value** are those with little fat or carbohydrate and a large amount of water. From **Fig 3**, name: (i) four foods with a high energy value, (ii) four foods with a low energy value.

4 Place the following foods in order of the number of calories they contain, from highest to lowest: 100 g white bread, 80 g jacket potato, 60 g chips, 40 g apple, 30 g rice, 20 g crispbread, 10 g milk chocolate. The necessary information to calculate the answer is given in **Fig 3**.

FURTHER WORK

1 Consider the day's intake of food in **Fig 2**: (i) Which foods shown here are unsuitable for a diabetic who cannot eat sugar? Suggest which foods shown in **Fig 1** should be eaten instead. (ii) Which foods should be omitted for a person on a low-fat diet? (iii) Which foods would not be eaten by a vegetarian – a person who does not eat meat? Suggest foods which could be eaten instead.

2 List the foods you ate yesterday. Do you consider you did, or did not, have a healthy diet? Give your reasons.

3 Carry out exercise 7, page 94, either using the foods shown in **Fig 2** or choosing your own selection from **Fig 1**.

73

Food preservation and additives

When food is stored for use at a later date it is important to prevent it being damaged by the activities of:

◆ microbes – bacteria and fungi,
◆ insects – flies, weevils, grubs,
◆ mammals – mice, rats,
◆ natural chemical changes (due to enzymes) which take place within the food.

This can be done in part by correct storage conditions. However, many foods need special treatment – preserving – if they are to be kept for any length of time.

Figure 1
Preserved foods

Kippers being cured

Meat sealed in a plastic bag

Pack of tomatoes

Chicken

Meat pie

FRIDGE

Vacuum pack of bacon

FREEZER

Ways of preserving food against microbes

Sterilisation (killing microbes and their spores)

◆ **Canning.** Food is heated to temperatures which are high enough to kill microbes and spores. Whilst the food remains in a sealed can it cannot be contaminated.
◆ **Irradiation.** Pre-packed food is given small doses of gamma rays to destroy any microbes or spores, and new microbes cannot get in until the pack is opened. No radiation remains in the food after it has been treated.

Preventing microbe activity

◆ **Drying.** Most of the water is removed from the food, and microbes cannot live without water.
◆ **Curing.** Salt or smoke are used to remove water.
◆ **Pickling.** Vinegar (ethanoic acid) is too acid for microbe activity.
◆ **Jam-making.** The high sugar content of jam prevents growth of microbes.

Delaying microbe activity

◆ **Pasteurisation.** Milk is heated to 63°C for 30 minutes or 72°C for 15 seconds, and then cooled rapidly. This method of heat treatment does not destroy all bacteria, but it kills those capable of causing disease.
◆ **Refrigeration.** Low temperatures reduce microbe activity, but do not stop it altogether. Refrigeration is therefore suitable for short-term storage only.
◆ **Freezing.** Temperatures of − 18°C can stop bacterial growth, but the bacteria will not be killed. When the temperature rises again, the bacteria become active and multiply. If the food is then re-frozen, it will contain an increased number of bacteria.

Food additives

Food additives are chemicals which are added to food. Additives have always been added to food to preserve it. Salt, sugar and vinegar are obvious examples but there were others. Nowadays more than 3000 substances are used as additives, many for purposes other than preservation such as to

make food look attractive,
make it smell appetising,
make it taste different,
disguise the ingredients,
make it easier and therefore cheaper to process,
give it a longer shelf-life – which makes food cheaper and more convenient.

E-numbers

Additives which are generally recognised as safe by the European Economic Community (EEC; the Common Market) are given a serial number – an **E-number**. The E-numbers enable the additives to be identified more easily and are simpler to use than many of the long and complicated chemical names. Foods containing additives with E-numbers can be moved between countries in the EEC.

Some types of additive

Colours (E100–E180)

Colours are used to make food more colourful and attractive or to change its colour.

Examples. Colouring is added to butter and margarine to make them yellow, to cheese to make it yellow or red, and to tinned peas to make them greener. Protein obtained from soya beans can be changed from its natural grey colour to the colour of meat.

Preservatives (E200–290)

Preservatives are added to prevent microbe growth and enable food to be stored for a longer time.

Examples. **Nitrates** and **nitrites** are used for preserving meat and meat products. Dried fruit, fruit juices and white wine can be preserved with **sulphur dioxide** (E220). **Vinegar – ethanoic (acetic) acid** (E260) – is used to flavour food as well as to preserve it.

Anti-oxidants (E300–E320)

Anti-oxidants prevent oxygen in the air from oxidising the food and making it unfit to eat.

Examples. **Butylated hydroxytoluene** (BHT, E321) is added to butter, margarine and lard to prevent the fat from turning rancid. **Vitamin C – ascorbic acid** (E300) is added to cut fruit to prevent discoloration.

Emulsifiers and stabilisers (some numbers between E322 and E494)

Emulsifiers allow oil and water to mix, and stabilisers prevent them from separating out again. They are used to thicken foods but, at the same time, they disguise the amount of fat or water that the food contains.

Examples. **Lecithin** (E322), an emulsifier which occurs naturally in eggs and soya beans, is used in confectionery and commercially prepared puddings. Some **polyphosphates** enable meat products such as frozen chicken and cooked ham to retain additional water.

Flavour enhancers

Enhancers improve the taste of food but have little flavour of their own.

Example. **Monosodium glutamate** (E621) is added to bring out the flavour by increasing the amount of saliva produced or by stimulating the taste buds.

Bulking agents

These are added to give bulk to food but they do not contain calories.

Examples. **Water** is the main additive of this type. Another is fibre – **cellulose** (E460).

Vitamins

These are added to:
◆ replace those lost in the processing,
◆ increase the vitamin content.

Examples. **Vitamins A** and **D** are added to margarine. **Vitamin C** is added to some fruit juices. Most breakfast cereals have **B vitamins** added.

Additives and ill-health

Any additive which was known to cause widespread ill-health would be withdrawn from the list of those permitted to be added to food. But some individuals seem to be sensitive to certain colourings, flavourings or preservatives, for example:

◆ **Tartrazine** (E102) – a commonly used yellow colouring in fizzy drinks, convenience foods and medicines. It can be the cause of skin rashes, hay fever, blurred vision, purple patches on the skin, and may possibly be linked with hyperactivity in some children, or with asthma.
◆ **Sunset yellow** (E110) – a yellow colour widely used in convenience foods. It may produce skin rashes.

QUESTIONS

1 Answer the questions **a–d**. Give examples from **Fig 1** of foods preserved in each of the ways mentioned in your answers.
  a Describe two ways in which food can be sterilised.
  b List four ways of preventing the activity of microbes.
  c What is pasteurisation?
  d Explain the difference between refrigeration and freezing.

2a What is meant by 'food additives'?
  b (i) Name three additives which have always been in use. (ii) Why have they been used?

  c For what purposes, other than preservation, are additives used these days?
  d (i) What are E-numbers? (ii) Why are they useful?

3 Give reasons, with examples, of why each of the following are added to food: (i) colours, (ii) preservatives, (iii) anti-oxidants, (iv) emulsifiers and stabilisers, (v) flavour enhancers, (vi) bulking agents, (vii) vitamins.

4a To which types of additive are some individuals sensitive?
  b Give two examples of additives which have been linked with ill-health.

FURTHER WORK

1 Study the labels from a variety of foods. What types of additives have been included?

2 Complete exercise 5, p. 94.

Mouth and teeth

Functions of the mouth

The mouth has several functions:
- ◆ It is the point of entry to the body for food and drink.
- ◆ It chews food and mixes with saliva to help with swallowing.
- ◆ It enables food to be tasted.
- ◆ It is an air passage to the lungs.
- ◆ It makes speech possible.
- ◆ It expresses feelings.

'Coated' tongue   The surface of the tongue is constantly shed and replaced (like the skin), with the debris being cleared away by saliva. If the flow of saliva is reduced due to thirst, fever or loss of appetite, the mouth feels dry and the debris is not removed. The surface of the tongue becomes white and is said to be 'coated' or 'furred'.

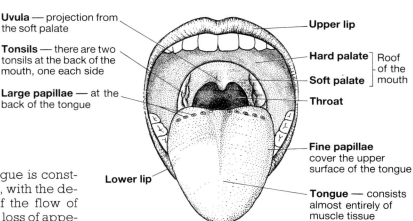

Uvula — projection from the soft palate

Tonsils — there are two tonsils at the back of the mouth, one each side

Large papillae — at the back of the tongue

Upper lip

Hard palate ⎤ Roof
Soft palate ⎦ of the mouth

Throat

Lower lip

Fine papillae cover the upper surface of the tongue

Tongue — consists almost entirely of muscle tissue

Figure 1 The mouth open and the tongue out

Teeth

Teeth are used for biting and chewing food. There are four different types:
- ◆ **Incisors** – situated in the front of the mouth and with chisel-like edges for biting.
- ◆ **Canines** – rather pointed and can be used for tearing off pieces of food.
- ◆ **Premolars** – have a flatter surface and are used for grinding food into small pieces.
- ◆ **Molars** – similar to premolars but larger. Generally, the upper molars have three roots, the lower molars two roots and the other teeth have a single root.

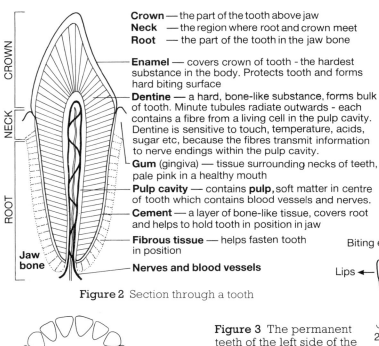

Crown — the part of the tooth above jaw
Neck — the region where root and crown meet
Root — the part of the tooth in the jaw bone

Enamel — covers crown of tooth - the hardest substance in the body. Protects tooth and forms hard biting surface

Dentine — a hard, bone-like substance, forms bulk of tooth. Minute tubules radiate outwards - each contains a fibre from a living cell in the pulp cavity. Dentine is sensitive to touch, temperature, acids, sugar etc, because the fibres transmit information to nerve endings within the pulp cavity.

Gum (gingiva) — tissue surrounding necks of teeth, pale pink in a healthy mouth

Pulp cavity — contains **pulp,** soft matter in centre of tooth which contains blood vessels and nerves.

Cement — a layer of bone-like tissue, covers root and helps to hold tooth in position in jaw

Fibrous tissue — helps fasten tooth in position

Nerves and blood vessels

CROWN NECK ROOT Jaw bone

Figure 2 Section through a tooth

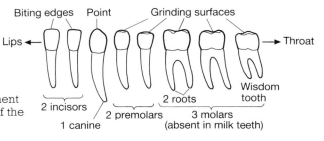

Biting edges   Point   Grinding surfaces

Lips ◄   ► Throat

2 incisors
1 canine
2 premolars
2 roots
3 molars (absent in milk teeth)
Wisdom tooth

Figure 3 The permanent teeth of the left side of the lower jaw

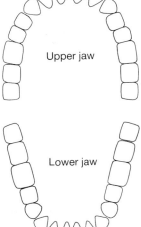

Upper jaw

Lower jaw

Figure 4 Plan of the teeth in the permanent set

The two sets of teeth   The first set of teeth – **milk teeth** (deciduous teeth) – begin to appear when the child is a few months old. There are twenty milk teeth, ten in each jaw – four incisors, two canines and four molars.

From the age of five onwards the roots of the milk teeth gradually disappear and the teeth fall out. They are replaced by larger, **permanent teeth**. When complete, the permanent set contains thirty-two teeth, sixteen in each jaw. Counting from the mid-line of the jaw, on each side there are two incisors, one canine, two premolars and three molars.

Tooth decay (caries)

Bacteria are always present in the mouth and some types help to keep it healthy. They become very active in the presence of sugar and produce acids, mainly **lactic acid**.

Sugar remains in the mouth for about half an hour after eating something sweet, or even longer if it was sticky food. The longer time that sugar is in the mouth, the more chance there is of tooth decay.

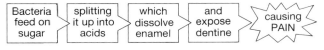

Figure 5 Usual pattern of tooth decay.

Plaque   Plaque consists of bacteria in a sticky paste which sticks onto and between the teeth, and is not washed away by saliva. It holds the acids onto the tooth surface, particularly at the gum margin.

Tartar   Tartar is calcified plaque – plaque made hard by materials deposited on the teeth from saliva. It provides shelter for bacteria and can also damage the gums.

Root abscess

The bacteria which cause a root abscess usually enter the tooth through an area of decay and then spread through the pulp to the root, **Fig 5**. The tooth often has to be extracted to relieve the pressure caused by the inflammation and pus. **Pus** contains living and dead bacteria, debris, damaged tissue, white cells and serum.

Infected gums (gingivitis)

Gums infected by bacteria become swollen and sore, cause an unpleasant taste in the mouth and make the breath smell. This condition may develop because the teeth are not being cleaned properly, allowing plaque and tartar to build up. **Bleeding gums** when the teeth are being brushed is a first sign of gingivitis.

The condition can usually be cured by a new toothbrush more thorough cleaning, and a mouth-wash such as dilute hydrogen peroxide. If allowed to continue for a long time, the jaw bone around the teeth can be destroyed, and the teeth may loosen and fall out.

Keeping teeth healthy

A number of things can be done to prevent teeth from decaying:

◆ **Sugary foods**, if eaten, should be taken all at one go, and then the teeth cleaned to remove sugar from the mouth. This applies to sweets and chocolates, sweet drinks and sweet foods.

◆ Drinking water should contain a minute amount of **fluoride** while the teeth are developing to help produce strong teeth. Fluoride toothpaste helps to keep them healthy by strengthening the enamel. The teeth of children who have too much fluoride become discoloured.

◆ A healthy diet for teeth includes plenty of foods which require **chewing** to keep the gums in good condition.

◆ Cleaning the teeth by brushing and flossing at least once a day removes plaque and prevents the build-up of bacteria. **Brushing** removes plaque from the surface of the teeth, and **flossing** removes plaque from between the teeth and from the crevices. Dental floss is like strong thread, and is pulled to and fro between the teeth to remove plaque near the gum where a toothbrush cannot reach.

◆ Regular **dental check-ups** enable any decay to be treated at an early stage and stopped by a small filling. Also, regular scaling and polishing removes tartar.

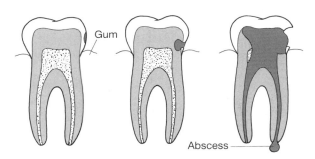

Figure 6 Development of a tooth abscess. An **abscess** is a collection of pus.

FURTHER WORK

1   Copy **Fig 4**. How many of each type of tooth – incisors, canines, premolars and molars – are present in the permanent set? Study your own teeth in the mirror, then mark on your plan any fillings or missing teeth.

2   **Discover how well you clean your teeth**
Disclosing tablets contain a harmless dye which stains plaque a pink colour:
1. Chew a disclosing tablet, swishing saliva around in the mouth as you do so.
2. Rinse the mouth out with water.
3. Inspect the teeth for pink-stained plaque.
4. Brush the teeth in your usual manner.
5. Inspect the teeth again to check if any plaque remains. This can be removed by using dental floss.

QUESTIONS

1a Give six functions of the mouth.
 b Name the two parts of the roof of the mouth.
2a Draw and label a section through a tooth.
 b Describe the: **(i)** crown, **(ii)** root, **(iii)** neck, **(iv)** pulp, **(v)** cement, **(vi)** fibrous tissue.
 c Name the hardest substance in the body and describe its functions.
 d Describe dentine and explain how this tissue is able to be sensitive to touch etc.
3a Name the two sets of teeth and give the number of teeth in each set.

 b Name and describe the four types of teeth. Draw one example of each type.
4a Describe the usual pattern of tooth decay.
 b Explain why tooth decay is encouraged by: **(i)** eating something sweet, **(ii)** plaque, **(iii)** tartar.
 c **(i)** What is an abscess? **(ii)** Describe pus. **(iii)** Draw diagrams to show the development of a root abscess.
 d **(i)** Name one sign of infected gums. **(ii)** Give three suggestions to help remedy the condition.
 e Give some suggestions for keeping teeth healthy.

Digestive system

The **digestive system** consists of the following:
- ◆ **Teeth** (p. 76).
- ◆ **Alimentary canal** – a long tube through which the food passes.
- ◆ **Digestive glands** which secrete digestive juices into the alimentary canal.

Alimentary canal

The alimentary canal – the **gut** – is a muscular tube extending from mouth to anus. Different parts are specialised for different functions and form the mouth, oesophagus, stomach, small intestine, large intestine, rectum and anus.

Figure 1 The digestive system

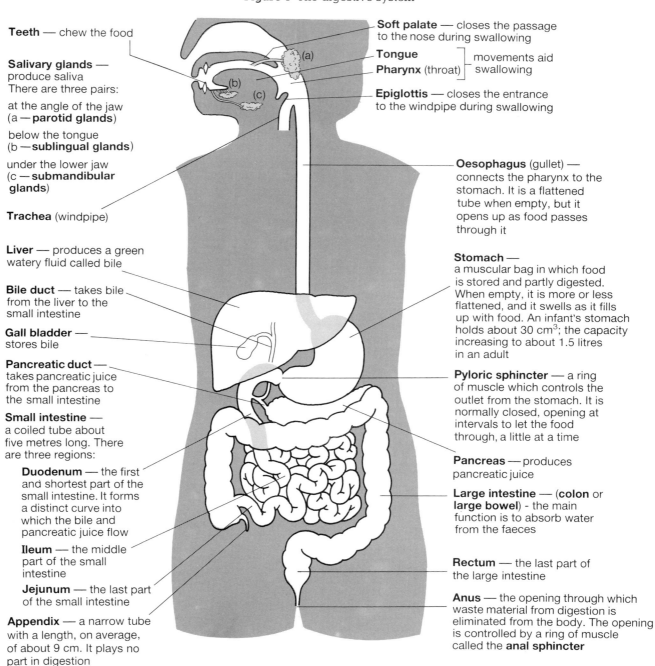

Teeth — chew the food

Salivary glands — produce saliva
There are three pairs:

at the angle of the jaw (a — **parotid glands**)

below the tongue (b — **sublingual glands**)

under the lower jaw (c — **submandibular glands**)

Trachea (windpipe)

Liver — produces a green watery fluid called bile

Bile duct — takes bile from the liver to the small intestine

Gall bladder — stores bile

Pancreatic duct — takes pancreatic juice from the pancreas to the small intestine

Small intestine — a coiled tube about five metres long. There are three regions:

Duodenum — the first and shortest part of the small intestine. It forms a distinct curve into which the bile and pancreatic juice flow

Ileum — the middle part of the small intestine

Jejunum — the last part of the small intestine

Appendix — a narrow tube with a length, on average, of about 9 cm. It plays no part in digestion

Soft palate — closes the passage to the nose during swallowing

Tongue
Pharynx (throat) } movements aid swallowing

Epiglottis — closes the entrance to the windpipe during swallowing

Oesophagus (gullet) — connects the pharynx to the stomach. It is a flattened tube when empty, but it opens up as food passes through it

Stomach — a muscular bag in which food is stored and partly digested. When empty, it is more or less flattened, and it swells as it fills up with food. An infant's stomach holds about 30 cm^3; the capacity increasing to about 1.5 litres in an adult

Pyloric sphincter — a ring of muscle which controls the outlet from the stomach. It is normally closed, opening at intervals to let the food through, a little at a time

Pancreas — produces pancreatic juice

Large intestine — (**colon** or **large bowel**) - the main function is to absorb water from the faeces

Rectum — the last part of the large intestine

Anus — the opening through which waste material from digestion is eliminated from the body. The opening is controlled by a ring of muscle called the **anal sphincter**

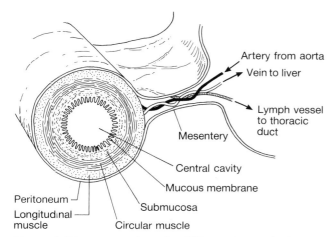

Figure 2 Diagram to show the different layers in the wall of the gut

Artery from aorta
Vein to liver
Lymph vessel to thoracic duct
Mesentery
Central cavity
Mucous membrane
Submucosa
Peritoneum
Longitudinal muscle
Circular muscle

Structure of the wall The wall of the alimentary canal consists of several layers, **Fig 2**:

◆ **Mucous membrane** (mucosa) lines the canal and continuously secretes **mucus**. This thick, sticky substance prevents the wall from being damaged by the digestive juices.

◆ **Submucosa** – a layer containing blood vessels, lymph vessels and nerves. Variations in the thickness of this layer creates folds and ridges.

◆ **Circular muscle** – a layer of smooth muscle in which the muscle fibres are arranged in a circular manner.

◆ **Longitudinal muscle** – the muscle fibres in this layer of smooth muscle are arranged lengthways.

◆ **Tough outer layer** covered by peritoneum which is smooth and moist and allows the alimentary canal to move smoothly against other organs.

Peritoneum

The peritoneum is a thin, tough, fibrous layer that lines the abdominal cavity and covers all the organs inside. It has a moist and slippery surface which allows easy movement of the organs against each other.

The intestines are loosely attached to the back of the abdomen by the **mesentery**. This is formed from a double layer of peritoneum, with arteries, veins and lymph vessels between the layers, **Fig. 2**.

Peristalsis Food is pushed through the oesophagus and intestines by peristalsis: **Fig 3**. **Peristalsis** is the name given to the rhythmic squeezing movements in the walls of tubes which push the contents forwards. These squeezing movements are produced by the alternate contraction and relaxation of two layers of smooth muscle (the longitudinal and circular layers), and they result in a wave of contraction which moves down the tube. The rate and force of the contractions are varied by the autonomic nervous system (p. 118).

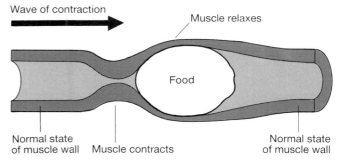

Wave of contraction
Muscle relaxes
Food
Normal state of muscle wall
Muscle contracts
Normal state of muscle wall

Figure 3 Peristalsis

QUESTIONS

1 (i) Copy **Fig 4** – Diagram of the digestive system. (ii) Label parts 1–20, using Fig 1 as a guide. (iii) Write brief notes about each of the parts labelled.

2a Describe the alimentary canal.
 b Describe the structure of the wall.
 c Explain the difference between peritoneum and mesentery.
 d Draw a diagram to show the different layers in the wall of the gut.

3a Describe how food is moved through the alimentary canal.
 b Draw a diagram to illustrate peristalsis.

FURTHER WORK

1 Demonstrate peristalsis by squeezing a tennis ball through a stocking. Pushing smoothly from behind demonstrates a peristaltic wave.

2 Obtain X-rays of a barium meal and a barium enema from the local hospital to demonstrate the anatomy of the digestive system.

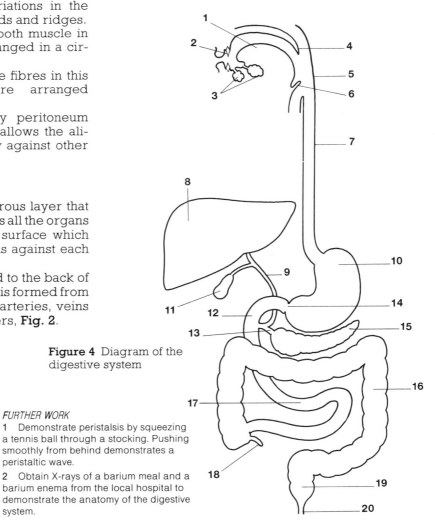

Figure 4 Diagram of the digestive system

Digestive glands and enzymes

The digestive glands are:

◆ the three pairs of salivary glands,
◆ the gastric glands in the stomach wall,
◆ the liver,
◆ the pancreas,
◆ the intestinal glands in the wall of the small intestine.

They secrete **digestive juices**, each of which has a part to play in digestion. All together they produce about 5 litres of digestive juice each day. Although the juices are mainly water, they contain enzymes and/or other important substances which help to digest (break down) food. Most of the 5 litres is reabsorbed, mainly in the large intestine.

Figure 1 Digestive glands, juices and enzymes

> Key: **Digestive glands** are named first, in large, bold type starting with a capital letter
> **digestive juices** are named in small, bold type
> *enzymes* are in italics

Digestive enzymes

Enzymes in general are discussed in more detail on p. 68. In this topic we are concerned only with the digestive enzymes. These are made in the digestive glands and secreted in the digestive juices. Their function is to speed up the rate at which food is digested. With the aid of these enzymes, food can be digested in a matter of hours. Without them, the same processes would take months.

Points to note about the enzymes involved in digestion

◆ They speed up the chemical reactions which break down large food molecules into smaller ones.
◆ Each enzyme acts only on one type of chemical reaction.
◆ Enzymes act most rapidly at the correct pH – acid, neutral or alkaline as the case may be. The enzymes in the mouth and small intestine prefer neutral or slightly alkaline conditions, whereas the stomach enzymes prefer acid conditions. An incorrect pH either slows down or stops enzyme action.

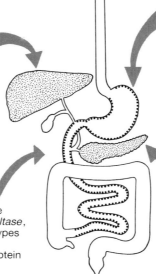

Salivary glands continuously secrete a little saliva into the mouth. Production is rapidly increased when food is in the mouth and, often, at the thought, smell and sight of food. Saliva contains the enzyme *amylase* (also called *ptyalin*) which digests starch

Gastric glands secrete **gastric juice**. It starts to be produced when food is in the mouth and continues while there is food in the stomach. Gastric juice contains hydrochloric acid and the enzyme *pepsin* which digests protein. Babies also produce *rennin*, an enzyme which clots milk

Liver secretes **bile** continuously and it is stored in the gall bladder until food enters the duodenum.
Bile contains bile salts but no enzymes. Bile salts emulsify fat—break it up into small droplets

Pancreas secretes **pancreatic juice**. Large amounts are rapidly produced soon after food is eaten.
Pancreatic juice contains sodium hydrogencarbonate (sodium bicarbonate) and three enzymes - *lipase* which digests fat, *amylase* which digests starch and *trypsin* which digests protein

Intestinal glands secrete **intestinal juice** when food is in the small intestine. This juice contains a number of enzymes including *maltase*, *sucrase* and lactase which digest different types of sugar, and a mixture of enzymes called *erepsin* which completes the digestion of protein

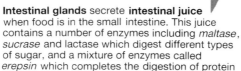

Experiment 1. To show the action of saliva on starch

Method

1. Pour water into two test-tubes to a depth of about 2 cm, then add a pinch of flour and a drop of iodine to each and shake well. The contents of the test-tubes will turn blue-black, showing that starch is present.
2. Label the test-tubes A and B.
3. Collect some saliva in a beaker; add saliva to A to a depth of about 1 cm. Shake well to mix. (To stimulate saliva production, think about appetising food.)
4. Place the tubes in a water bath or warm place and keep at 37°C. Watch for any colour change.

Result The contents of A gradually lose their black colour as the starch disappears. This indicates that the saliva is responsible for removing the starch (see next Topic, p. 82).

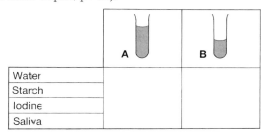

	A	B
Water		
Starch		
Iodine		
Saliva		

a Copy and complete the table by placing a tick in the appropriate column if the substance is present in tube A and/or B.
b What colour does starch become when mixed with iodine?
c When the blue-black colour disappears, what does this indicate?
d The blue-black colour disappeared because the enzyme in saliva removed the starch by breaking it down (digesting it). Name the enzyme in saliva.
e Why was there no colour change in B?
f What would have been the result if, at the beginning of the experiment, the saliva had been boiled before being added to A? Explain.
g What would have been the result if hydrochloric acid had been added to A at the beginning of the experiment? Explain.
h Carry out experiments to test your answers to f and g.

Experiment 2. To show the effect of the enzyme pepsin on protein

Method

The protein used in this experiment is egg albumin which is found in egg-white. The white of one egg is made into a solution by mixing well with five times as much water, then straining through a fine sieve to remove the lumps.

1. Pour 2 cm depth of the egg-white solution, which is cloudy, into four test-tubes labelled A, B, C and D.
2. Add a little dilute hydrocholoric acid to A and C.
3. Add a little pepsin powder to B and C.
4. Leave the tubes in a warm place and examine from time to time to see if any changes have taken place.

Result The contents of C turned from cloudy to clear; the other tubes all remained cloudy. This indicates that both pepsin and hydrochloric acid are necessary for the protein to be changed.

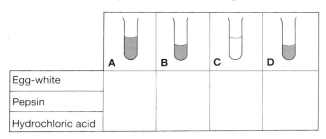

	A	B	C	D
Egg-white				
Pepsin				
Hydrochloric acid				

a Copy and complete the table by placing a tick in the appropriate column if the substance is present in the tube above.
b Name the enzyme used in this experiment.
c Name the type of protein used.
d What other substance needed to be present before the protein was changed?
e Which digestive juice contains both the acid and enzyme used in this experiment?
f Where is that digestive juice made?
g What result would you have expected if the test-tubes had been placed in a refrigerator instead of a warm place? Why?
h What result would you expect if sodium hydrogencarbonate (sodium bicarbonate) was used instead of hydrochloric acid? Why?
i Carry out an experiment to test your answer to h.

QUESTIONS

1 Copy the table on the right and complete the words by using information from **Fig 1**.

2a What is the function of the digestive enzymes?
 b List four points to note about the enzymes involved in digestion.

FURTHER WORK

1 Carry out **Experiment 1** and complete a–h. Carry out **Experiment 2** and complete a–i.

2 Devise experiments to check the statements made in the section 'Points to note about the enzymes involved in digestion'.

Gland(s)	Digestive juice	Enzymes	Other substances
1. S_____ g_____	s_____	a_____	
2. G_____ g_____	g_____ j____	p_____	h_____ a___
		r_____	
3. L____	b___		b___ s____
4. P_____	p_____ j____	l_____	s_____
		a_____	_____
		t_____	
5. I_____	i_____ j____	e_____	
g_____		m_____	
		l_____	
		s_____	

Digestion

Digestion is a breaking down process

During digestion large insoluble pieces of food are broken down into soluble substances which are small enough to be absorbed through the intestine wall and into the blood stream. Digestion of food involves physical and chemical actions.

Physical digestion involves:

◆ **chewing** to break solid food into smaller pieces,
◆ **churning** by the stomach to help break up food and to mix it with gastric juice,
◆ **warmth** of the body to melt fat.

Chemical digestion uses enzymes to break down:

◆ **carbohydrates** to simple sugars (see p. 62).
◆ **fats** to fatty acids and glycerol (see p. 63).
◆ **proteins** to amino acids (see p. 64).

Some substances remain unchanged:

◆ **glucose**
◆ **vitamins** are already small enough to be absorbed;
◆ **minerals**
◆ **water**
◆ **fibre** – cannot be digested by human enzymes and therefore cannot be absorbed.

Digestion in the mouth

When food enters the mouth (is **ingested**) it is chewed and mixed with saliva. Saliva moistens the food, making it easier to swallow, and the enzyme it contains – **salivary amylase** – begins to change starch into the sugar called **maltose**.

Swallowing The tongue rolls the food into a **bolus** which is easy to swallow and it is then pushed to the back of the mouth and into the oesophagus (gullet). The food is prevented from going the wrong way because the soft palate closes the entrance to the nose and the epiglottis covers the entrance to the windpipe. Peristalsis then pushes the food through the oesophagus to the stomach.

Digestion in the stomach

Gentle movements of the stomach wall churn the food up with gastric juice and it becomes turned into a semi-liquid state called **chyme**. The warmth of the body also melts fat.

The **hydrochloric acid** in gastric juice kills germs and also helps the enzymes to work. **Pepsin** digests protein by splitting it up into peptides. **Rennin** clots milk and is important in infancy.

At intervals, the pyloric sphincter opens to allow a little food to pass through into the small intestine.

Digestion in the small intestine

The small intestine is the region in which the greater part of digestion takes place. Here, the food is mixed with bile, pancreatic juice and intestinal juice which have the following effects:

◆ **Sodium hydrogencarbonate** (sodium bicarbonate) neutralises the hydrochloric acid from the stomach; this stops the action of pepsin and allows the enzymes in the small intestine to act on the food.
◆ **Bile salts** emulsify fat, that is, they split it up into minute droplets.
◆ **Lipase** splits up fat into fatty acids and glycerol.
◆ **Trypsin** continues the digestion of protein to peptides.
◆ **Erepsin** splits up peptides to amino acids.
◆ **Amylase** continues the digestion of starch to maltose.
◆ **Maltase** splits up maltose to glucose.
◆ **Sucrase** digests sucrose to glucose and fructose.
◆ **Lactase** digests lactose to glucose and galactose.

Absorption

Absorption is the movement of digested food from the gut into the blood stream.

Most of the absorption of food takes place in the small intestine, although a small amount of water, glucose, alcohol and other substances which do not need to be broken down further may be absorbed in the stomach. The wall of the small intestine provides a **large surface area** through which absorption can take place because:

◆ it is **very long** – about 5 metres in an adult,
◆ the inner surface is much folded,
◆ the inner surface is covered with tiny finger-like projections called **villi** (each is a **villus**).
◆ the cells of the villus wall have **microvilli**.

Structure of a villus Each villus has a very thin wall and contains **capillaries** and a **lacteal**. This means that the contents of the small intestine come very close to the blood stream.

Glucose, amino acids, vitamins and **minerals** pass through the villus wall and into the capillaries, and are then carried away in the blood stream to the **hepatic portal vein** which takes them to the liver.

Fat is absorbed through the intestine wall either in the form of **fat droplets** or as **fatty acids** and **glycerol**, and goes into the **lacteal**. Lacteals are part of the lymphatic system and the fat is carried away in lymph vessels and enters the blood stream near the heart (p. 50).

Assimilation

After the food has been absorbed, it is transported by the blood to the tissues. It is assimilated into the body when it enters the cells of the tissues.

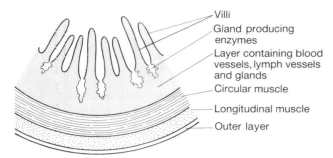

Figure 1 Section through the wall of the small intestine

Labels in Figure 1:
Villi
Gland producing enzymes
Layer containing blood vessels, lymph vessels and glands
Circular muscle
Longitudinal muscle
Outer layer

Figure 2 Section through a villus

Labels in Figure 2:
Epithelium of villus (Mucous membrane)
Network of capillaries
Lacteal
From artery
To hepatic portal vein
To lymph vessel

The large intestine

The material which passes from the small intestine into the large intestine is mainly water and undigested matter such as fibre. As it moves slowly along, most of the water is absorbed through the wall of the large intestine. Enormous numbers of bacteria live in the large intestine and feed on the contents, and produce **vitamin K**.

Defaecation (egestion; elimination) The large intestine acts as a storage place for waste matter – **faeces** or **stools** – and from time to time is discharged from the body through the rectum and anus. Besides the undigested remains of food, faeces contain vast numbers of bacteria, both living and dead. Most are harmless but some of the live bacteria are a possible source of disease. The anal sphincter operates in a similar manner to the sphincter controlling the outlet to the bladder (p. 91).

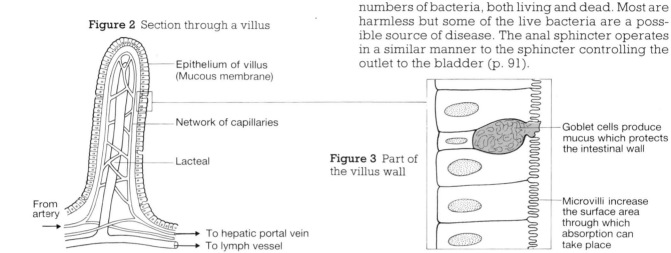

Figure 3 Part of the villus wall

Labels in Figure 3:
Goblet cells produce mucus which protects the intestinal wall
Microvilli increase the surface area through which absorption can take place

QUESTIONS

1 Copy and complete the table below:
Summary of digestion

Summary of digestion	Enzymes etc.	Action on food
Mouth	s_____ a_____	begins digestion of starch → m_____
Stomach	h_____ a____ p_____	acidifies stomach contents begins digestion of protein → p_____
Small intestine	s_____ h_____ _____ b____ a_____ m_____ t_____ e_____ l_____ s_____ l_____	neutralises intestinal contents emulsifies f__ continues digestion of starch → m_____ splits up maltose → g_____ continues digestion of protein → p_____ splits up peptides → a_____ a_____ splits up fat → f____ a____ and g_____ splits up sucrose → g_____ and f_____ splits up lactose → g_____ and g_____

2a Why does mixing food with saliva make it easier to swallow?
 b How is food swallowed?
 c How is food prevented from going the wrong way?

3a How is the food which is swallowed turned into chyme?
 b Name two effects of hydrochloric acid in the stomach.
 c When is rennin important and why?
 d How does the food get into the small intestine?

4a Name three substances that can be absorbed in the stomach.
 b Where is most of the food absorbed?
 c Name four ways in which the small intestine provides a large surface area for absorption.
 d Draw a diagram to show the structure of a villus.
 e What substances are absorbed into the capillaries and where are they taken to?

f In what form is fat absorbed into the lacteal and how does it get into the blood stream?

5 Match each of these words with one of the descriptions below: absorption, egestion, digestion, assimilation, ingestion.
 (i) The act of taking food into the alimentary canal through the mouth.
 (ii) The conversion of large, insoluble molecules into smaller, soluble, absorbable molecules.
 (iii) The uptake of the digested food into the blood stream.
 (iv) The incorporation of the digested food into body tissue.
 (v) The expulsion from the alimentary canal of undigested remains of food.

FURTHER WORK

1 Describe with the aid of diagrams how the structure of the small intestine relates to its functions.

2 Complete exercise 4, p. 94.

Digestive disorders

Heartburn (reflux oesophagitis)

The stomach lining is designed to resist the acid which the stomach produces, but the lining of the gullet is not. When acid from the stomach flows backwards (refluxes) into the gullet (oesophagus), it causes inflammation and pain. Heartburn can be relieved:

◆ **without medicines** by:
   small, regular meals (a full stomach makes heartburn more likely),
   wearing loose-waisted clothes,
   sleeping propped up.
◆ **by medicines** to:
   neutralise the acid (antacids),
   reduce the amount of acid produced,
   line the gullet with a protective layer.

Ulcers

An **ulcer** is a break in any of the body surfaces – the skin on the outside or the mucous membranes inside – in which healing is delayed.

Mouth ulcers   These are common, small but painful, and usually heal quickly without treatment.

Peptic ulcers   These occur in the stomach (**gastric ulcers**) or duodenum (**duodenal ulcers**), producing a gnawing or burning pain in the middle of the abdomen. The pain is relieved by milk, food and antacids, and tends to come and go – come for a few days or weeks, then go for a few weeks or months. **Treatment** involves:
◆ stopping smoking,
◆ avoiding foods which produce pain, eg alcohol and spicy foods,
◆ taking antacids to neutralise the acid,
◆ medicines (eg ranitidine) to stop acid secretion by the stomach, or medicines to strengthen and protect the mucosa.

Bleeding from peptic ulcers   A **big bleed** is obvious because either the blood appears in vomit – it can be bright-red fresh blood or dark like 'coffee grounds' – or the blood comes out in the stools (faeces) – making them black. Urgent medical attention is required.

When the bleeding is only a slow trickle, it goes unnoticed, but anaemia (p. 36), slowly develops.

Constipation

Constipation is the infrequent passing of hard, dry stools. The normal range of frequency of bowel action is between three per day and three per week. The desire to empty the bowel comes when it is stretched by the presence of a stool. A stool held in the bowel for a long time dries out, becomes hard and, when it is finally passed, may be painful, tear the anus and cause bleeding.

Constipation can be due to:
◆ repeatedly ignoring the signals to empty the bowel,
◆ a diet lacking fibre,
◆ repeated use of laxatives,
◆ repeated use of some pain-relievers,
◆ lack of exercise,
◆ illness – when no food or exercise are taken.

Treatment   A diet rich in fibre helps to prevent constipation. If it should occur, a gentle laxative will empty the bowel. Laxatives should be used for a few days at a time only, and not as a regular habit. The **laxative habit** makes the bowel dependent on drugs and it will then not work without its regular dose.

Flatulence

Flatulence – 'wind' – is gas in the stomach or intestines. It can cause discomfort and may be relieved by burping or belching, or passing wind from the anus. The gas is often air which has been swallowed when eating or drinking. It may also be produced by the activity of bacteria in the large intestine, particularly with certain foods such as beans and bran.

Hernia

A **hernia** is a place where one part of the body protrudes unnaturally into another part. For example, it can occur in men just above the groin – the intestine bulges through the abdominal wall and forms a swelling under the skin. If the blood supply to the bulge becomes cut off, the hernia becomes a **strangulated hernia** and surgery is then urgent to save the patient's life. A **hiatus hernia** occurs when part of the stomach bulges through the diaphragm and into the thorax. This condition may give rise to heartburn.

Hernias are more likely to occur as people get older, and are encouraged by increased pressure in the abdomen that comes from bending, or coughing (often by smokers).

Irritable bowel syndrome (spastic colon; mucous colitis)

The muscles of the colon wall go into spasm (tighten) and their peristaltic movements (p. 78) fail to coordinate. The result is pain in the lower left side of the abdomen with diarrhoea or constipation.

This condition is painful, but not a sign of more serious disease. It may be eased by more fibre in the diet, and there are various medicines which help.

Piles (haemorrhoids)

These are swollen veins (varicose veins) in the side of the anus. They may be painful and irritate, and may bleed, causing anemia. If small, they can be treated by injection. If larger or protruding, they may have to be removed surgically.

Diarrhoea

Diarrhoea is the frequent passing of loose, watery stools. Most acute (short-term) diarrhoea is due to infection of the intestines with bacteria or viruses. Chronic (long-term) diarrhoea needs medical advice.

Appendicitis

Appendicitis is inflammation of the appendix. The pain usually starts in the middle of the abdomen, and 12 to 24 hours later, moves to the right side of the lower abdomen. Other symptoms are slight fever, nausea, vomiting (sometimes), loss of appetite and constipation.

Peritonitis

Peritonitis is inflammation of the **peritoneum** – the membrane which surrounds the organs within the abdomen and links them together. It is caused by bacterial infection from, for example, a burst appendix or an abdominal wound.

Indigestion (dyspepsia)

Indigestion is a term used to describe a variety of symptoms – discomfort, distension (internal pressure or swelling), ache or pain.

Treatment Taking antacid preparations may give relief. If indigestion lasts for more than a week, or if attacks recur regularly, medical advice should be sought so that the cause can be diagnosed.

Antacids

These are medicines which neutralise acid produced by the stomach, and they relieve the pain of gastritis (p. 86), hiatus hernia and peptic ulcer.

Many different types of antacids are available in liquid or tablet form and containing a variety of ingredients. Some types of antacid also relieve ulcer pain by covering the ulcer with a layer which protects it from being attacked by the acid.

All antacids give temporary relief from pain caused by acid. People usually find that some suit them better than others, but they:
◆ do not cure the problem;
◆ will be ineffective for other digestive disorders;
◆ can cause health problems if taken in large amounts over a long period of time.

Possible causes of indigestion

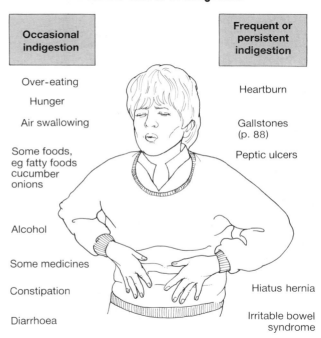

Occasional indigestion	Frequent or persistent indigestion
Over-eating	Heartburn
Hunger	
Air swallowing	Gallstones (p. 88)
Some foods, eg fatty foods cucumber onions	Peptic ulcers
Alcohol	
Some medicines	
Constipation	Hiatus hernia
Diarrhoea	Irritable bowel syndrome

QUESTIONS

1a Give eight possible causes of occasional indigestion.
b Give five possible causes of frequent or persistent indigestion.
c Describe the treatment for indigestion.
d (i) What is an antacid? (ii) What do antacids give temporary relief from? (iii) What will antacids not do?

2a (i) What is flatulence? (ii) Where does the gas come from?
b Describe heartburn.
c Give four ways of relieving heartburn.

3a Describe: (i) hernia, (ii) strangulated hernia, (iii) hiatus hernia.
b What encourages a hernia?

c (i) Give the technical name for piles. (ii) Describe the condition. (iii) How can they be treated.

4a What is: (i) an ulcer, (ii) a peptic ulcer, (iii) treatment of peptic ulcers?
b Describe the effects of bleeding from a peptic ulcer.

5a Explain the difference between diarrhoea and constipation.
b (i) Give five causes of constipation. (ii) What is the recommended treatment? (iii) Why should laxatives be used only for a few days at a time?
c Describe irritable bowel syndrome.
d What is the difference between appendicitis and peritonitis?

FURTHER WORK
Study the labels on packets or bottles of antacids: (i) What are they recommended for? (ii) List their contents. (iii) Compare the different brands.

Gastro-enteritis

Gastro-enteritis is inflammation of the lining of the stomach (gastritis) and intestine (enteritis). The symptoms of this common complaint vary from nausea (feeling sick) or slight looseness of the bowel, to a severe fever with abdominal pain, vomiting, diarrhoea and thirst. Gastro-enteritis is usually due to contaminated food or drink.

Causes of gastro-enteritis

The two main causes of gastro-enteritis are:
- **Diseases** such as typhoid, cholera, dysentery. These are more often found in countries with a hot climate, or without clean water and a sewage system. The gastro-enteritis is severe.
- **Food poisoning** – a term used to describe gastro-enteritis which is generally milder and shorter than that due to the diseases mentioned above. Causes are:
  - **infections**, eg *Salmonella, Campylobacter*, certain viruses,
  - **bacterial toxins**, eg those produced by *Staphylococcus, Clostridium*,
  - **allergy**, eg to shellfish,
  - **poisoning**, eg due to poisonous toadstools, toxic chemicals.

Bacterial food poisoning

Food poisoning caused by bacteria is the most common cause of gastro-enteritis in Britain.

Conditions in which the bacteria multiply Bacteria thrive in warm, moist foods, particularly those containing protein, for example meat and poultry, milk and cream.

Rate of increase Bacteria multiply by dividing into two, and when conditions are right this can happen every twenty minutes. After several hours, very large numbers will have built up in the food.

Food hygiene The essential rules to prevent bacterial food poisoning are:
- Keep food clean.
- Keep food cold.
- Wash your hands and scrub under the nails before handling food.
- Cook food thoroughly to destroy any bacteria.

Treatment for food poisoning

Adults and older children The best treatment is to rest the stomach and intestines by drinking only water or weak orange or lemon squash. The patients usually recover within 1–2 days, and no harm comes from not eating during this time as long as there is a good fluid intake to keep the kidneys functioning normally. Kaolin mixtures can be used to treat the diarrhoea.

Young children need more care. They can easily lose too much water from the body, and become dehydrated and seriously ill very quickly. A mixture of salt and sugar given to them aids recovery – 1 teaspoon of sugar (5 g) and 8 teaspoons of salt (40 g) in one litre of water. This replaces water and minerals lost in the stools and provides simple nutrition.

Babies with gastro-enteritis need urgent medical advice. With older children and adults, it depends how ill they are.

Figure 1 A food poisoning story

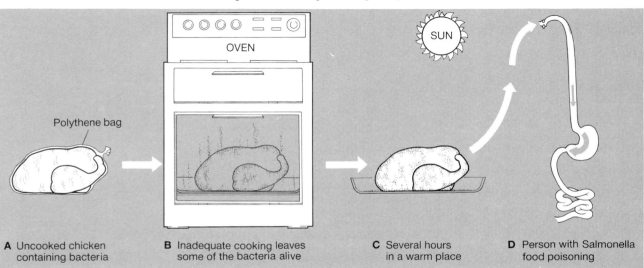

A Uncooked chicken containing bacteria

B Inadequate cooking leaves some of the bacteria alive

C Several hours in a warm place

D Person with Salmonella food poisoning

Salmonella infection

These bacteria are found in the intestines of animals such as cattle and poultry, and in human carriers. They get into food when it is contaminated with infected excreta of humans or animals, or by water which has been polluted by infected sewage. Once inside human intestines, they grow and multiply and, about 12 hours after being eaten, symptoms of gastro-enteritis occur. If food is thoroughly cooked, the bacteria are killed and will not be harmful.

The severity of the illness depends on
◆ the number of bacteria eaten,
◆ the ability of the individual to resist infection – young children and old people have least resistance,
◆ the particular species of Salmonella involved.

Campylobacter infection

This has recently become recognised as a common form of food poisoning. Sources of infection include milk, poultry, dogs and cats.

Staphylococcus food poisoning

These bacteria are found in many places including the nose, throat, boils and pus from infected wounds. When these bacteria get into warm moist food, they grow and multiply and produce a toxin – a poisonous substance. It is the toxin which causes food poisoning. The bacteria are killed by cooking but the toxin is only gradually destroyed. The symptoms of food poisoning usually occur within 2–4 hours, but they can occur almost immediately if a large dose of toxin is consumed.

Clostridium food poisoning

These bacteria can only grow in the absence of oxygen, for example, in the large intestine, and they are able to produce **spores** which can survive for a long time in dust and soil. Food can therefore be contaminated by:
◆ bacteria in human and animal excreta – cooking will destroy them.
◆ spores in dust and dirt.
The spores are very hardy and may even survive normal cooking processes. When in warm, moist food, they will turn into active bacteria again and multiply rapidly.

Different species of Clostridium produce different illnesses, eg C. perfringens (C. welchii) causes mild food poisoning, and C. botulinum causes botulism – a rare but very serious form of food poisoning.

Traveller's diarrhoea

(Montezuma's revenge, Delhi belly, the Aztec two-step, gippy tummy etc)
When travelling to other countries, particularly warm ones, it is not uncommon to have a short, sharp attack of diarrhoea and sometimes vomiting. The cause is often a local strain of E. coli (Escherichia coli) bacteria new to the traveller's body and to which it has not built up a natural resistance.

QUESTIONS

1a What is gastro-enteritis?
 b Give the symptoms of gastro-enteritis.
 c Name the two main causes of gastro-enteritis.
 d List four causes of food poisoning.

2a What is the most common cause of gastro-enteritis in Britain?
 b Describe the conditions in which bacteria multiply.
 c List four rules to prevent bacterial food poisoning.

 d Describe the treatment for food poisoning in: (i) adults and older children, (ii) young children, (iii) babies.

3a Name two types of bacteria which cause illness when eaten.
 b Name two types of bacteria which cause food poisoning by producing toxins in food before it is eaten.
 c What often causes traveller's diarrhoea?

FURTHER WORK

1 Explain **Fig. 1** in detail.

2 Describe, in words or by diagrams, how the following bacteria are able to cause food poisoning: (i) Staphylococcus, (ii) Clostridium.

Liver, pancreas and spleen

Liver

The liver is the largest organ in the body and weighs about 1½ kg. It is situated beneath the diaphragm in the upper right side of the abdomen, and is protected by the ribs. In appearance it is a dark red-brown colour and has a very smooth surface. As can be seen from **Fig 1**, four vessels are linked to the liver.

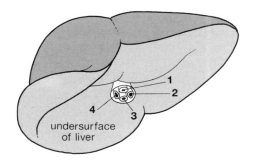

1. **Hepatic artery** — brings oxygenated blood to the liver from the aorta
2. **Hepatic vein** — removes blood from the liver to the inferior vena cava
3. **Bile duct** — removes bile made by the liver to the small intestine
4. **Hepatic portal vein** — brings blood containing digested food to the liver from the small intestine

Figure 1 Under-surface of the liver

Functions The liver has a wide range of functions, many of which are concerned with keeping the composition of the blood constant (homeostasis, p. 120):

◆ It **regulates** the amount of sugar in the blood (see opposite).
◆ It **stores** glycogen, vitamins A and B_{12} and some iron.
◆ It **converts** excess amino acids to urea (deamination, p. 64) for excretion by the kidneys.
◆ It **destroys** substances such as alcohol and nicotine.
◆ It **detoxifies** substances such as drugs and unwanted hormones so that they can be excreted more easily by the kidneys.
◆ It **secretes** bile containing bile salts to aid the digestion of fat.
◆ It **disposes** of the waste products from worn out red cells in the bile (bilirubin gives bile its yellowish-green colour).
◆ It **makes** fibrinogen.
◆ It **protects** by producing white cells which can destroy germs and make antibodies.
◆ It **produces heat** from many of the continuous chemical activities which take place in the liver. These help to maintain body temperature.

Disorders of the liver

Hepatitis Hepatitis is inflammation of the liver due to infection, chemicals (eg cleaning fluid) or drugs. The disease interferes with the production of bile, and the yellow pigments which are normally excreted in the bile then circulate in the blood stream, causing **jaundice** – yellowing of the skin and eyeballs, and dark yellow urine. Other common symptoms of hepatitis are fever, nausea, and vomiting, with loss of appetite and weight.

The usual cause of hepatitis is a virus infection. There are two main types of virus:
Hepatitis A is spread from person to person by food contaminated with faeces.
Hepatitis B (serum hepatitis) is spread by blood, semen and vaginal secretions.

Cirrhosis Cirrhosis is a liver disorder in which liver tissue becomes replaced by fibrous tissue which interferes with the normal working of the liver. It is usually caused by excessive intake of alcohol over several years. The only satisfactory treatment is to stop taking alcohol and allow the liver to recover.

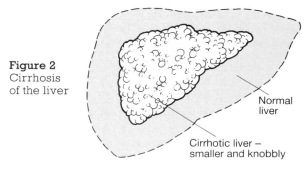

Figure 2 Cirrhosis of the liver

Normal liver

Cirrhotic liver – smaller and knobbly

Gallstones These develop in the gall bladder and are quite common, especially in overweight women. The stones are usually formed from cholesterol when excessive amounts are being excreted in the bile. Gallstones become troublesome when they:

◆ irritate the gall bladder lining – causing pain in the upper right hand side of the abdomen or indigestion when fat is eaten.
◆ block the bile duct – causing pain and jaundice.

Gallstones usually give no symptoms, but when they are repeatedly troublesome, they are usually removed by surgery (cholecystectomy).

Figure 3 Gall bladder with gallstones

Pancreas

The pancreas is a large, whitish gland about 20–25 cm long and is situated at the back of the abdomen behind the lower part of the stomach. It is linked to the duodenum by the pancreatic duct through which pancreatic juice flows during digestion.

Functions The pancreas produces:
◆ **Pancreatic juice** – p. 80.
◆ **Hormones** – made in special groups of cells in the pancreas called **islets of Langerhans**. There are about 2 000 000 islets and these small nodules secrete two hormones:

> **insulin** – reduces the level of glucose in the blood by encouraging glucose to enter the cells of muscles and liver for storage as glycogen.
> **glucagon** – raises the level of glucose in the blood by releasing glucose from liver glycogen. (Muscles use the glycogen stored in them for energy.)

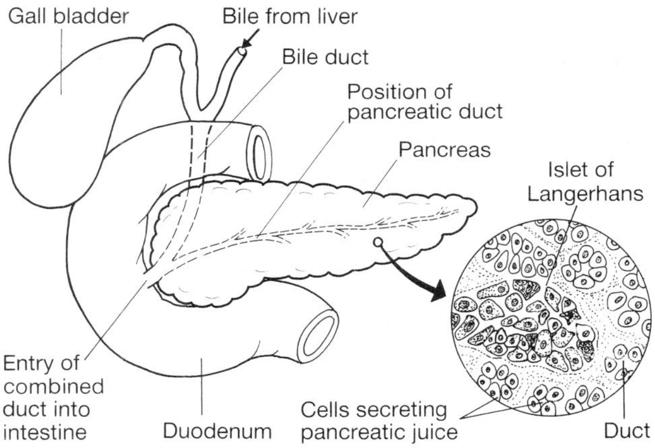

Sugar diabetes (diabetes mellitus)

Diabetes affects about 1–2% of the population. It is caused by lack of effective insulin and, as a result, the glucose level builds up in the blood and the excess passes into the urine.

Young diabetics The first symptoms of diabetes in young people are – excessive thirst, frequent passing of large quantities of urine, weight loss and general exhaustion. The treatment is by:
◆ **diet** – have a regular pattern of meals; control quantities of starchy foods in each meal; cut out sugar; cut down on fat; include foods containing fibre, eg vegetables, fruit, pulses, wholemeal bread.
◆ **regular injections of insulin**, usually two to three times a day.

Mature diabetics Diabetes which comes on in middle or old age, more often in people who are overweight, is usually mild. It can often be controlled by:
◆ **diet** (as above).
◆ **medicines** to lower the blood sugar level.
Insulin injections are rarely required.

Figure 4 Pancreas and gall bladder

Diabetic comas

Hypoglycaemic coma (a 'hypo'). When the level of glucose in the blood becomes too low, a 'hypo' develops. This condition comes on quickly and makes the person pale, sweaty, sometimes aggressive, and start to lose consciousness. Food or drink containing sugar needs to be taken immediately to prevent **coma** (loss of consciousness). The reason for the 'hypo' is usually too much insulin or too much physical exercise (which uses up the glucose).
Hyperglycaemic coma. When the blood sugar level stays too high for a day or two, the person passes a lot of water, becomes dehydrated, and then becomes more and more drowsy before passing into a coma. Urgent medical attention is required.

Spleen

This dark red-brown organ, about the size of a hand (see **Fig. 1**, p. 50), sits high up against the diaphragm on the left side of the abdomen and is protected by the ribs. The spleen is a fibrous sponge filled with lymphoid tissue which filters blood as it passes through. The functions of the spleen are to:
◆ destroy worn-out red cells.
◆ make antibodies.
The spleen is not essential to adults as its functions are shared with other organs, but people who have had their spleens removed are more prone to infection.

QUESTIONS

1a (i) Draw and label a diagram of the liver.
  (ii) Describe its position in the body.
 b List ten functions of the liver.

2a (i) What is hepatitis? (ii) What is the usual cause? (iii) What is the difference in the way the two types of hepatitis virus are spread?
 b What is the cause of jaundice?
 c Describe: (i) cirrhosis of the liver, (ii) the usual cause, (iii) treatment.
 d Draw a diagram to show where gallstones develop.
 e (i) When do gallstones become troublesome? (ii) What is the recommended treatment?

3a Describe the pancreas and its position.
 b Draw and label a diagram of the pancreas.
 c Give two functions of the pancreas.
 d How do the actions of the pancreatic hormones insulin and glucagon differ?

4a What is the cause of diabetes?
 b Describe diabetes and its treatment in: (i) young diabetics, (ii) mature diabetics.
 c (i) What is meant by coma? (ii) Describe 'hypo' and what to do about it.

5a With the aid of a diagram, describe the spleen and its position in the body.
 b Give two functions of the spleen.

FURTHER WORK

1 How many diabetics are there likely to be in your: (i) school or college, (ii) town, (iii) country. How does diabetes affect the lives of those who suffer from it?

2 Complete exercise 6, p. 94.

Renal system

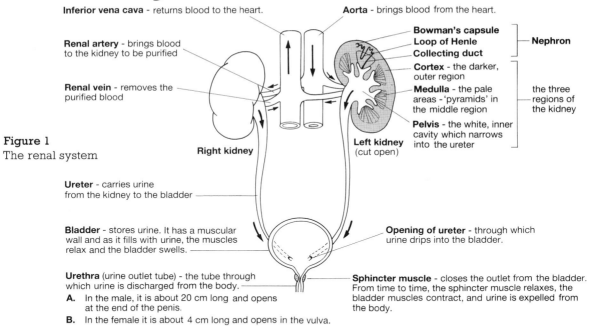

Inferior vena cava - returns blood to the heart.

Aorta - brings blood from the heart.

Renal artery - brings blood to the kidney to be purified

Renal vein - removes the purified blood

Bowman's capsule
Loop of Henle — **Nephron**
Collecting duct

Cortex - the darker, outer region
Medulla - the pale areas - 'pyramids' in the middle region
Pelvis - the white, inner cavity which narrows into the ureter

the three regions of the kidney

Right kidney

Left kidney (cut open)

Figure 1
The renal system

Ureter - carries urine from the kidney to the bladder

Bladder - stores urine. It has a muscular wall and as it fills with urine, the muscles relax and the bladder swells.

Opening of ureter - through which urine drips into the bladder.

Urethra (urine outlet tube) - the tube through which urine is discharged from the body.
A. In the male, it is about 20 cm long and opens at the end of the penis.
B. In the female it is about 4 cm long and opens in the vulva.

Sphincter muscle - closes the outlet from the bladder. From time to time, the sphincter muscle relaxes, the bladder muscles contract, and urine is expelled from the body.

The **renal system** (urinary system) consists of two kidneys and ureters leading to a bladder and urethra. Each kidney connects with an artery and a vein. About 600 cm³ (1 pint) of blood passes through the kidneys every minute, and they are so efficient that it is possible for the body to function normally with only one. This may happen if a kidney is removed because of disease or accident, or for transplanting into another person.

The kidneys

The kidneys are dark reddish-brown in colour, bean-shaped, about 11 cm long, 6 cm wide and 3 cm thick. They are situated high up on the wall of the abdomen, one each side of the backbone. The right kidney is usually slightly lower than the left kidney (as if the right kidney were pushed down by the liver above it).

Protection The kidneys are delicate organs but they are well protected by the:
   bones of the lower ribs and spine,
   abdominal wall and intestines,
   bulky mucles of the back,
   surrounding layer of fat,
   tough membrane which encloses each.

Functions The main functions are:
◆ **Regulation** of salt and water balance in the body.
◆ **Excretion** of waste substances:
   urea and other nitrogenous waste,
   excess salt (sodium chloride) and other minerals.

Nephrons Nephrons – kidney tubules – are about 3–5 cm long with a definite looped shape, and there are about a million inside each kidney. The blind end of the nephron lies in the cortex and is expanded into the cup-shaped **Bowman's capsule**, which encloses a small knot of capillaries called the **glomerulus**.

After leaving the Bowman's capsule, the tubule coils, loops into the medulla to form the **loop of Henle**, returns to the cortex and coils again before joining the collecting duct which leads to the centre of the kidney.

How the kidney works
The kidney works by:
◆ **filtering** liquid from the blood into the kidney tubules – a total of about 180 litres of liquid per day, then
◆ **re-absorbing** various substances from the liquid back into the blood, and
◆ **removing** the unwanted substances as **urine** – about 1½ litres per day. Details of these processes are given in **Fig 2**.

Micturition (passing urine) The sphincter controlling the outlet to the bladder contains two types of muscle, skeletal muscle in the **external sphincter** which is under voluntary control, and smooth muscle in the **internal sphincter** which is under reflex control. When the pressure of urine in the bladder reaches a certain level, it triggers the reflex to relax the internal sphincter. Voluntary control of the external sphincter can override the reflex and prevent urine from being released. Loss of control of the external sphincter results in **incontinence**, as happens, for example, to those who are paralysed from the waist down.

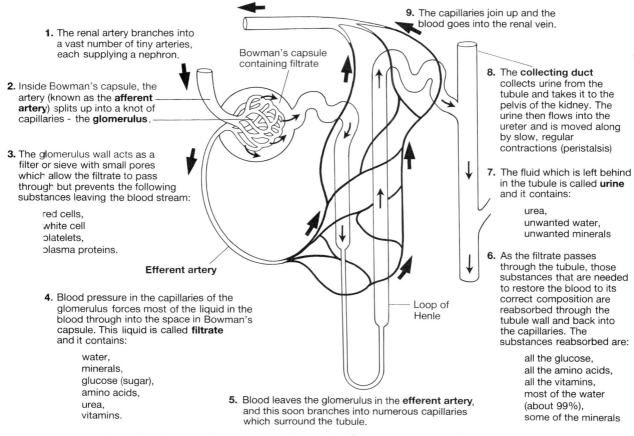

1. The renal artery branches into a vast number of tiny arteries, each supplying a nephron.

2. Inside Bowman's capsule, the artery (known as the **afferent artery**) splits up into a knot of capillaries - the **glomerulus**.

3. The glomerulus wall acts as a filter or sieve with small pores which allow the filtrate to pass through but prevents the following substances leaving the blood stream:

　　red cells,
　　white cell
　　platelets,
　　plasma proteins.

Efferent artery

4. Blood pressure in the capillaries of the glomerulus forces most of the liquid in the blood through into the space in Bowman's capsule. This liquid is called **filtrate** and it contains:

　　water,
　　minerals,
　　glucose (sugar),
　　amino acids,
　　urea,
　　vitamins.

Bowman's capsule containing filtrate

5. Blood leaves the glomerulus in the **efferent artery**, and this soon branches into numerous capillaries which surround the tubule.

Loop of Henle

9. The capillaries join up and the blood goes into the renal vein.

8. The **collecting duct** collects urine from the tubule and takes it to the pelvis of the kidney. The urine then flows into the ureter and is moved along by slow, regular contractions (peristalsis)

7. The fluid which is left behind in the tubule is called **urine** and it contains:

　　urea,
　　unwanted water,
　　unwanted minerals

6. As the filtrate passes through the tubule, those substances that are needed to restore the blood to its correct composition are reabsorbed through the tubule wall and back into the capillaries. The substances reabsorbed are:

　　all the glucose,
　　all the amino acids,
　　all the vitamins,
　　most of the water (about 99%),
　　some of the minerals

Figure 2 Diagram of a nephron with details of how nephrons and kidneys work

QUESTIONS

1 Copy **Fig 3** and label 1–14.

2 Match each of the following parts of the kidney with one of the descriptions below:
　　glomerulus, Bowman's capsule, urethra, nephron, collecting duct, loop of Henle, ureter, bladder, afferent artery, efferent artery.
a a kidney tubule.
b the cup-shaped end of the tubule.
c a small knot of capillaries.
d the loop of the nephron in the medulla.
e collects urine from the tubule.
f carries urine from kidney to bladder.
g stores urine.
h urine outlet tube.
i splits up to form the glomerulus.
j collects blood from the glomerulus.

3a Name the two main functions of the kidney.
b Where are the kidneys situated?
c How are the kidneys protected?

4 Copy and complete the following account of how the kidney works.
　The kidney works by:
　(i) **Filtering** liquid from the blood. This filtrate contains:
　　　(list 6 items)
　(ii) **Re-absorbing** those substances the body needs:
　　　(list 5 items)
　(iii) **Removing** unwanted substances as urine:
　　　(list 3 items)

Figure 3 Diagram of the renal system

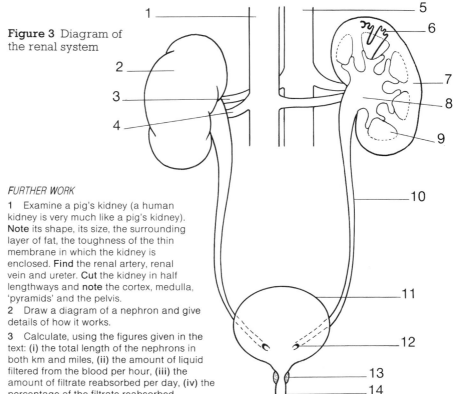

FURTHER WORK

1 Examine a pig's kidney (a human kidney is very much like a pig's kidney). **Note** its shape, its size, the surrounding layer of fat, the toughness of the thin membrane in which the kidney is enclosed. **Find** the renal artery, renal vein and ureter. **Cut** the kidney in half lengthways and **note** the cortex, medulla, 'pyramids' and the pelvis.

2 Draw a diagram of a nephron and give details of how it works.

3 Calculate, using the figures given in the text: (i) the total length of the nephrons in both km and miles, (ii) the amount of liquid filtered from the blood per hour, (iii) the amount of filtrate reabsorbed per day, (iv) the percentage of the filtrate reabsorbed.

Urine

Urine is the watery yellow fluid produced by the kidneys. It consists of water and the waste products of the metabolic activities of cells dissolved in this water, together with other substances which are in excess in the body and need to be excreted. If these waste substances build up, they are toxic and poison the body's cells – a situation which occurs in kidney failure.

Colour The yellow colour is due to the pigment urochrome. Urine may become pink after eating beetroot or red sweets, or after taking certain medicines.

Jaundice and other disorders of the liver can result in the excretion of bile pigments in the urine, making it a dark yellow or orange colour.

Smell Fresh urine normally has very little smell. When it becomes contaminated with bacteria, the urea in the urine is converted to ammonia, which gives a strong smell.

Cystitis (see below) may cause the urine to have a strong, unpleasant smell.

Quantity The daily output of urine varies considerably. Reasons for this are:
- fluid intake,
- type of food eaten,
- amount of exercise taken and therefore the volume of water lost as sweat;
- surrounding conditions, such as the weather or room temperature, which affect the rate at which water is lost as sweat.

pH	Urine is usually acid
Glucose	When present it is usually, but not always, a sign of sugar diabetes
Ketones	Present when the intake of food is low, and in poorly controlled diabetes
Protein	Due to leaking of plasma proteins and usually a sign of kidney or bladder disease
Blood	Minute amounts which cannot be seen are usually a sign of kidney or bladder disease
Bilirubin	Present in the urine in most forms of jaundice
Nitrites	Often found in the urine when infection is present

Figure 1 Left: A test strip (dip-stick) for detecting substances in urine. Right: Chart of substances

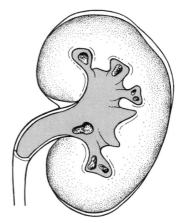

Figure 2 Kidney stones

Composition

The composition of urine varies widely, depending on the amount of waste substances to be excreted.
- **The main substances in urine** and the approximate quantities excreted daily are:

  water – $1\frac{1}{2}$ litres. When there is less water to be excreted, the urine is stronger.

  urea – 30 g (p. 89).

  salt (sodium and chloride ions) – 15 g. Usually, we eat more salt than we lose in sweat or faeces, and the excess is excreted in the urine. When the body is short of salt, then almost complete reabsorption takes place in the kidney tubules and very little or none is lost in the urine.

- **Small amounts** of many other substances are normally found in urine, eg

  uric acid and **creatinine** (both are nitrogen compounds),

  hormones.

  minerals, eg ions of **potassium, calcium, magnesium**.

- **Traces** of **alcohol, steroids,** or certain **drugs** or **medicines** appear in the urine if these substances are taken.

Disorders of the renal system

Kidney stones Occasionally stones form in the kidney or bladder, where they may cause bleeding into the urine and cystitis. If a stone leaves the kidney and passes down the ureter it can cause **renal colic** – severe pain in the small of the back and diagonally round to the front. Kidney stones which are troublesome can be removed by surgery.

Cystitis is inflammation of the bladder, usually caused by bacterial infection. It causes pain in the lower abdomen, stinging on passing urine, and the feeling of wanting to pass water much more frequently than usual, but often only very small quantities are passed.

It is quite a common complaint, especially in women. This is because the urethra is so much shorter in the female than the male, there are more bacteria present in the outlet area, and bacteria can more easily pass up into the bladder. Drinking large quantities of water may help to relieve the symptoms, but medical advice should be obtained.

Kidney dialysis

If both kidneys are seriously diseased, their function of removing toxic substances from blood can be replaced by dialysis. There are two dialysis techniques:

Haemodialysis Blood is taken from the patient's artery to an **artificial kidney** where it passes over selectively permeable membranes in the machine. The blood is then returned to a vein **Fig. 3A**.

As the blood passes over the membranes, urea and other unwanted substances diffuse into the dialysis fluid, which circulates on the other side of the membranes, and they are carried away. The patient needs to have this treatment for several hours, two or three times a week.

Peritoneal dialysis The walls of the abdominal cavity and intestines are surrounded by a thin membrane – the peritoneum – which contains blood vessels. In peritoneal dialysis, fluid is passed into the abdominal cavity **Fig. 3C**. Toxic substances in the blood in the peritoneum diffuse into this fluid, which is then drained off. The process can be repeated as often as necessary.

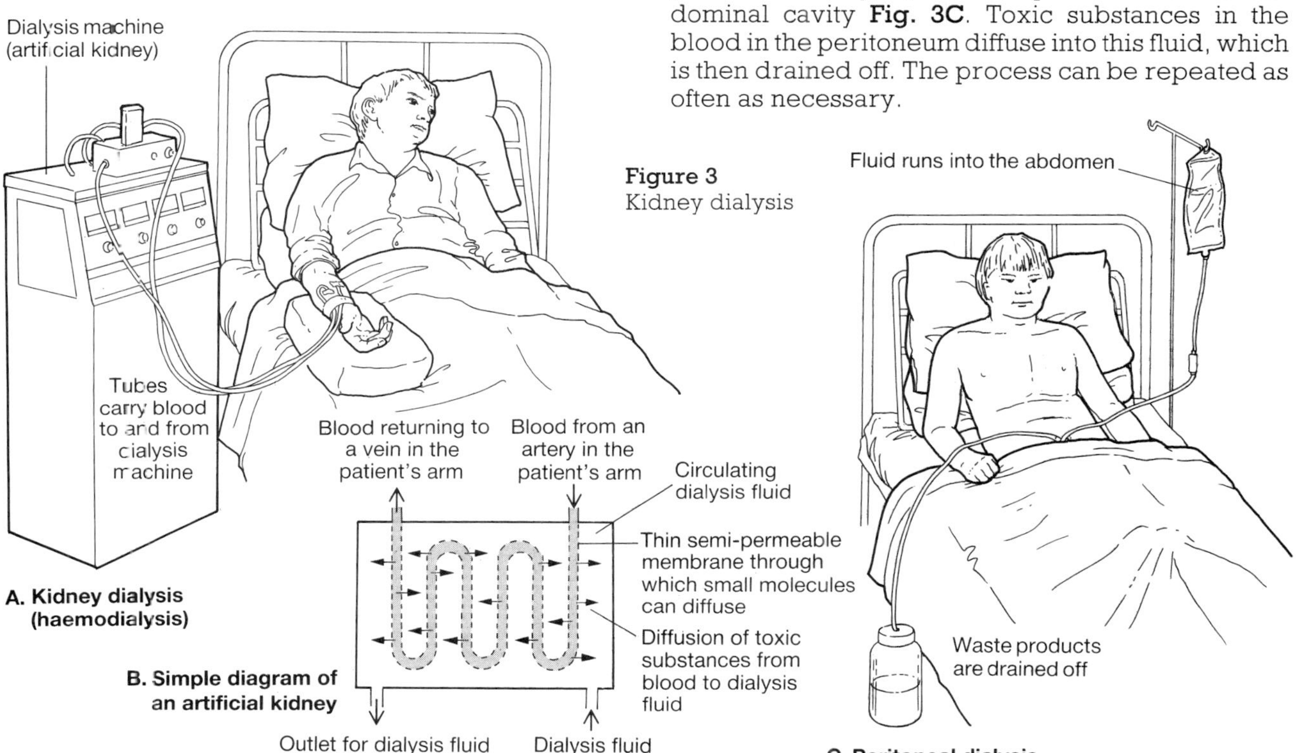

Dialysis machine
(artificial kidney)

Tubes carry blood to and from dialysis machine

A. Kidney dialysis (haemodialysis)

B. Simple diagram of an artificial kidney

Blood returning to a vein in the patient's arm

Blood from an artery in the patient's arm

Circulating dialysis fluid

Thin semi-permeable membrane through which small molecules can diffuse

Diffusion of toxic substances from blood to dialysis fluid

Outlet for dialysis fluid which takes with it impurities from the patient's blood

Dialysis fluid being pumped into the machine

Figure 3 Kidney dialysis

Fluid runs into the abdomen

Waste products are drained off

C. Peritoneal dialysis

QUESTIONS

1a Give four reasons why the daily output of urine varies.
b Name the three main substances in urine and state approximately how much of each is excreted daily.
c When does urine contain little or no salt?
d Give examples of other substances which are present in urine: (i) in small amounts, (ii) if the substances have been taken.
2 When the following substances occur in urine what may be the cause? (i) glucose, (ii) albumin, (iii) blood, (iv) a pink colour, (v) a strong smell of ammonia.
3a What is cystitis and what does this condition cause?
b Why is cystitis more common in women than in men?
c What is the cause of renal colic and where is the pain felt?
4a Describe haemodialysis.
b Draw a simple diagram of an artificial kidney.
c Describe peritoneal dialysis.

FURTHER WORK

Urine analysis Test urine samples by using a test strip (dip-stick) or by testing separately for the substances listed below.
(i) **pH** – using Universal Indicator.
(ii) **Water** – turns dry cobalt chloride paper from blue to pink.
(iii) **Glucose** – using a Clinitest tablet – as for diabetes, or with Benedict's solution (p. 63).
(iv) **Protein** – using Albustix (obtainable from a pharmacist), or by the Biuret test (p. 65).
(v) **Urea** – using urease. This enzyme breaks down urea to produce ammonia gas which can be detected when wet, turning red litmus paper blue: Fig 4.

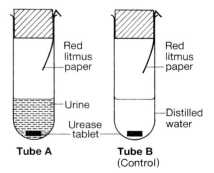

Red litmus paper

Urine

Urease tablet

Tube A

Red litmus paper

Distilled water

Tube B (Control)

Leave in a warm place (about 37°C) for a few hours and note any changes

Figure 4 Experiment to find out if urine contains urea

Section 3 EXERCISES

1 Match each of the terms with the correct statement in the list below.

(a) **amino acids ATP cholesterol enzymes glycogen iodine metabolism minerals vitamin B$_1$ vitamin C**

animal starch
building blocks for proteins
inorganic substances
thiamine
chemical reactions in living cells
adenosine triphosphate
speed up chemical reactions
ascorbic acid
needed for thyroid hormones
essential for cell membranes   [10]

(b) **duodenum gastro-enteritis liver nephron peristalsis peritoneum rickets urea ureter urethra**

lines abdominal cavity
rhythmic squeezing movements
first part of small intestine
inflammation of stomach and intestines
largest organ in the body
produced from amino acids
carries urine from kidney to bladder
tube through which urine is discharged from the body
kidney tubule
caused by lack of vitamin D   [10]

2 Give two ways in which each item in the pie chart is used in the structure or functioning of the body.   [10]

Main components of the body (average proportions)

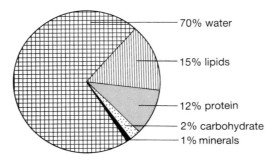

- 70% water
- 15% lipids
- 12% protein
- 2% carbohydrate
- 1% minerals

3 (a) Draw a diagram of the human digestive system to show: mouth, oesophagus, stomach, liver, pancreas, small intestine, large intestine and rectum.   [8]
(b) Draw guidelines to mark accurately the place where:

protein is first acted upon by enzymes – A
fats are broken down into minute droplets – B
most digested food is absorbed – C
water is absorbed from undigested remains – D
insulin is produced – E
peristalsis takes place – F
the digestion of carbohydrate begins – G
bile is produced – H
faeces are stored – I
pH 4 is most likely – J
pH 7 is most likely – K
pH 8 is most likely – L   [12]

4 (a) Discuss the central role of the liver in building up, breaking down, storing and releasing chemical substances in the body. Include in your answer reference to the blood supply to and from the liver.   [14]
(b) Outline the principles by which:
(i) food 'in large, more or less solid lumps' is converted into 'small dismantled molecules' in the gut,
(ii) oxygen and carbon dioxide are exchanged at the 'interface with the outside world'.   [8]
(c) (i) With reference to the skin-environment interface, describe **three** ways in which the structure of the skin functions as a barrier between the external and internal environment.
(ii) With reference to the lung-environment interface, how may dust particles in the air be prevented from reaching the gas exchange surface?   [8]
(AEB: Biology of Man)

5 The diagram on the right represents a section from the intestine wall with four villi:

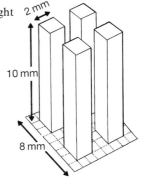

2 mm
10 mm
8 mm

(a) Calculate the surface area of this part of the intestine wall, (i) if no villi were present, (ii) when four villi are present.
(b) How many times greater is the surface area because the villi are there?

6 The figure below shows an MRI (magnetic resonance image) through the abdomen. Identify five of the parts, giving a reason for each identification   [10]

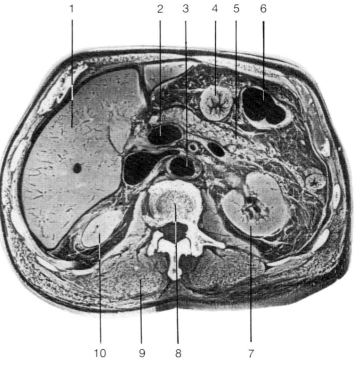

7 Figure 2 on page 72 shows the food consumed by one person in a day. Use the information given on pages 72 to 73, together with the guide below, to calculate the number of kilojoules or kilocalories consumed by this person in one day.

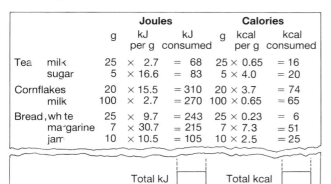

			Joules			Calories	
		g	kJ per g	kJ consumed	g	kcal per g	kcal consumed
Tea	milk	25	× 2.7	= 68	25 × 0.65		= 16
	sugar	5	× 16.6	= 83	5 × 4.0		= 20
Cornflakes		20	× 15.5	= 310	20 × 3.7		= 74
	milk	100	× 2.7	= 270	100 × 0.65		= 65
Bread, white		25	× 9.7	= 243	25 × 0.23		= 6
	margarine	7	× 30.7	= 215	7 × 7.3		= 51
	jam	10	× 10.5	= 105	10 × 2.5		= 25

Total kJ consumed in one day [ ] Total kcal consumed in one day [ ]

8 The nutritional information on a tin of baked beans is shown below. Study it and answer the questions.

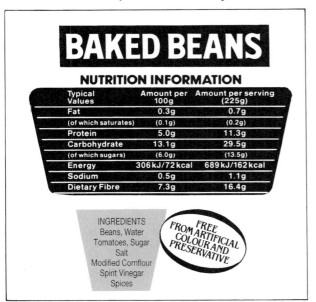

BAKED BEANS

NUTRITION INFORMATION

Typical Values	Amount per 100g	Amount per serving (225g)
Fat	0.3g	0.7g
(of which saturates)	(0.1g)	(0.2g)
Protein	5.0g	11.3g
Carbohydrate	13.1g	29.5g
(of which sugars)	(6.0g)	(13.5g)
Energy	306kJ/72kcal	689kJ/162kcal
Sodium	0.5g	1.1g
Dietary Fibre	7.3g	16.4g

INGREDIENTS
Beans, Water
Tomatoes, Sugar
Salt
Modified Cornflour
Spirit Vinegar
Spices

FREE FROM ARTIFICIAL COLOUR AND PRESERVATIVE

(a) (i) Which mineral is named?
(ii) What type of carbohydrate is the remaining 7.1 g per 100 g likely to be?
(iii) What will the remaining 0.2 g per 100 g of fat be called?
(iv) Is dietary fibre a desirable ingredient? Give a reason.
(b) Which of the items listed will provide the most energy:
(i) per serving,
(ii) per gram?
(c) (i) Give the total weight of ingredients listed per 100 g.
(ii) What substance is the remainder likely to be?
(d) (i) What is a preservative?
(ii) Why was none required for this food? [10]

9 Explain:
(a) The role of the liver in nitrogenous excretion.
(b) How the secretions of the liver and pancreas bring about the digestion of fat.

SECTION 4
Co-ordination

Nervous system

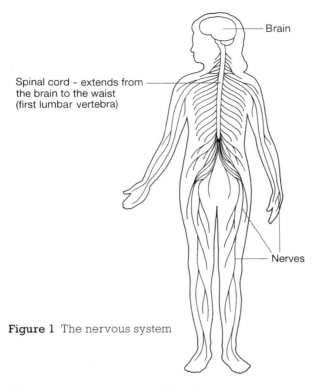

Brain

Spinal cord - extends from the brain to the waist (first lumbar vertebra)

Nerves

Figure 1 The nervous system

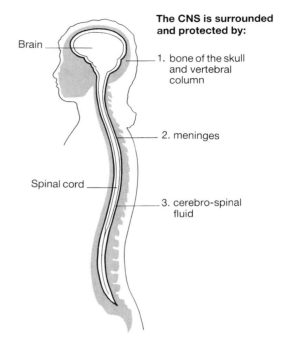

Brain

Spinal cord

The CNS is surrounded and protected by:

1. bone of the skull and vertebral column

2. meninges

3. cerebro-spinal fluid

Figure 2 Protection of the CNS

The nervous system consists of:
- **brain**
- **spinal cord** } **central nervous system (CNS)**
- **nerves – peripheral nervous system**

The nervous system is a network of millions of nerve cells called **neurones**, which each have a cell body and one or more nerve fibres. **Nerves** are bundles of nerve fibres running parallel to each other. Some nerves have ganglia – a **ganglion** is a cluster of nerve cell bodies outside the CNS. Connective tissue called **neuroglia** forms a network of spidery cells amongst the neurones of the CNS to support them.

Function The function of the nervous system is to carry messages – called **impulses** – rapidly from one part of the body to another.

Central nervous system (CNS)

The brain and spinal cord consist of two types of matter – grey and white:
- **Grey matter** contains nerve cells and is well supplied with blood vessels.
- **White matter** contains nerve fibres and only a few blood vessels.

Most of the brain has grey matter forming the outside, with white matter inside (Fig 2, p. 98). The position is reversed in the spinal cord, with white matter outside and grey matter inside. In a cross-section of the spinal cord, the grey matter can be seen centrally and in the shape of an 'H': **Fig 3**.

Meninges Three membranes called **meninges** surround, support and protect the brain and spinal cord, **Fig 2**. These are:
- a tough protective outer layer.
- a middle layer, which is a delicate net-like membrane which has spaces filled with **cerebro-spinal fluid (CSF)**. This fluid acts as a shock-absorber.
- an inner membrane containing blood vessels to supply the nervous tissue.

Meningitis is inflammation of the meninges and it is caused by infection with viruses or, less often and more seriously, bacteria.

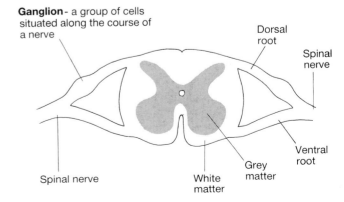

Ganglion- a group of cells situated along the course of a nerve

Dorsal root

Spinal nerve

Spinal nerve

White matter

Grey matter

Ventral root

Figure 3 Section through the spinal cord

Neurones (nerve cells)

Neurones are unusual cells in that they can be extremely long. For example, neurones which connect the brain to the base of the spinal cord may be half a metre long, and those that connect the toes to the spinal cord may be one metre or more in length.

There is great variety in the shape and size of neurones but they can be classified according to their function:

◆ **Sensory neurones** relay impulses from the sense organs to the CNS.
◆ **Motor neurones** relay impulses from the CNS to muscles and glands.
◆ **Intermediate neurones** (connecting neurones) relay impulses between neurones.

Structure of neurones Each neurone has a cell body with granular cytoplasm and a large, centrally placed nucleus. The cell body gives rise to thin threads – **nerve fibres** – which are called:

dendrites if they conduct impulses towards the cell body,

axons if they conduct impulses away from the cell body.

It is usual for long nerve fibres to be surrounded by a **myelin sheath** which insulates the nerve fibre and allows impulses to be conducted along it more quickly. It also gives the nerve a white colour due to the presence of the fatty substance – **myelin**.

The myelin sheath is in sections. Each section has been formed by a **Schwann cell** which wraps itself around the axon: **Fig 5**. The junction between two sections of the sheath is called a **node of Ranvier**.

Nerves

There are 43 pairs of nerves which leave the central nervous system. 12 pairs of nerves – the **cranial nerves** – are connected to the undersurface of the brain and pass outwards through holes in the skull. The other 31 pairs – the **spinal nerves** – are connected to the spinal cord and pass outwards between the vertebrae. All other nerves are branches of these 43 pairs.

Structure of nerves Nerves vary in thickness from being as thick as the little finger to very thin threads containing only one or two fibres. Each nerve consists of one or more bundles of nerve fibres: **Fig 4**. By repeatedly branching, nerves penetrate to all parts of the body.

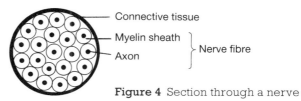

Figure 4 Section through a nerve

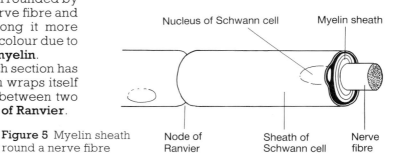

Figure 5 Myelin sheath round a nerve fibre

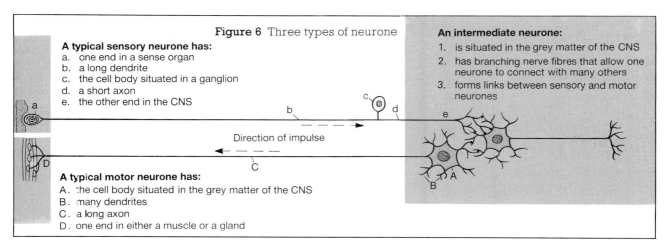

Figure 6 Three types of neurone

A typical sensory neurone has:
a. one end in a sense organ
b. a long dendrite
c. the cell body situated in a ganglion
d. a short axon
e. the other end in the CNS

Direction of impulse

A typical motor neurone has:
A. the cell body situated in the grey matter of the CNS
B. many dendrites
C. a long axon
D. one end in either a muscle or a gland

An intermediate neurone:
1. is situated in the grey matter of the CNS
2. has branching nerve fibres that allow one neurone to connect with many others
3. forms links between sensory and motor neurones

QUESTIONS

1a What is the function of the nervous system?
b What does CNS stand for?
c Name the two parts of the CNS.
d Draw and label **Fig 2** to show how the CNS is protected.

2a What is the difference between grey and white matter?
b Draw a section through the spinal cord to show the grey and white matter.
c What is a ganglion?

3a How many pairs of nerves leave the CNS?
b How many pairs of these nerves are connected to: (i) the brain, (ii) the spinal cord?
c (i) What does a nerve consist of?
(ii) Draw a section through a nerve.
d Give the difference between motor nerves, sensory nerves and mixed nerves.

4a In what way are neurones unusual?
b Describe the cell body of a neurone.
c What is the difference between dendrites and axons?

d (i) Where is a myelin sheath found?
(ii) What is its function?
e Name three types of neurone and give the function of each.

FURTHER WORK

1 Use labelled diagrams to explain the differences between motor neurones and sensory neurones.
2 Complete Exercise 5, p. 125.

Brain

The brain weighs about 1500 g in an adult and sits within the skull in a bath of fluid – cerebro-spinal fluid (CSF) – which both supports it (like your body in a swimming pool) and acts as a shock absorber. It is necessary to protect the brain because brain tissue – the white and grey matter (p. 97) – is very delicate and, if damaged, cannot be replaced.

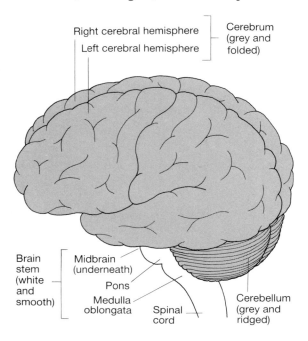

Figure 1 The main parts of the brain

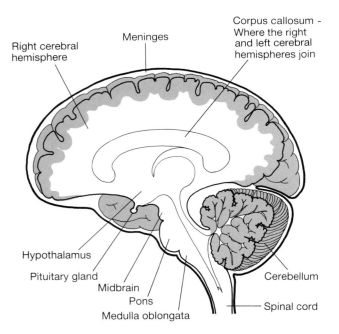

Figure 2 Section through the brain

The brain is connected with the rest of the head by the cranial nerves which go to the eyes, ears, nose and mouth, and also control facial sensations and expression. It is connected with the body and limbs by the **brain stem** and spinal cord.

Functions The brain has four major functions:
◆ It receives information from the sense organs.
◆ It controls muscle movements.
◆ It is the centre of the autonomic nervous system (p. 118).
◆ It controls consciousness, intelligence, reasoning, memory, personality and 'knowing who we are'.

Cerebrum

This is the largest part of the brain and it is divided into two halves – **right** and **left cerebral hemispheres** – which are connected together.

A layer of grey matter called the **cerebral cortex** covers the cerebrum. The many folds in the cortex allow the number of nerve cells in this layer to be much increased. Each nerve cell connects with many others, and the millions and millions of nerve cells form a complex and elaborate network which is only just beginning to be understood.

Certain areas of the cortex are specialised for different functions as shown in **Fig 3**.

Cerebellum

The cerebellum is situated below and at the back of the cerebrum. It is divided, like the cerebrum, into two hemispheres which are linked together. Each hemisphere has a ridged and folded outer layer of grey matter enclosing white matter, so arranged that in section it resembles a tree with branches.

The function of the cerebellum is to coordinate and **control the skeletal muscles** to:

◆ give **smoothness of action** when, for example, walking, talking, writing, feeding,
◆ maintain the body's **balance**,
◆ maintain **muscle tone**.
If the cerebellum is damaged, movements are clumsy, and control of balance may be lost.

Medulla oblongata

The medulla oblongata is continuous with the spinal cord. It contains the '**vital centres**' controlling the reflexes for breathing (respiratory centre), heart rate and blood pressure – vital because these functions are essential for life.

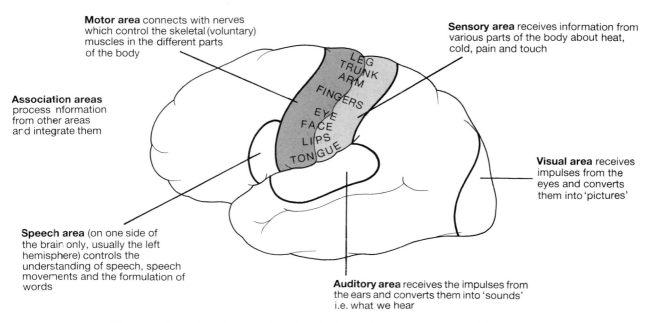

Motor area connects with nerves which control the skeletal (voluntary) muscles in the different parts of the body

Sensory area receives information from various parts of the body about heat, cold, pain and touch

Association areas process information from other areas and integrate them

LEG
TRUNK
ARM
FINGERS
EYE
FACE
LIPS
TONGUE

Visual area receives impulses from the eyes and converts them into 'pictures'

Speech area (on one side of the brain only, usually the left hemisphere) controls the understanding of speech, speech movements and the formulation of words

Auditory area receives the impulses from the ears and converts them into 'sounds' i.e. what we hear

Figure 3 Map of the left cerebral hemisphere showing the areas of the cortex known to be related to particular functions

Memory

It is thought that information goes into the brain in the form of an electro-chemical 'pattern' which can be stored for recall later on.

Short-term memory – much information can be recalled for a few days, eg what you ate yesterday. Most of this is then lost permanently, although a certain amount is locked away as **long-term memory**. Short-term memory tends to become reduced in the elderly.

Notes on Fig 3:

The **motor**, **sensory** and **visual areas** in each hemisphere **relate to the opposite side of the body**. For example, if the motor area in the right side of the brain is damaged, the left side of the body is paralysed.

Different functions of the two sides of the brain The left side of the brain is more concerned with language, mathematical ability and logic. The right side of the brain is more concerned with colour, shape, creativity, imagination and day-dreaming.

QUESTIONS

1a Why is it necessary to protect the brain?
b How is the brain protected by fluid?
c Give four functions of the brain.
d Copy **Fig 4** and complete the labelling.

2a Describe the: (i) cerebrum, (ii) cerebral cortex.
b (i) Draw a map of the brain and label the areas known to be connected with certain functions.
c What is the effect of damage to the motor area of the right side of the brain?
d Do the two sides of the brain have different functions.
e How is memory thought to function?

3a Describe the cerebellum.
b What is the function of the cerebellum?
c What is the effect of damage to the cerebellum?

4a Name the three parts of the brain stem.
b What functions are controlled by the medulla oblongata?

Figure 4 Diagram of the brain

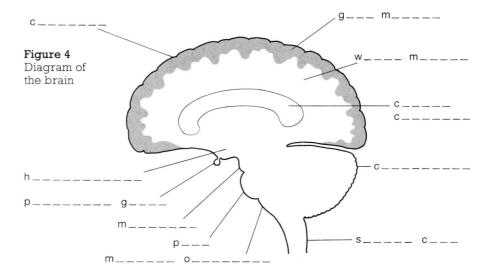

c _ _ _ _ _ _

g _ _ _ m _ _ _ _ _

w _ _ _ _ m _ _ _ _ _

c _ _ _ _ _

c _ _ _ _ _

c _ _ _ _ _ _ _

h _ _ _ _ _ _ _ _

p _ _ _ _ _ _ _ g _ _ _ _

m _ _ _ _ _ _

p _ _ _

m _ _ _ _ _ _ o _ _ _ _ _ _ _

s _ _ _ _ _ c _ _ _

FURTHER WORK

1 (i) What does CSF stand for? (ii) Describe the difference between the two tissues of the brain, white matter and grey matter. (iii) Name the parts of the brain which have grey matter outside, and those which have white matter outside. (iv) Whereabouts in the brain is the corpus callosum?

2 Complete Exercise 3, p. 124

99

How the nervous system works

The nervous system works continually to control our actions whether we are awake or asleep. Whatever the type of action, the instructions which control it are sent through the neurones (nerve cells) as impulses.

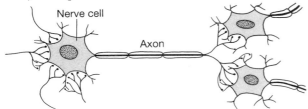

Figure 1 A neurone may be connected with many other neurones. It will then receive impulses from some, and transmit impulses to others

Nerve impulses

An **impulse** is a short burst of electrical current which passes along a neurone.

◆ **All-or-none response** A neurone can only 'fire' or 'not fire'. If it 'fires' it produces an impulse which is always of the same strength. Otherwise, it does not 'fire' at all.
◆ **How impulses start** Neurones are stimulated to produce impulses by other nerve cells, or by decisions in the brain, or by sense organs.
◆ **Strength of the stimulus** A strong stimulus causes impulses to be sent at a high rate per second. A weak stimulus results in only a few impulses per second. If the stimulus does not reach a certain level – **threshold level** – there is no impulse.
◆ **Impulses always pass through a neurone in the same direction: Fig 2.** For a message to be sent in the opposite direction, the impulses must pass through other neurones.
◆ **The speed at which impulses travel** depends on the thickness of the nerve fibre and the presence or absence of a myelin sheath. Impulses travel most quickly – at a rate of 130 m per second – in thick fibres with myelin sheaths. The impulse only travels at about 0.5 m per second in fibres which conduct slowly – in thin fibres without myelin sheaths.
◆ **When impulses reach the end of the neurone,** depending on where the neurone ends, they either cross a synapse to another neurone, **Fig 4**, or they stimulate a muscle or gland to take action.

Figure 2 A neurone transmits impulses in one direction only

Reflex actions

A reflex action (also called a **reflex**) is an automatic response to a stimulus **Fig 3**. When the body receives a certain stimulus it gives the same response, for example, the knee-jerk reflex, **Fig 2**, p. 124. Reflex actions are carried out quickly and without thinking, and often have a protective function. Many reflexes are inborn, others are learnt.

Control of reflex actions Many of the functions of the body such as breathing, heartbeat, digestion and excretion are controlled mainly by reflex actions. Some of these actions can also be temporarily under voluntary control. Breathing is an example: it is possible to hold the breath only for a short while until the reflex takes over again.

Inborn reflexes

Inborn reflexes are inherited and do not have to be learnt. Examples of inborn reflexes are:
◆ **Knee-jerk reflex** – when the knee is tapped below the knee cap, the lower leg jerks forward.
◆ **Pupil reflex** – when the light intensity or the focus changes, the size of the pupil changes.
◆ **Coughing** – when unwanted matter gets into the windpipe, it is cleared by coughing.
◆ **Blinking** – when something moves close to the eyes, the eyelids close.
◆ **Producing saliva** – when food enters the mouth, saliva is produced. Thinking about food, or smelling it, can also produce the same result.
◆ **Response to pain** – when the foot stands on a pin, the foot is quickly removed.

Learnt reflexes

Learnt reflexes are actions which have to be learnt before they become automatic. Examples:

Talking, reading, writing, dancing, playing an instrument etc, are all skills which have to be learnt. **Driving a car** and **riding a bicycle** become mainly automatic after enough practice.

The learning process Every time an action is repeated, the impulse passes along the same pathway in the nervous system, and eventually the action becomes automatic.
Unlearning Once these reflexes have been learnt they are difficult to unlearn and change.
Habits Habits are a type of learnt reflex. They are actions which have been repeated so often that they have become automatic, eg smoking after a meal, swearing, nail-biting.
Conditioned reflex This is a type of learnt reflex where the response has no natural relationship to the stimulus. For example, a dog will produce saliva in response to the sound of a bell – if the bell has always before been rung when the dog was fed.

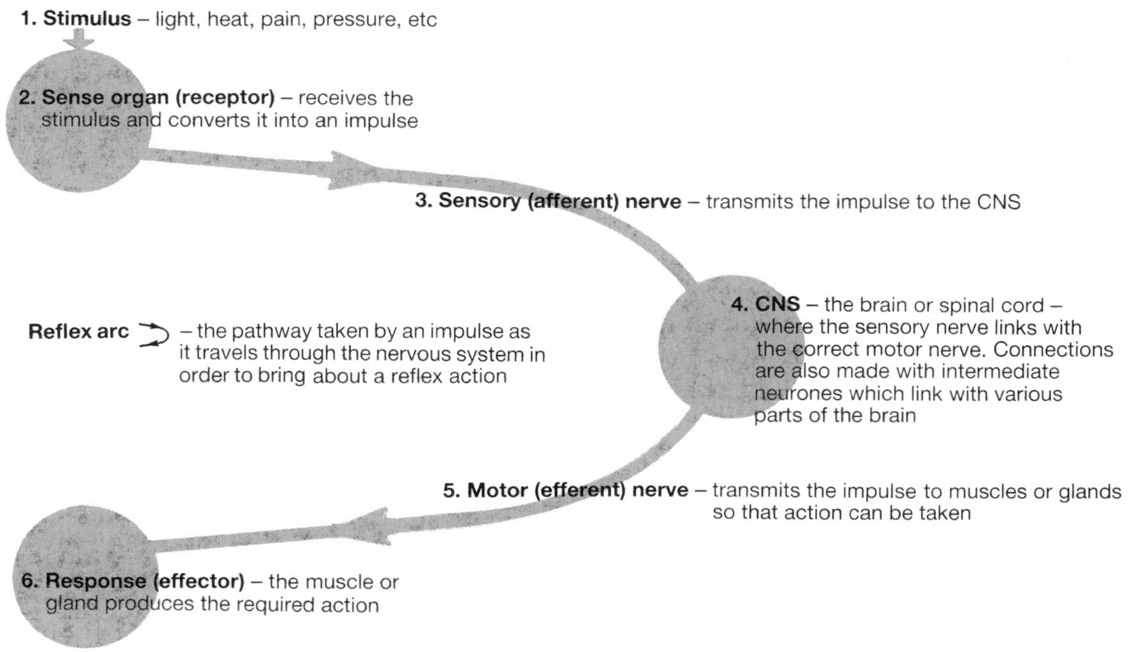

1. Stimulus – light, heat, pain, pressure, etc

2. Sense organ (receptor) – receives the stimulus and converts it into an impulse

3. Sensory (afferent) nerve – transmits the impulse to the CNS

Reflex arc – the pathway taken by an impulse as it travels through the nervous system in order to bring about a reflex action

4. CNS – the brain or spinal cord – where the sensory nerve links with the correct motor nerve. Connections are also made with intermediate neurones which link with various parts of the brain

5. Motor (efferent) nerve – transmits the impulse to muscles or glands so that action can be taken

6. Response (effector) – the muscle or gland produces the required action

Figure 3 Pattern of a reflex action

Voluntary actions

Voluntary actions are actions which the brain decides to carry out (decided by the cells of the cerebral cortex). We choose these actions and are aware of them, and they can be altered, stopped or repeated.

Examples of voluntary actions   A person has to decide when to get up, whether to have breakfast, go out or stay indoors, and so on throughout the day.

Synapse

A synapse is the junction between two neurones. Although very close together, the neurones do not quite touch each other and there is a gap between them. When electrical impulses reach a synapse, they stimulate the production of chemicals called **neuro-transmitters** (such as **acetylcholine** or **dopamine**). These chemicals cross the gap and cause an electrical impulse to start travelling along the next neurone.

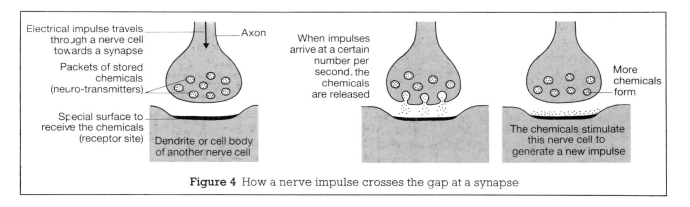

Electrical impulse travels through a nerve cell towards a synapse

Axon

Packets of stored chemicals (neuro-transmitters)

Special surface to receive the chemicals (receptor site)

Dendrite or cell body of another nerve cell

When impulses arrive at a certain number per second, the chemicals are released

More chemicals form

The chemicals stimulate this nerve cell to generate a new impulse

Figure 4 How a nerve impulse crosses the gap at a synapse

QUESTIONS

1a What is an impulse?
 b Where are impulses started?
 c Draw a diagram to show the direction of an impulse through a neurone.
 d Name two factors which affect the speed at which impulses travel.
 e What happens when impulses reach the end of a neurone?

2a What is a synapse?
 b Draw diagrams to show how an impulse crosses the gap at a synapse.

3a What is: (i) a reflex action, (ii) a reflex arc?
 b Draw a diagram to show the pattern of a reflex action.
 c Describe, with examples, the difference between: (i) inborn reflexes, (ii) learnt reflexes, (iii) habits, (iv) conditioned reflexes.

4a What are voluntary actions?
 b Give some examples of voluntary actions.

FURTHER WORK

1   Complete Exercise 4, p. 124.

2   Carry out an experiment on reaction times as described on p. 119. The **reaction time** is the time between stimulus and response.

Disorders of the nervous system

Disorders of the nervous system fall into three groups:
◆ **Mental handicap**
   (mental retardation)
◆ **Mental illness**
   (psychiatric disorder)
◆ **Diseases of the nervous system**
   (neurology)

Mental handicap

Mental handicap is due to failure of the brain to develop normally from an early age. A mentally handicapped person has reduced powers of reasoning, learning, and memory. Although there is no cure, the development of skills can be encouraged by special training.

Brain damage, caused by head injury, meningitis and poisoning (eg by lead) may have similar effects to mental handicap.

Causes of mental handicap

◆ **Genetic defect**, eg
   Down's syndrome (mongolism) – p. 131
   phenylketonuria – p. 151
   thyroid deficiency – p. 151

◆ **Conditions in the womb**, eg
   German measles infection during early pregnancy

◆ **Damage during birth,** eg
   oxygen starvation

Mental illness

In mental illness, the brain has usually developed normally and is undamaged, but there is a behaviour disorder, often as a result of emotional stress. The illness may last for weeks, months or years, and during this time, the way in which the affected person behaves differs from the socially accepted norms. There are two groups of mental illness – neurosis and psychosis.

Neurosis   It is normal to feel anxious, worried or depressed from time to time. They are normal responses to adverse circumstances, for example illness of a close relative, difficulties at work, and money problems. However, if the anxiety or depression becomes so excessive that it interferes with normal living, a person may be suffering from neurosis. People with neuroses remain fully aware both of their problems and the effects upon them.

There are different forms of neurosis:
◆ **Anxiety neurosis**   A few people become so anxious about trivial matters that their normal life style is seriously affected. The anxiety can be the cause of fainting, dizziness, headache, tremor, sweating, poor concentration, diarrhoea, breathlessness and sexual difficulties. It may be sufficiently severe to interfere with normal relationships with family and friends.
◆ **Depression** – an excessive lowering of mood. There is loss of interest in people and activities, lack of self-confidence with feelings of being inadequate, hopeless and helpless. Often the patient feels very tired and suffers from insomnia with early morning wakening. The appetite may increase or decrease.
◆ **Phobia** – extreme fear of a particular object, or situation, for example:
   agoraphobia – fear of open spaces,
   claustrophobia – fear of enclosed spaces,
   fear – of spiders, snakes, or flying.

Psychosis   In psychosis, the sufferers are out of touch with reality and are unaware that their behaviour is considered abnormal. There are different forms of psychosis:
◆ **Schizophrenia** – the person is emotionally distant and cool and withdraws into an unreal world with delusions and hallucinations. This illness usually starts in adolescence, and its cause is unknown. A complete cure is unusual but treatment can result in long periods of normality.
◆ **Manic depression** – behaviour is either extremely over-active to no purpose (mania), or extremely depressed to the point of immobility and complete withdrawal. The patient does not want to do anything or have any contact with people.

Disease of the nervous system

The brain, spinal cord and nerves are exactly like other parts of the body in that they can be affected by disease. Some examples follow.

Multiple sclerosis (MS)   With this disease of the nervous system, small scattered patches of nerve tissue in the brain and spinal cord degenerate – they lose their myelin sheaths and their ability to conduct impulses. The symptoms of MS depend on which parts of the CNS are affected – perhaps blurred vision, uncoordinated movements, slurred speech and unsteady walking.

MS affects people of both sexes, usually starting between the ages of 20 and 50. The disease comes and goes, affecting different parts of the nervous system in turn. Recovery between episodes is often not complete. In severe cases, the episodes recur after short intervals and the patient becomes gradually more disabled.

Epilepsy This disorder is characterised by temporary loss of consciousness. When the only symptom is an absence of consciousness for a few seconds, the condition is known as **petit mal** (petit = little; mal = illness).

When unconsciousness is accompanied by convulsion (a fit) it is known as **grand mal** – GM (grand = big). An attack of GM epilepsy has 3 stages:

First stage The patient goes rigid (the face turns blue) and falls unconscious, often with a cry. This stage lasts about half a minute.

Second stage Jerking movements of the body – arms, legs, face and jaw take place, and frothing at the mouth. The bladder may empty. This stage lasts from a half to two minutes, during which the patient remains unconscious.

Third stage The patient relaxes and usually goes into a deep sleep for up to an hour.

Dementia This is caused by a loss of brain cells resulting in absent mindedness, confusion, loss of the ability to think, and loss of personality. This condition occurs usually in older people, eg as a result of many small strokes, or Alzheimer's disease.

Migraine This usually takes the form of a severe one-sided headache lasting from a few hours to a whole day. A migraine often begins with flashing lights before the eyes, and is associated with nausea, vomiting, and dislike of bright light. Migraine is sometimes brought on by certain foods and by the contraceptive pill.

Figure 1 Treatment during an attack of epilepsy: Roll the patient onto his side and loosen anything tight around the neck, but do not restrain the patient's movements except to prevent him hurting himself, for example, by falling from a chair or bed. Remove objects that could cause damage. Do not put your fingers into the patient's mouth as they can be badly bitten.

Headaches

Headaches are very common and are due to many causes: **Fig 3**. They can often be relieved by rest and relaxation or a mild analgesic (pain-reliever). A headache which persists for more than a few days may need medical advice to discover the cause and give guidance.

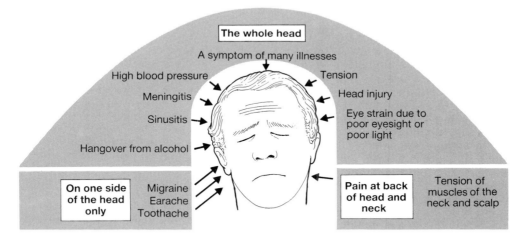

The whole head

A symptom of many illnesses

High blood pressure

Tension

Meningitis

Head injury

Sinusitis

Eye strain due to poor eyesight or poor light

Hangover from alcohol

On one side of the head only

Migraine
Earache
Toothache

Pain at back of head and neck

Tension of muscles of the neck and scalp

Figure 2 Causes of headache

QUESTIONS

1a Give three groups of disorders of the nervous system.
 b What is the difference between mental handicap and mental illness?
 c List six causes of mental handicap.
2a Describe the difference between neurosis and psychosis.
 b Give three forms of neurosis.
 c Give two forms of psychosis.
 d (i) What is a phobia? (ii) Give some examples.

3a What is the difference between the two forms of epilepsy?
 b Describe multiple sclerosis.
4a Draw a diagram to show the causes of headache.
 b How can headaches be relieved.
 c Describe a migraine.

FURTHER WORK

1 Describe an attack of GM epilepsy and the treatment of a patient during an attack.

2 Complete Exercise 2, p. 124

Sense organs

The **sense organs (receptors)** are parts of the body which contain sensory cells – cells that are sensitive to stimuli:
◆ Rods and cones in the **eyes** are sensitive to the stimulus of light.
◆ Organs of Corti in the **ears** are sensitive to the stimulus of sound.
◆ Taste buds on the **tongue** and olfactory cells in the **nose** are sensitive to chemical stimuli.
◆ Sensory nerve endings in the **skin** are sensitive to the stimuli of touch, pain, heat and cold.

How the sense organs work   The sense organs all work in the same way – when the sensory cells are stimulated they send impulses (messages) to the brain. Depending on which part of the brain the impulses reach, they will be interpreted as noise, sight, taste etc.

Sensory adaptation   When a stimulus is applied continuously or frequently to a sense organ, its effect becomes reduced with time. This is known as adaptation. The degree of adaptation depends on the type of sense organ. Touch adapts rapidly, for example we soon forget we are wearing a wrist watch; warning sensations such as pain and cold adapt only very slowly and incompletely.

Tongue

The tongue is made of muscle fibres which go in several directions. This enables the tongue to alter its shape and position for its various functions of helping with:
◆ chewing,
◆ swallowing,
◆ speech,
◆ taste,
◆ sensitivity to touch and temperature.

The upper surface of the tongue   This looks rough (but feels smooth) because it is covered with tiny projections of varying size called **papillae**. They are sometimes mistaken for taste buds, but the taste buds are very much smaller and found in the sides of the papillae: **Fig 1**.

Taste buds   A **taste bud** is a round structure with a small **pore** opening on to the surface. It contains 4–20 slender **taste cells**. Each taste cell has a short **taste hair** which is sensitive to chemicals in solution.

Tasting   One of the functions of saliva is to moisten the food taken into the mouth. As the food becomes moist, some of the chemical substances which the food contains dissolve in the saliva and reach the taste buds. When the chemicals stimulate the taste cells, impulses are sent along nerve fibres to the brain where they are interpreted as tastes.

There are four basic tastes – sweet, sour, salty and bitter – and each is most easily detected by different areas of the tongue: **Fig 2**.

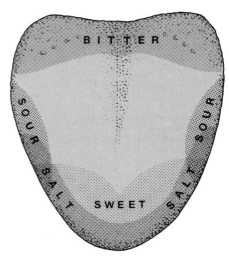

Figure 2 Taste areas of the tongue

Figure 1 Section through the surface of the tongue to show: **A.** the position of the taste buds,
B. the structure of a taste bud

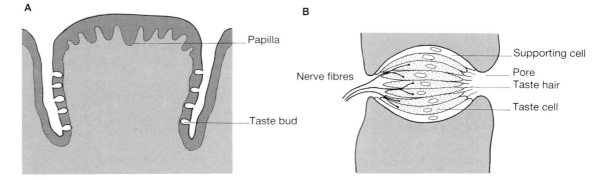

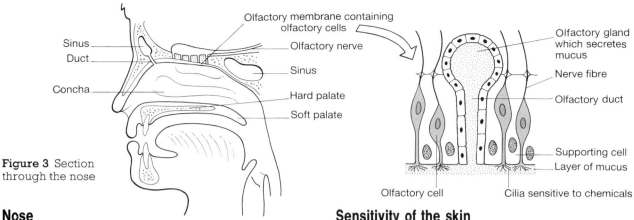

Figure 3 Section through the nose

Nose

The nose extends from the face as far back as the end of the palate: **Fig 3**. It is divided into two **nasal cavities** and lined with mucous membrane. The surface area within the nose is increased by the presence of three flaps of bone (**conchae**) which extend inwards from the sides. A small area in the upper part of each nasal cavity contains the **olfactory cells** which are sensitive to chemicals in solution.

Smelling   The inner surface of the nose is kept moist by mucus. Chemicals in the air entering the nose dissolve in the mucus and are then able to stimulate the olfactory cells to send impulses to the brain, where they are interpreted as smell. The olfactory area of the brain can distinguish many different smells

Flavour   Our sense of flavour depends on the sense of smell as well as the sense of taste. This is obvious when the nose is blocked due to a 'cold' and food seems to have little flavour.

Sinusitis   This is inflammation of the sinuses (see p. 4). It may be caused by infection with bacteria or viruses, or by allergy to dust, pollen etc. The mucous membrane lining these cavities becomes inflamed, swells, and produces abundant mucus which may block the nose, giving rise to headache, stuffiness of the nose, and a 'nasal' voice.

Sensitivity of the skin

The skin is a sense organ. It contains nerve endings of different types which are sensitive to touch, pain, warmth and cold: **Fig 4**.

Figure 4 Sensory nerve endings in the skin

Proprioceptors

Nerve endings (receptors) in muscles, ligaments, joints and tendons are known as proprioceptors. They supply information to the brain about:
- muscle contractions,
- the positions of the joints.

This information gives an awareness of the state of the muscles and positions of the limbs for example, awareness of:
- the position of the hands when behind the back,
- aching muscles after unaccustomed exercise,
- the heaviness of a weight which is being lifted.

QUESTIONS

1a Complete the table:

Sense organ	Sensory cells or nerve endings	Stimulus
Eyes	Rods and cones	Light
Ears		
Tongue		
Nose		
Skin		

b Describe how sense organs work.
c What is meant by adaptation?
2a What is the tongue made of?
b List five functions of the tongue.

c (i) Describe the upper surface of the tongue. (ii) Draw a section through a papilla.
d (i) Describe a taste bud. (ii) Draw a section through a taste bud.
e Describe the process of tasting.
f (i) Name the four basic tastes. (ii) Draw a diagram to show the taste areas.
3a How far does the nose extend back from the face?
b (i) Whereabouts are the olfactory cells? (ii) Draw a diagram of olfactory cells.
c Describe the process of smelling.
d Flavour depends on two senses; name them.
4 Draw a diagram to show the different types of sensory ending in the skin. Say what each type is most sensitive to.

FURTHER WORK

1 Devise experiments to find out:
(i) whether your tongue has similar taste areas to those shown in **Fig 2**,
(ii) if flavour depends on both taste and smell, (iii) if it is possible to tell the difference between butter and margarine.

2 Test different areas of the skin for two-point discrimination, p. 215.

3 What are proprioceptors? With the eyes closed, carry out some actions involving proprioceptors, eg touching the tip of the nose; comparing two weights, one held in each hand. Describe the actions and say how accurately each was able to be carried out.

Eyes

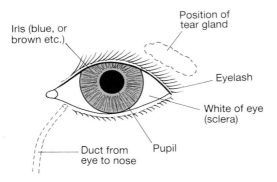

Figure 1 The left eye – front view

The eyes are situated in sockets in the skull – the **orbits**. Each eye has the shape of a small ball about 2–2½ cm in diameter, with a transparent bulge in front through which light can enter the eye. A large nerve – the **optic nerve** – comes from the back of the eyeball and connects with the brain.

Six muscles are attached to the eyeball and control its movements, **Fig 2**. When all these muscles are relaxed, the eyeball faces forwards. Contraction of one or more of the muscles causes the eye to move. It can then receive light rays from a different direction. Contraction of all six muscles in succession makes the eyes 'roll'.

Structure of the eye

The eye has a three-layered wall, made up of the **sclera**, **choroid** and **retina**. The inside of the eye contains transparent substances – **vitreous humour** and **aqueous humour** – which fill the eyeball and maintain its shape: **Fig 3**.

Tear glands (lachrymal glands)

A tear gland, situated deep above the upper, outer corner of each eye, continuously secretes fluid which:
◆ keeps the eyeball moist,
◆ cleans the surface,
◆ prevents infection because it contains antiseptic (**lysozyme** – an enzyme) which destroys bacteria.

Blinking spreads this fluid over the eyeball, and any excess drains away through a duct from each eye into the side of the nose.

If the eye is irritated by foreign particles such as dust, or by chemicals such as onion juice or tear gas, the glands secrete extra fluid (tears) to wash the irritant out. Emotions such as sadness or happiness can cause tears – 'I cried with joy.'

The crust which collects in the inner corner of the eye is dried tear fluid.

First Aid

Foreign bodies or chemicals which enter the eye should be quickly washed out with water. If eye damage is suspected, the patient should be taken to hospital immediately.

Eye conditions

Cataract – the lens becomes cloudy (opaque) making the centre of the eye look milky-white. Vision is blurred or lost completely in the affected eye.
Treatment: The lens is removed from the eye by surgery. The eye then has some sight but, for useful vision, either a plastic lens is implanted or strong glasses need to be worn to do the job of the missing lens – that is, to focus the rays on the retina.

Blindness – the absence of useful sight. Total blindness is rare. It occurs following loss of both eyes, injury to the optic nerves or damage to the visual areas of the brain.

Conjunctivitis ('pink eye') – infection or irritation (by smoke, tear gas etc) of the conjunctiva which makes the eyes look red and inflamed, and feel gritty and painful.
Treatment: Apply the correct antibiotic or avoid the irritant.

Detached retina – the retina, or part of it, comes away from the wall of the eye. Vision is lost from the affected area.
Treatment: It is often possible to stick the retina back in place by surgery, sometimes using a laser beam.

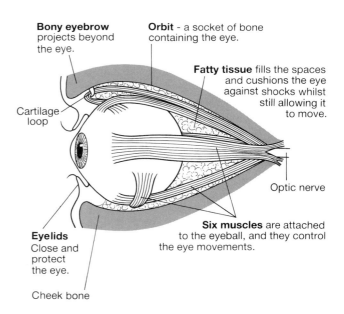

Bony eyebrow projects beyond the eye.

Orbit - a socket of bone containing the eye.

Fatty tissue fills the spaces and cushions the eye against shocks whilst still allowing it to move.

Cartilage loop

Optic nerve

Eyelids Close and protect the eye.

Cheek bone

Six muscles are attached to the eyeball, and they control the eye movements.

Figure 2 Protection and movement of the eyeball

Eye-strain – tired and sore eyes which result from working in a poor light or because of not wearing glasses when they are needed. Permanent damage to the eyes does not occur.

Squint – the eyes look in different directions because the muscles controlling the eyeball are not working together properly. A mild squint is normal in the first six months of life, but if it persists after that, or develops in later life, corrective treatment is necessary to prevent blindness developing in one eye.
Treatment: This includes exercises for the eye muscles and the wearing of glasses, or surgery.

Scratches – slight scratches of the cornea are painful but quickly heal. If the scratch is deep, it should be checked by a doctor because a scar on the cornea can interfere with vision permanently.

Glaucoma – too much fluid (aqueous humour) within the eyeball causes pressure on the optic nerve. The result is eye pain and blurred vision and, if left untreated, blindness.
Treatment: The fluid is reduced by eye drops, tablets or simple surgery. If glaucoma is diagnosed early, no permanent damage will be done to the optic nerve. Correct treatment should keep the condition under control.

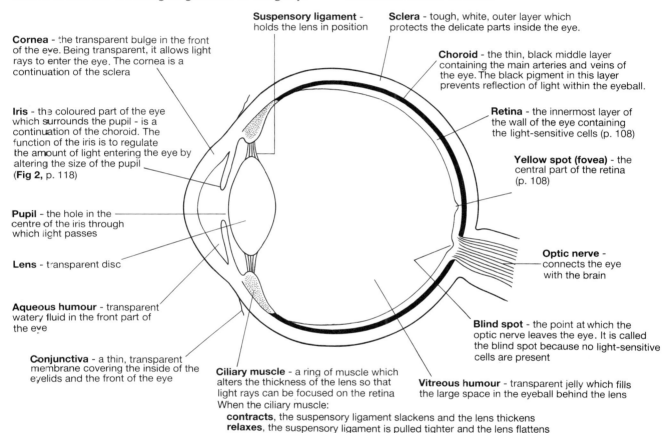

Suspensory ligament - holds the lens in position

Sclera - tough, white, outer layer which protects the delicate parts inside the eye.

Cornea - the transparent bulge in the front of the eye. Being transparent, it allows light rays to enter the eye. The cornea is a continuation of the sclera

Choroid - the thin, black middle layer containing the main arteries and veins of the eye. The black pigment in this layer prevents reflection of light within the eyeball.

Iris - the coloured part of the eye which surrounds the pupil - is a continuation of the choroid. The function of the iris is to regulate the amount of light entering the eye by altering the size of the pupil (**Fig 2,** p. 118)

Retina - the innermost layer of the wall of the eye containing the light-sensitive cells (p. 108)

Yellow spot (fovea) - the central part of the retina (p. 108)

Pupil - the hole in the centre of the iris through which light passes

Lens - transparent disc

Optic nerve - connects the eye with the brain

Aqueous humour - transparent watery fluid in the front part of the eye

Blind spot - the point at which the optic nerve leaves the eye. It is called the blind spot because no light-sensitive cells are present

Conjunctiva - a thin, transparent membrane covering the inside of the eyelids and the front of the eye

Ciliary muscle - a ring of muscle which alters the thickness of the lens so that light rays can be focused on the retina
When the ciliary muscle:

Vitreous humour - transparent jelly which fills the large space in the eyeball behind the lens

contracts, the suspensory ligament slackens and the lens thickens
relaxes, the suspensory ligament is pulled tighter and the lens flattens

Figure 3 Diagram of a horizontal section through a right eye as seen from above a right eye because of the direction of the optic nerve.

Figure 4
To demonstrate the presence of the blind spot

Hold the book about 20 cm (8 inches) away from the face. Cover the left eye and focus the right eye on the cross. Move the book towards and away from the face. At one point the black circle will disappear. At this point the light rays from it are falling on the blind spot, and therefore the brain is not registering an image.

+   ●

FURTHER WORK

1   Study your eyes in a mirror. Draw your right eye (using **Fig 1** as a guide).

2   Dissect a bullock's eye to find all the parts labelled in **Fig 3**.

3   Demonstrate the presence of the blind spot, **Fig. 4**.

4   Apply a nose clip, then demonstrate the effect of onions on the production of tear fluid and the congestion of the nose which follows as the tear fluid drains into it.

QUESTIONS

1a Draw a section through the eye (**Fig 3**) and name all the parts.
 b Describe each of the parts in the diagram.

2a How are the eye movements controlled?
 b Name four structures shown in **Fig. 2** which help to protect the eye.
 c Name the three layers in the wall of the eye.
 d What fills the eyeball and maintains its shape?

3a Describe the position of the tear gland.
 b Give: (i) three functions of tear fluid, (ii) one function of blinking.

4   Describe the following eye conditions: (i) detached retina, (ii) cataract, (iii) glaucoma, (iv) conjunctivitis, (v) squint, (vi) eye-strain, (vii) scratches on the eye, (viii) blindness.

Seeing

1. Light rays reach the retina by passing through the transparent:
 cornea
 aqueous humour
 lens
 vitreous humour

3. When the impulses reach the area of the brain concerned with vision they are interpreted as 'pictures'

2. The light stimulates the light-sensitive cells of the retina and impulses are sent along the optic nerve to the brain

Figure 1 Diagram to illustrate sight.

The function of the eye is to receive light rays and convert them into nerve impulses which are sent to the brain, where they are interpreted as 'seeing'.

Refraction (bending light rays)

Light rays entering the eye are bent (refracted) and brought into focus on the retina by:
◆ the **cornea** – where the greatest amount of refraction takes place,
◆ the **lens** – which adjusts for fine focusing.

Accommodation (focusing the lens)

The lens is continually altering in thickness as the eye looks at objects which are nearer, or further away.
To focus on near objects: the lens thickens and becomes more convex and so causes greater bending (refraction) of the light rays.
To focus on distant objects: the lens flattens so that there is less refraction.

Keeping an object in focus As the eyes watch an object which is moving closer:
◆ the eyeballs turn inwards to keep the pupils pointed at it,
◆ the pupils contract (get smaller),
◆ the lens thickens (to bend the light rays more).
The opposite takes place when watching an object as it moves away from the eyes.

Retina

The retina contains cells which are sensitive to light – the **rods** and **cones**. The rods and cones are connected to nerve fibres which pass across the surface of the retina to the blind spot. The nerve fibres then leave the eye as the optic nerve.
◆ **Rods** are not sensitive to colour and they work best in dim light.
◆ **Cones** are sensitive to colour and they only work in brighter light.
There are three types of cone – one type is sensitive to red light, another to green light, and the third type to blue light. Equal stimulation of all three types of cone gives a sensation of white.

Seeing in the dark

The rods only function when a substance called **visual purple** is present in them. Visual purple is bleached in bright light and re-forms when the light becomes dim. Consequently, when a person moves from a bright light to a dim light, nothing can be seen at first, but as visual purple gradually re-forms it becomes possible to see – not in colour, but in various shades of grey.

Dazzled by bright lights When going from dim light to a bright light, the eyes are at first dazzled. The pupils get smaller, the visual purple breaks down, and the eyes are then adapted to bright light and colour.

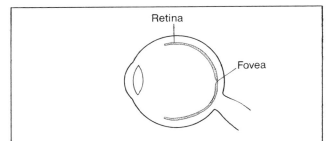

Cones are more numerous in the part of the retina opposite the pupil. The **yellow spot** (fovea) in the exact centre has only cones. In daylight, an object is most clearly seen when the light rays from it are focused directly on the yellow spot. The other objects surrounding it will be indistinct.

Moving outwards from the yellow spot, the number of **cones** decreases and the **rods** increases. In a dim light the pupil will be wide open, which allows light to reach the rods at the sides of the retina.

Figure 2 Distribution of rods and cones: There are far more rods than cones and they are not evenly distributed

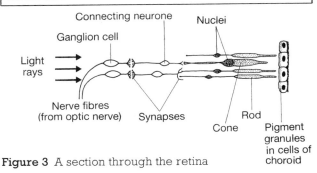

Figure 3 A section through the retina

Normal sight

People with normal sight have no difficulty in seeing things which are close to the eyes or some distance from them. The lens rapidly adjusts so that the light rays are always focused on the retina: Fig 4, **A** and **B**.

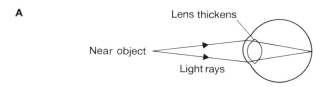

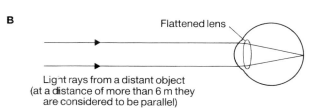

Figure 4 Normal sight
A. When looking at objects close to the eyes
B. When looking at distant objects

Binocular vision – seeing with two eyes – gives a larger field of vision and is necessary for stereoscopic vision.

Stereoscopic vision When an object is viewed with both eyes, each eye receives light from a slightly different angle and sends a slightly different picture to the brain. The brain combines both pictures to give a single picture with a three-dimensional effect. This gives an impression of depth and allows more accurate judgement of distances.

Seeing the right way up The light rays reaching the retina form an image (picture) which is upside down and back to front: **Fig 5**. The picture is corrected by the brain.

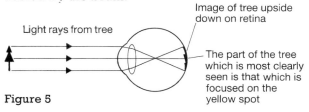

Figure 5

Short sight (myopia)

People who are short-sighted can only see clearly things which are close to the eyes; everything else is blurred. It can be caused by:
◆ the eyeball – which is too long from front to back, or
◆ the lens – which is too rounded.
Correction: wear glasses with lenses which bend the light rays outwards before they reach the eyes.

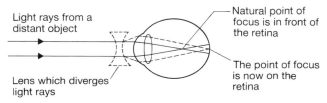

Figure 6 Short sight and its correction

Long sight (hypermetropia)

People who are long-sighted can see things in the distance clearly but everything close to the eyes appears blurred because:
◆ the eyeball is too short from front to back, or
◆ the lens is too flat, or
◆ the lens has hardened, as often happens as people become older. This condition is called **presbyopia** – old sight.
Correction: wear glasses with lenses which bend the light rays inwards before they reach the eyes.

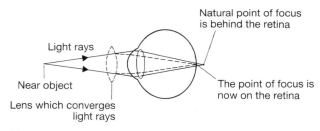

Figure 7 Long sight and its correction

Astigmatism This defect of the eye makes things look crooked or out of shape because the cornea is out of shape. It can occur with short sight, or long sight, or on its own.
Remedy: wearing glasses with lenses to correct the fault.

QUESTIONS

1a Name the two types of light-sensitive cell in the retina.
 b Which of these types is: (i) present in greater numbers, (ii) sensitive to colour, (iii) only functions in dim light, (iv) the only type present in the yellow spot?
 c Draw a diagram to show the structure of the retina.
2a How are we able to see in the dark?
 b Why are we dazzled when we move from darkness into bright light?

3a Give two advantages of having two eyes.
 b What is meant by: (i) stereoscopic vision, (ii) refraction, (iii) myopia, (iv) hypermetropia, (v) presbyopia?
4 Draw diagrams to show:
a focusing on: (i) near objects, (ii) distant objects;
b short sight and its correction;
c long sight and its correction.

FURTHER WORK

1 Demonstrate stereoscopic vision: Catch a ball thrown at you with (i) one eye open, (ii) two eyes open. Which makes catching easier?

2 Examine spectacles used to correct short sight and long sight. Can you tell the difference between them?

3 Find out about contact lenses. List, in two columns, the differences between spectacles and contact lenses.

4 Complete Exercise 6, p. 124.

Ears

Only the **outer ear** is visible. The rest of the ear – the **middle** and **inner** parts – are small and delicate and situated inside the bone of the skull.

Functions

The ears have two functions:

◆ **Hearing** – sound waves are converted into impulses and transmitted to the brain where they are interpreted as sounds.
◆ **Balance** – movements of the head are detected by the inner ear and this information is sent to the brain.

The importance of two ears The possession of two ears, situated one on each side of the head, enables a person to know from which direction sounds are coming. Sound waves from the side reach one ear before the other, so the first ear sends impulses to the brain before the other, enabling it to decide the direction of the sound.

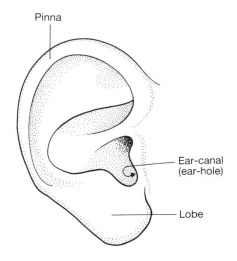

Figure 1 The outer ear

Figure 2 Structure of the ear

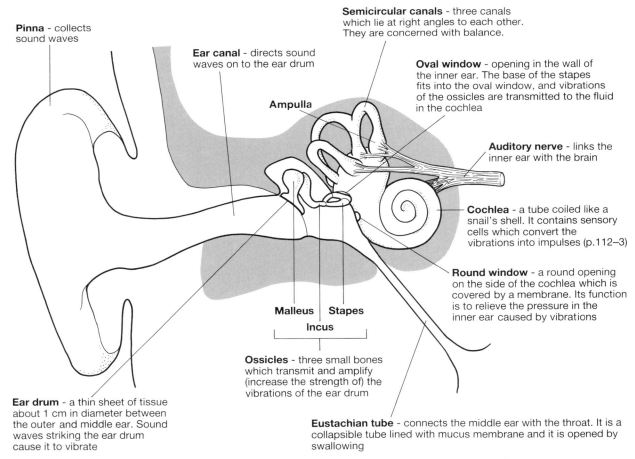

Pinna - collects sound waves

Ear canal - directs sound waves on to the ear drum

Ampulla

Semicircular canals - three canals which lie at right angles to each other. They are concerned with balance.

Oval window - opening in the wall of the inner ear. The base of the stapes fits into the oval window, and vibrations of the ossicles are transmitted to the fluid in the cochlea

Auditory nerve - links the inner ear with the brain

Cochlea - a tube coiled like a snail's shell. It contains sensory cells which convert the vibrations into impulses (p.112–3)

Round window - a round opening on the side of the cochlea which is covered by a membrane. Its function is to relieve the pressure in the inner ear caused by vibrations

Malleus **Stapes**

Incus

Ossicles - three small bones which transmit and amplify (increase the strength of) the vibrations of the ear drum

Ear drum - a thin sheet of tissue about 1 cm in diameter between the outer and middle ear. Sound waves striking the ear drum cause it to vibrate

Eustachian tube - connects the middle ear with the throat. It is a collapsible tube lined with mucus membrane and it is opened by swallowing

Outer ear

This part of the ear consists of:

the ear flap (called **pinna** or **auricle**),
the ear canal (ear-hole or **external auditory meatus**:
    external = outer; auditory = hearing; meatus
    = canal).
and ear drum (**tympanic membrane**).

The pinna is flexible and bends easily. Apart from the lobe at the bottom, it is made of elastic cartilage. The lobe contains softer tissue which can be pierced easily and without much pain. Several muscles are attached to the ear but they remain undeveloped. (The detection of sound for survival is not so important for humans as it is for other mammals such as cats and rabbits who are able to turn their ears in the direction of the noise.) A few people are able to use these muscles to 'wiggle their ears'.

Wax   Wax is secreted by glands in the wall of the ear canal. It protects in three ways:
- It lubricates the ear drum and keeps it supple.
- The bitter taste keeps insects away from the ear canal.
- It keeps the ear clean because dirt sticks to it and is removed when the wax falls out – as it does naturally.

Middle ear

The middle ear is a cavity (space) containing air, with three small bones – **ossicles** – linking the ear drum with the inner ear. Because of their shapes, these bones are known as the **malleus** (hammer), **incus** (anvil) and **stapes** (stirrup).
    The ossicles are held in place by ligaments.

Inner ear

The inner ear consists of fluid-filled tubes embedded in bone. It has two parts – the **cochlea** which is concerned with hearing and the **semi-circular canals** which are concerned with balance.

Balance   The three semicircular canals contain fluid, and at one end of each canal in the **ampulla**, are sensory cells which are sensitive to any movement of the fluid.
    When the position of the head changes, the fluid in the semicircular canals stays still and this stimulates the sensory cells to send impulses to the brain. The brain is then made aware of the position of the head. If the person 'loses balance', the brain immediately sends impulses (messages) to the appropriate muscles so that they can restore the body to its correct position.

Dizziness   Spinning round and round and then stopping causes dizziness. This is because the fluid in the semicircular canals continues moving after the body has stopped.

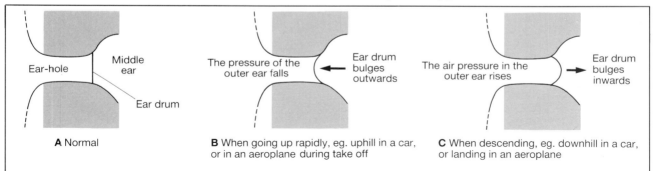

A Normal

B When going up rapidly, eg. uphill in a car, or in an aeroplane during take off

C When descending, eg. downhill in a car, or landing in an aeroplane

Figure 3 Effect on the ear drum of unequal pressures. If the pressure becomes unequal, the ear drum bulges towards the lower pressure. This stretching is painful. Swallowing, yawning or sucking a sweet helps to equalise pressure by opening the eustachian tube. Air is then allowed into or out of the middle ear to equalise the pressure on the two sides of the ear drum – and a slight 'popping' is felt as the ear drum returns to its right position.

QUESTIONS

1a The ear has two functions. Name them.
 b Why is having two ears important?
 c Where are the middle and inner parts of the ear situated?

2a Draw and label a diagram of the ear: Fig 2.
 b Give one function for each of the parts that you have labelled on your diagram.

3   Use the following words to complete the paragraph below: auditory nerve, cochlea, ear drum, ossicles, brain, ear canal, sensory cells.
  Hearing. Sound waves pass through the ___ ___ to the ___ ___ making it vibrate. The vibrations pass through the _____ to the fluid

in the ___. Vibrations of this fluid stimulate _____ ___ to send impulses along the _____ ___ to the ___ where they are interpreted as hearing.

4a Whereabouts in the ear is wax produced?
 b Give three ways in which wax protects the ears.

5a (i) What happens when the air pressures on each side of the ear drum become unequal?
  (ii) How does swallowing help to equalise the pressures?
 b Draw diagrams to illustrate your answer.

6a Name the two parts of the inner ear. Describe how the body keeps its balance.

c Why do we become dizzy after spinning round and round?

FURTHER WORK
To demonstrate that the fluid in a container stays still when the container moves – float a small piece of paper on the surface of a beaker of water, then twist the beaker round.

111

Hearing

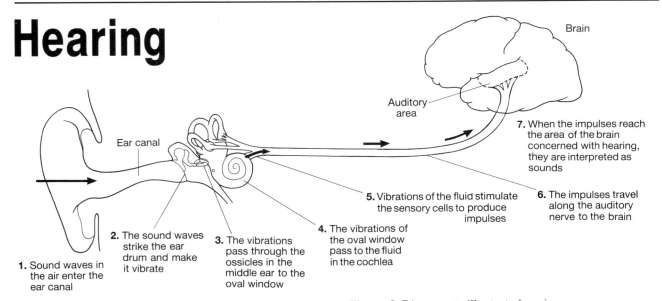

1. Sound waves in the air enter the ear canal

2. The sound waves strike the ear drum and make it vibrate

3. The vibrations pass through the ossicles in the middle ear to the oval window

4. The vibrations of the oval window pass to the fluid in the cochlea

5. Vibrations of the fluid stimulate the sensory cells to produce impulses

6. The impulses travel along the auditory nerve to the brain

7. When the impulses reach the area of the brain concerned with hearing, they are interpreted as sounds

Figure 1 Diagram to illustrate hearing

Sound

Sound is produced by vibrations. The size of the vibration and the frequency of vibrations determines the type of sound produced: **Fig 2**.

Pitch Pitch, whether high or low, is determined by the frequency of the vibrations. A high frequency (fast vibrations) gives high notes. The slower the vibrations, the lower the note.

The young human ear can detect a frequency range of 30–20 000 vibrations per second. The top limit comes down with age and therefore high notes become less easy to hear as a person gets older.

Loudness Loudness depends on the size of the vibration (which reflects the energy content of the sound). Large vibrations give loud sounds, and small vibrations give soft sounds.

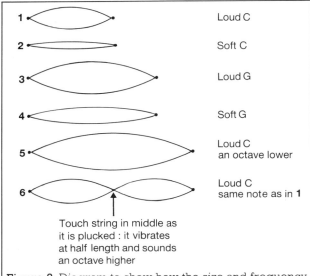

Figure 2 Diagram to show how the size and frequency of vibrations affects the sounds produced

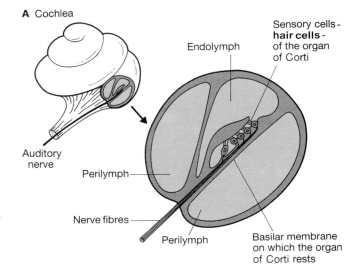

A Cochlea

B Cross-section through the cochlea

Figure 3

Deafness

Deafness can occur in one or both ears and be:
- **temporary** – due to an ear infection or a build-up of wax,
- **permanent** – because of damage to the ear, auditory nerve, or a part of the brain responsible for hearing.

Deafness can also be:
- **total** – no sounds can be heard; it is rare for people to be totally deaf;
- **partial** – some sounds are heard but not others, and this makes it difficult to understand what other people are saying.

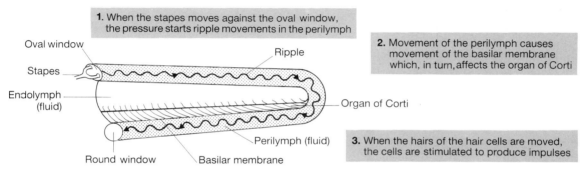

1. When the stapes moves against the oval window, the pressure starts ripple movements in the perilymph

2. Movement of the perilymph causes movement of the basilar membrane which, in turn, affects the organ of Corti

3. When the hairs of the hair cells are moved, the cells are stimulated to produce impulses

Oval window
Ripple
Stapes
Endolymph (fluid)
Organ of Corti
Perilymph (fluid)
Round window
Basilar membrane

Figure 4 Diagram of an uncoiled cochlea to show how it works

Causes of deafness

Outer ear deafness
◆ Wax can block the ear canal and prevent sound waves from reaching the ear drum. Wax is continually being produced and then gradually pushed out of the ear canal. If more is produced than drops out, it accumulates and blocks the ear canal.
◆ A bead or other small object pushed into the ear canal can be the cause of deafness. Small children sometimes do this.

Middle ear deafness
◆ An ear drum and/or ossicles damaged by long-term infection, will result in less efficient conversion of sound waves into vibrations.
◆ The bones of the middle ear become fixed (otosclerosis) and are no longer able to transmit vibrations from the outer to the inner parts of the ear.
◆ The common cold and similar infections sometimes cause deafness in babies and young children. They often find it difficult to hear when they have a cold, and some become very deaf. The eustachian tube becomes blocked by mucus and this interferes with the functioning of the middle ear. Pressure builds up in the middle ear and causes earache.

Inner ear deafness
◆ Damage to the sensory cells in the cochlea prevents the conversion of vibrations into impulses.
◆ Damage to the auditory nerve stops impulses from reaching the brain.

Noise and deafness

Sound is measured in decibels (dB). A loud sound of 120 decibels causes discomfort, but exposure to 140 decibels gives pain, and the ear may be permanently damaged. Even much lower noise levels may produce damage if the ear is exposed to them for long periods. Rock musicians are liable to high-tone deafness.

Noise at work The International Standards Organisation has set the upper limits for loudness of noise at work as:
> 70 dB for the highest frequencies (a high-pitched whistle).
> 91 dB at the lowest frequency that the human ear can pick up (a low rumble).
Deep, low-frequency noises are much less damaging than high-frequency ones.

Reducing noise damage to the ears Safeguards taken at work to reduce noise damage to the ears include:
◆ Wearing protective ear plugs and ear muffs.
◆ Muffling the sound to make it less noisy.
◆ Using acoustic screening – a screen to reduce the amount of noise reaching people.
◆ Rotating of jobs so that a worker is not constantly exposed to loud noise. Loud noises are less dangerous if exposure is brief.
◆ Improving the design of the machinery to reduce the noise.

Why we do not recognise our own voices

When we hear a recording of our voice we find that it is different from the way we think we sound. This is because when we speak we not only hear the sound through our ears but also sound which is conducted from the larynx through the skull bones and which resonates in the air sinuses before it reaches the cochlea.

QUESTIONS

1 List seven stages in hearing.

2 Draw a diagram to show how the size and frequency of vibrations affects the sound produced.

3a Give two causes of temporary deafness.
 b What can be the cause of permanent deafness?
 c What is the difference between total and partial deafness?

4a Name the unit in which sound is measured.
 b How many decibels: (i) cause discomfort, (ii) cause pain?
 c What limits have been set for noise at work?
 d Give four measures aimed at reducing noise damage to the ears.

FURTHER WORK

1 Draw diagrams to show the structure of the cochlea and how it works.

2 Draw a diagram similar to **Fig 1** and use it to explain causes of deafness in the outer, middle and inner parts of the ear.

3 Use a guitar string to demonstrate pitch and loudness.

4 In a recent study 20% of school leavers had significant noise-induced hearing loss. This may go unnoticed in the young but becomes a major disability in the old. Discuss the causes and effects of hearing loss.

5 Complete Exercise 7, p. 124.

Hormones

A **hormone** is a chemical substance which is produced by an endocrine gland in one part of the body and transported in the blood stream to affect tissues or organs in another part. For this reason, hormones are referred to as **chemical messengers**. Although each hormone travels to all parts of the body it only affects certain cells.

Hormones control a wide variety of processes. Some hormones act quickly, eg adrenaline; but others such as growth hormone produce a slower response and control many important long-term processes.

Endocrine glands

Hormones are produced in **endocrine glands**. These glands are often called **ductless glands** as the hormones are released directly from the glands which secrete them into the blood stream. Endocrine glands differ in this respect from exocrine glands. **Exocrine glands** are glands with ducts through which the secretions are removed, eg sweat glands and salivary glands. The pancreas, ovaries and testes have both endocrine and exocrine functions.

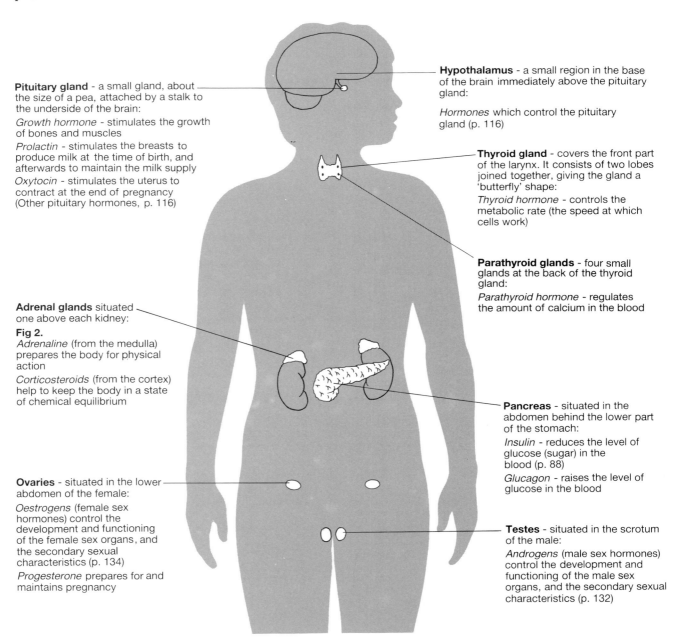

Pituitary gland - a small gland, about the size of a pea, attached by a stalk to the underside of the brain:
Growth hormone - stimulates the growth of bones and muscles
Prolactin - stimulates the breasts to produce milk at the time of birth, and afterwards to maintain the milk supply
Oxytocin - stimulates the uterus to contract at the end of pregnancy
(Other pituitary hormones, p. 116)

Adrenal glands situated one above each kidney:
Fig 2.
Adrenaline (from the medulla) prepares the body for physical action
Corticosteroids (from the cortex) help to keep the body in a state of chemical equilibrium

Ovaries - situated in the lower abdomen of the female:
Oestrogens (female sex hormones) control the development and functioning of the female sex organs, and the secondary sexual characteristics (p. 134)
Progesterone prepares for and maintains pregnancy

Hypothalamus - a small region in the base of the brain immediately above the pituitary gland:
Hormones which control the pituitary gland (p. 116)

Thyroid gland - covers the front part of the larynx. It consists of two lobes joined together, giving the gland a 'butterfly' shape:
Thyroid hormone - controls the metabolic rate (the speed at which cells work)

Parathyroid glands - four small glands at the back of the thyroid gland:
Parathyroid hormone - regulates the amount of calcium in the blood

Pancreas - situated in the abdomen behind the lower part of the stomach:
Insulin - reduces the level of glucose (sugar) in the blood (p. 88)
Glucagon - raises the level of glucose in the blood

Testes - situated in the scrotum of the male:
Androgens (male sex hormones) control the development and functioning of the male sex organs, and the secondary sexual characteristics (p. 132)

Figure 1 Endocrine glands and hormones they secrete. The hormones are in italics

114

Thyroid gland

Thyroid hormone is the main hormone produced by this gland and is essential for:

◆ **Normal development of children.** A baby with an inactive thyroid develops into a **cretin** – undersized and mentally handicapped. To prevent this condition, blood is tested at birth for thyroid hormone (p. 148). If none is present, regular doses of thyroid hormone are given to enable the baby to grow and develop normally.

◆ **Normal rate of metabolism** (p. 68) In some people, the thyroid gland may not function properly:

Over-activity (thyrotoxicosis) – too much thyroid hormone is produced. This makes the body burn up energy faster and results in restlessness, irritability, tremor of the hands, increased appetite and loss in weight.
Treatment: Tablets to stop the thyroid from producing excess thyroid hormone, or removal of part of the gland by surgery, or by radio-active iodine.

Under-activity (myxoedema) – failure to produce enough thyroid hormone. This results in a general slowing down – slower movements, placid temperament, increase in weight, feeling cold, no sweating, a gruff voice, dry skin and hair.
Treatment: Regular doses of thyroid hormone.

Goitre Enlargement of the thyroid gland is called goitre. This can be due to a shortage of iodine (iodine is required to make thyroid hormone).

Adrenal glands

There are two separate parts to each adrenal gland, an outer part – the **cortex** – which surrounds the central part – the **medulla**.

Adrenal medulla When a person feels angry, excited or frightened, **adrenaline** is secreted by the adrenal medulla. This hormone prepares the body for physical action ('fight or flight') by:
◆ increasing the rate of heartbeat,
◆ increasing the rate of breathing,
◆ converting glycogen to glucose,
◆ diverting blood from the skin and gut to the muscles; it is the reason for:
    turning 'white with anger' or 'pale with fear',
    a 'sinking feeling' in the stomach'.
◆ removing excreta:
    looseness of the bowels,
    the need to pass water,
◆ dilating the pupils.

Adrenal cortex The adrenal cortex secretes a number of hormones called **corticosteroids** which include:
◆ **cortisol** – helps to control the use of glucose,
◆ **aldosterone** – helps to control blood pressure and salt balance.
When corticosteroids are given as medicine they are often called **steroids** for short.

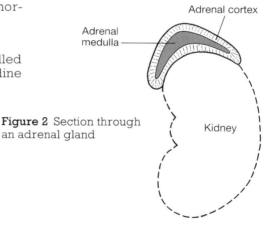

Figure 2 Section through an adrenal gland

QUESTIONS

1 Use information from **Fig 1** to complete the table below.

Endocrine gland	Position in body	Hormone(s)	Function of hormone(s)

2a What is a hormone?
 b Why are endocrine glands called ductless glands?
  (i) What are exocrine glands?
  (ii) Name two examples.
 d Give the names of two glands which are both endocrine and exocrine glands.

3a What effect does an inactive thyroid have on the development of a baby?
 b Contrast the effects on the body of over-activity and under-activity of the thyroid gland.
 c (i) What is a goitre? (ii) Name the usual cause.

4a Name the two parts of the adrenal gland.
 b (i) When is adrenaline secreted?
  (ii) What does it prepare the body for?
  (iii) In what ways is the body prepared?
 c Name the hormones secreted by the adrenal cortex.

FURTHER WORK

1 The output of various hormones alters in response to changes in age, stress, food intake, menstrual cycle etc. Give some examples. Other hormones are essential throughout life. Give some examples.

More about hormones

Hormone production

Endocrine glands do not secrete their hormones continuously. They are produced a little at a time when they are needed. Many important hormone levels are controlled by the working together of the hypothalamus and the pituitary gland which regulate the amount of a hormone in the blood.

Hypothalamus

The hypothalamus is the link between the nervous system and the endocrine system. It produces hormones – **releasing hormones** – which regulate hormone secretion by the pituitary gland. The pituitary gland then produces hormones which control other endocrine glands.

The hypothalamus is connected by nerve fibres to many areas of the brain and receives information from them about the emotions and about conditions in other parts of the body. It is also sensitive to the state of the blood which flows through it.

Pituitary gland

There are two distinct parts to the pituitary gland – anterior and posterior.

Anterior pituitary   It secretes six hormones:

◆ **Two affect other organs:**
   Growth hormone (GH; somatotrophin) stimulates growth of bones and muscles.
   Prolactin stimulates the breasts to produce milk.

◆ **Four control other endocrine glands:**
   TSH (thyroid-**s**timulating **h**ormone) controls the secretion of thyroxine.
   ACTH (**a**dreno**c**ortico**t**rophic **h**ormone) controls the secretion of hormones from the adrenal cortex.
   FSH (**f**ollicle-**s**timulating **h**ormone) controls the production of eggs in ovaries and sperm in testes.
   LH (**l**uteinising **h**ormone) controls the secretion of sex hormones.

Posterior pituitary   The posterior pituitary secretes two hormones:

◆ **Oxytocin** stimulates the uterus to contract at the end of pregnancy.
◆ **ADH** (**a**nti-**d**iuretic **h**ormone) decreases urine production.

Figure 1 Factors which affect the hypothalamus which, in turn, influences hormone production by the pituitary gland

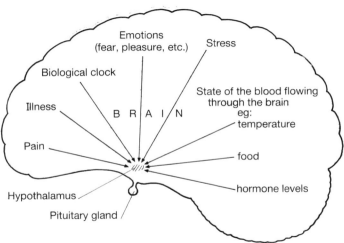

Sex hormones

The male sex hormones are called **androgens**, and the female sex hormones are called **oestrogens** (p. 114). Normal males also have a small amount of oestrogens, and normal females also have a small amount of androgens.

Testosterone is the most important male sex hormone and its presence increases protein production and the formation of muscle tissue as well as the development of the male secondary sexual characteristics.

Oestradiol is the most important female sex hormone.

Anabolic steroids (often referred to just as 'steroids') Anabolic steroids are artificial hormones which resemble testosterone but with less masculinising effects – they increase muscle tissue but have less effect on other male characteristics.

Athletes who take 'steroids' to increase the bulk and power of their muscles run the risk of grave side effects:

In males: sperm production declines,
                there is the possibility of impotence.

In females: skin becomes coarser and more hairy,
                voice deepens,
                periods are irregular.
                there is an increased build up of cholesterol in blood vessels.

Placental hormones

During pregnancy the placenta acts as a temporary endocrine gland. It secretes several hormones including **human chorionic gonadotrophin (HCG)** which is the basis of the pregnancy test. From the eighth week of pregnancy onwards the placenta produces **oestrogen**.

Hormone replacement therapy (HRT)

The menopause occurs when the hormones of the menstrual cycle are reduced. This is a gradual process and may give rise to hormone imbalance which produces menopausal symptoms – 'hot flushes', sweats, vaginitis, and the depression which may accompany the symptoms. Women who suffer severe symptoms may be offered hormone treatment – HRT. Cycles of female sex hormones are given to correspond with the menstrual cycle.

After the menopause, calcium is lost from the skeleton at an increased rate, and HRT is sometimes given to reduce the loss and thus help to slow the process of osteoporosis.

Figure 2 Hormones produced by the anterior and posterior pituitary gland

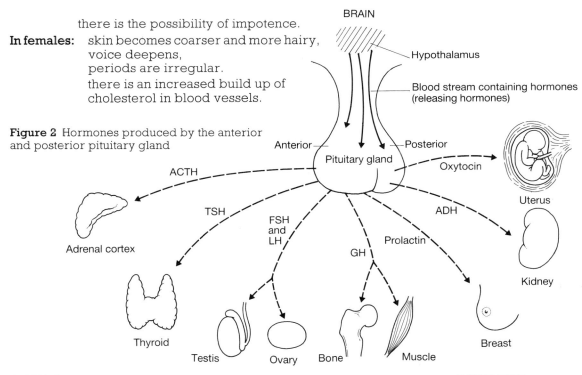

QUESTIONS

1a **(i)** Which two systems are linked by the hypothalamus? **(ii)** Describe the connection.
  b Draw a diagram to show the factors which affect the hypothalamus which, in turn, influence hormone production by the pituitary gland.
2a Name the two parts of the pituitary gland.
  b Name two hormones produced by the anterior pituitary which affect other organs and give the action of each.
  c Name four hormones produced by the anterior pituitary which control other endocrine glands and give the action of each.
  d Name two hormones secreted by the posterior pituitary and give the action of each.
3a Name the most important androgen and give its effects.
  b What are anabolic steroids?
  c Give the side effects of anabolic steroids in: **(i)** males, **(ii)** females.
  d Name two hormones produced by the placenta.

FURTHER WORK

1 **Drugs in sport.** Some athletes have been known to take drugs of various kinds in the hope of improving their athletic performance. Give reasons why is this not allowed. What action is taken by the Sports Authorities to try to prevent this type of drug-taking?

2 Explain what is meant by hormone replacement therapy and why it is given.

Autonomic nervous system

The autonomic system is part of the nervous system – the part that regulates the internal organs. It controls the activities of smooth muscle, cardiac muscle, endocrine glands and secretory glands. The actions controlled by the autonomic nervous system are almost entirely reflex actions.

Functions The autonomic system regulates functions such as:
 circulation,
 breathing,
 digestion,
 excretion,
 hormone production.

Structure

The autonomic nervous system consists of nerves which link the central nervous system (brain and spinal cord) with various organs in the head and trunk. The nerves in this system:

◆ are mostly motor (effector) nerves – nerves which carry impulses away from the CNS (brain and spinal cord),
◆ control smooth muscle, heart muscle or glands,
◆ are working in balance the whole time,
◆ all belong either to the sympathetic or to the parasympathetic system.

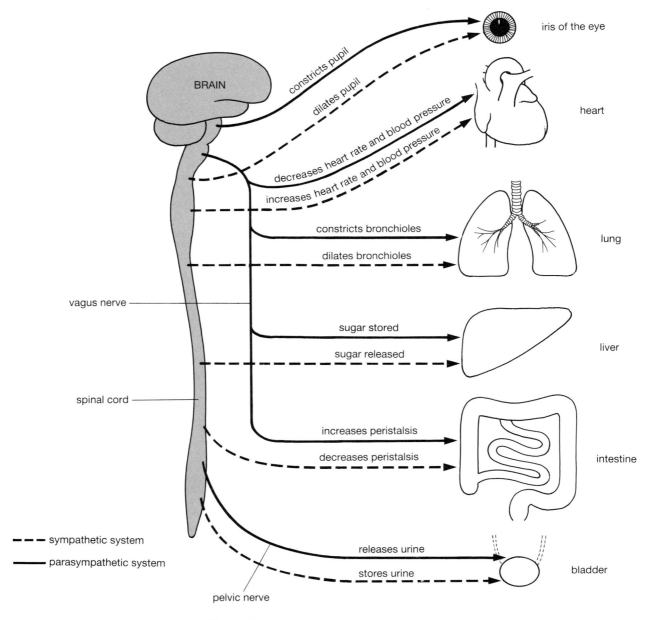

Figure 1 Autonomic nervous system

Sympathetic system and parasympathetic system These are two sub-divisions of the autonomic nervous system. The effects of one system counteracts and balances the effects of the other system.

The **sympathetic system** prepares for the action – 'fight or flight'. Sympathetic nerves arise from the whole length of the spinal cord. These nerves act by releasing noradrenaline at synapses.

The **parasympathetic system** prepares the body for rest, excretion and reproduction. The most important parasympathetic nerve, the **vagus nerve**, starts from the base of the brain. The other nerve, the **pelvic nerve**, starts from the lower end of the spinal cord. Both nerves act by releasing acetylcholine at synapses.

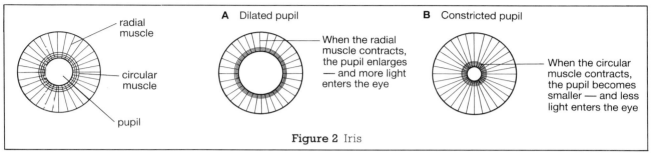

Figure 2 Iris

QUESTIONS

1a The autonomic nervous system is a part of the nervous system. Which part?

b Give examples of functions controlled by the autonomic nervous system.

2 Describe the structure of the autonomic nervous system.

3a Name the two subdivisions of the autonomic nervous system.

b Describe the difference between the sympathetic and parasympathetic systems.

4 Copy and complete the table using information from **Fig 1**.

Organ	Action of the sympathetic system	Action of the parasympathetic system
Iris of the eye	Dilates pupil	Constricts pupil

FURTHER WORK

1 Use diagrams of the iris to illustrate the opposing actions of the sympathetic and parasympathetic systems.

2 Draw two diagrams, one showing the sympathetic system, the other showing the parasympathetic system. Compare them.

Investigating reaction times using a falling ruler

The **reaction time** in this experiment is the time taken for the eyes to detect movement of the ruler, the brain to process the information, and the muscles to carry out the action.

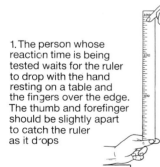

1. The person whose reaction time is being tested waits for the ruler to drop with the hand resting on a table and the fingers over the edge. The thumb and forefinger should be slightly apart to catch the ruler as it drops

2. A partner holds the top of the ruler so that 0 mm mark is level with the top of the other person's fingers

3. The distance the ruler drops before it is caught is recorded, ie. the distance from 0 mm to the top of the fingers

Table giving the distance a ruler will drop in a given period of time

Time (in seconds)	Distance of drop (in mm)
0.05	12
0.10	49
0.15	110
0.20	196
0.25	307
0.30	441

(i) Calculate the average distance of drop from ten drops.

(ii) Use the information in the Table to draw a graph.

(iii) From the graph, find the average **reaction time**. (When the distance the ruler drops is known, the time it took can be obtained from the graph.)

(iv) Find the average reaction time of each member of the class, and compare with the average reaction time of the class.

(v) Draw and label a diagram to show the parts of the nervous system and the muscles involved in this particular reaction.

(vi) Devise an experiment to find out whether reaction time is affected by time of day, tiredness, sedative drugs, age, alcohol or other factors.

(vii) Devise a **mechanism** to release the ruler by remote control.
Draw a detailed plan of the mechanism.
Construct the mechanism.
Test the mechanism to see if it is suitable for its purpose.
Evaluate: Does your mechanism work better, as well as, or less well than releasing a handheld ruler? Give your reasons.

Homeostasis

Homeostasis means maintaining a steady state (homeo = same; stasis = state). The conditions outside the body (the external environment) are continuously varying, but the body has mechanisms – **homeostatic controls** – for adjusting conditions within the body (the internal environment) to keep conditions surrounding the cells steady.

Internal environment

Cells are surrounded by tissue fluid which, when kept in a constant state, allows the cells to function well and the body to remain healthy. This makes it possible for people to live in a wide variety of conditions from the arctic to the tropics, and to move from one to the other with relative ease. Each of the conditions which together make up the steady state can vary slightly within a limited range, but too great an alteration of any one of them leads to disease.

Homeostatic control

Homeostasis is achieved by using both the nervous system and endocrine system, but in different ways.

The nervous system
◆ It is faster.
◆ It controls particular activities over a short period of time by making rapid adjustments.
◆ Messages are sent as impulses along nerves.
◆ Impulses travel to a particular part of the body.
◆ Each impulse controls certain muscle or gland cells.

The endocrine system
◆ It is slower.
◆ It controls long-term or continuous processes such as metabolism, growth and development.
◆ Messages are sent as hormones in the blood.
◆ Hormones travel in the blood stream to all parts of the body.
◆ Each hormone controls a certain type of cell.

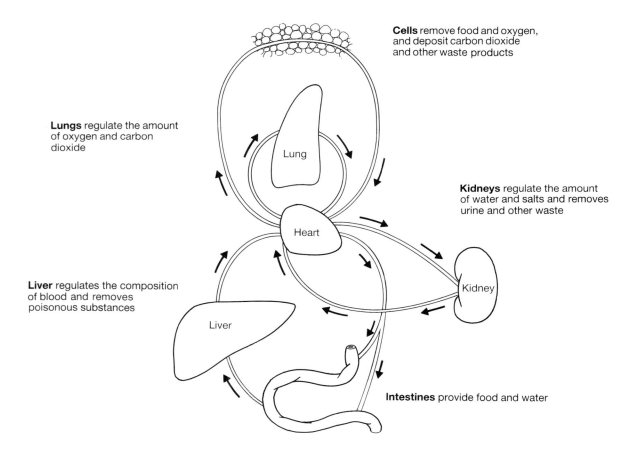

Cells remove food and oxygen, and deposit carbon dioxide and other waste products

Lungs regulate the amount of oxygen and carbon dioxide

Kidneys regulate the amount of water and salts and removes urine and other waste

Liver regulates the composition of blood and removes poisonous substances

Intestines provide food and water

Figure 1 Diagram to illustrate some of the processes involved in the homeostasis of blood. Each process is controlled by its own particular nerves and hormones

Examples of homeostasis

Conditions which are kept constant include:
- pH,
- temperature,
- blood pressure,
- blood sugar levels,
- levels of circulating hormones.

pH The pH scale of 1–14 is used to express the degree of acidity or alkalinity of a solution: pH 7 is neutral less than 7 is acid, more than 7 is alkaline.

The pH of blood is 7.4, and the range of blood pH compatible with life is only 7.0–7.8. An incorrect pH slows down enzyme action and therefore activity within living cells.

Another method of measuring acidity or alkalinity is by the **cH** scale – the concentration of hydrogen ions in the solution.

Feed-back systems

A **feed-back system** is any circular situation in which the output is used to control the input. A **negative feed-back system** is one in which the output is used to reduce the input. Control of the level of thyroid hormone in the blood is an example of a negative feed-back system – when the level of thyroid hormone is too high, it suppresses TSH production by the anterior pituitary.

Figure 2

EXAMPLES OF HOMEOSTATIC CONTROL

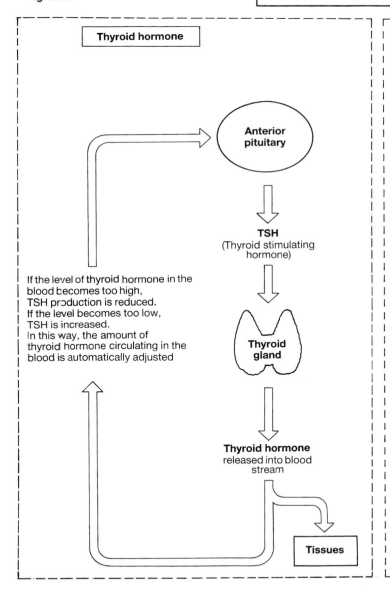
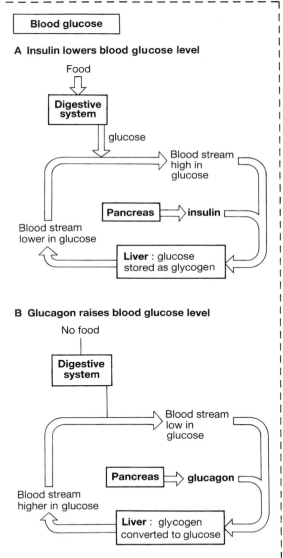

QUESTIONS

1　What is meant by: **(i)** homeostasis, **(ii)** the external environment, **(iii)** the internal environment?

2　How does the nervous system differ from the endocrine system?

3a　Give five conditions which are kept constant by homeostasis.
　b　**(i)** What is meant by pH? **(ii)** Give the pH of blood.

Temperature regulation and water balance

Temperature regulation

The temperature of the body remains remarkably constant at about 37°C, a little higher in the late afternoon and a little lower in the early morning. It is controlled by the brain (hypothalamus) which continuously balances heat production with heat loss.

Heat production   Heat is produced in living cells during metabolism. The liver and muscles produce most heat because they are the largest and most active parts of the body. The liver produces heat continuously, and muscles produce heat when they are working.

Heat loss   Heat is lost from the body mainly through the skin by:
>   **evaporation** of sweat,
>   **radiation** of heat,
>   **convection** of air.

A little heat is lost through breathing, and a very small amount in urine and faeces.

Variation in body temperature

There are a number of reasons why the body temperature may be above or below normal.

Higher than normal   An increase in body temperature can be due to either or both:
◆ **increased heat production**
>   exercise,
>   fever.
◆ **too little heat loss**
>   hot, humid surroundings,
>   too much clothing.

Lower than normal   A drop in body temperature can be due to either or both:
◆ **increased heat loss**
>   cold surroundings,
>   too little clothing.
◆ **too little heat produced**
>   lack of exercise,
>   lack of suitable food,
>   inability of babies and old people to adjust to low temperatures.

Changes associated with ovulation   The temperature rises a little at ovulation and falls back to normal just before a period.

Regulation of body temperature

The skin plays an important part in keeping body temperature more or less constant – maintaining homeostasis (p. 120) of body temperature.

When the body is too hot   As the temperature rises:
◆ **Heat loss is increased** when:
>   **blood vessels** in the skin dilate (open) and allow more blood to flow close to the surface, causing the skin to look flushed, and increasing the amount of heat lost by radiation and convection.
>   **sweat glands** increase the rate of sweat production so that a continuous layer of moisture covers the skin. Heat from the body is used up as evaporation of sweat takes place. If the air is both hot and humid, eg in a sauna, heat loss by evaporation is much more difficult.
◆ **Less heat is produced:**
>   people are less active.

When the body is too cold   As the temperature falls:
◆ **Heat loss is reduced** when
>   **blood vessels** in the skin constrict (close) and reduce the amount of blood flowing near to the surface – causing the skin to become cold and look pale and blue. This results in much less heat being lost by radiation.
>   **sweat glands** reduce the rate of sweat production. The skin is then dry and little heat is lost by evaporation.
◆ **More heat is produced** by:
>   **shivering**: heat is produced by the muscles which cause shivering. ('Goose pimples' appear which in other mammals would have the effect of raising the hair to trap a layer of air around the body and help prevent heat loss.)
>   **muscle movements** from stamping the feet, swinging the arms etc.

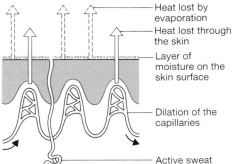

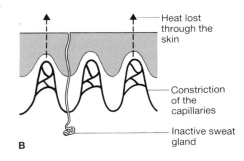

Figure 1 Regulation of body temperature by the skin
   A. When the body is too hot
   B. When the body is too cold

Water

Water (H_2O) is the main substance in the body. It accounts for 60–70% of body weight – which in a person weighing 70 kg is about 45 litres. Younger people contain a higher percentage of water than older people, men more than women, and thin people more than fat people.

About two-thirds of the water in the body is in the cells (**intracellular fluid**). The rest (**extracellular fluid**) is in the body's fluids – plasma, tissue fluid, lymph, etc. There is rapid and continuous movement of water between the cells and the extracellular fluids.

Water is essential for life – although people can live for weeks without food, they can survive for only a few days without water, especially in hot climates.

Functions Water has many functions in the body including the following:

◆ It is an essential part of protoplasm.
◆ It is a solvent. Many substances are able to dissolve in water and to enter and leave blood capillaries and cells, eg oxygen, carbon dioxide, glucose, salt.
◆ It provides a liquid medium in which many thousands of chemical reactions take place which are essential for life.
◆ It is a transport medium. The fluids in the body are mainly water, eg blood, lymph, urine, bile, and they carry many substances from one place to another.
◆ Sweat helps regulate body temperature.

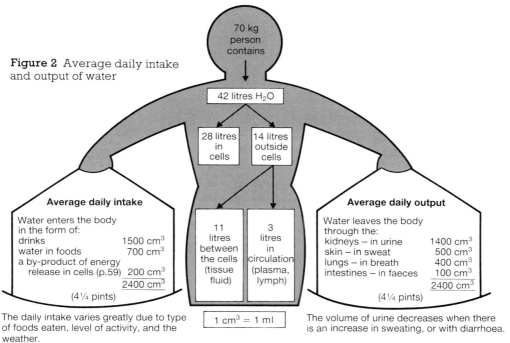

Figure 2 Average daily intake and output of water

70 kg person contains

42 litres H_2O

28 litres in cells | 14 litres outside cells

Average daily intake

Water enters the body in the form of:
drinks	1500 cm³
water in foods	700 cm³
a by-product of energy release in cells (p.59)	200 cm³
	2400 cm³

(4¼ pints)

11 litres between the cells (tissue fluid) | 3 litres in circulation (plasma, lymph)

Average daily output

Water leaves the body through the:
kidneys – in urine	1400 cm³
skin – in sweat	500 cm³
lungs – in breath	400 cm³
intestines – in faeces	100 cm³
	2400 cm³

(4¼ pints)

The daily intake varies greatly due to type of foods eaten, level of activity, and the weather.

$1 cm^3 = 1 ml$

The volume of urine decreases when there is an increase in sweating, or with diarrhoea.

QUESTIONS

1a What is normal body temperature?
 b How is heat produced in the body?
 c How is heat lost from the body?
 d Give two reasons for higher than normal body temperature.
 e Give two reasons for lower than normal body temperature.
2 Describe ways in which the skin helps to regulate body temperature when the body becomes: (i) too hot, (ii) too cold. Draw diagrams to illustrate your answers.
3a How much water does the body contain?
 b Whereabouts in the body does water occur?
 c Give two functions of water in the body.
4a How is the amount of water in the body maintained at a more or less constant level?
 b Describe: (i) average daily intake of water, (ii) average daily output.

FURTHER WORK

1 Describe the case of hypothermia shown in **Fig 3**.

2 Describe in your own words how the body maintains homeostasis of: (i) body temperature, (ii) water balance.

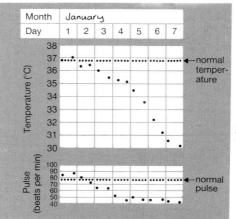

Figure 3 A case of hypothermia

Section 4   EXERCISES

1 Match each of the terms with the correct statement in the list below:

(a) **accommodation cataract cerebrum cones meninges nerve reflex action refraction retina synapse**

    surround brain and spinal cord
    bundle of nerve fibres
    largest part of the brain
    junction between two neurones
    automatic response to a stimulus
    cloudy lens
    layer of light-sensitive cells
    bending of light rays
    focusing of lens
    cells sensitive to colour   [10]

(b) **adrenaline autonomic nervous system cochlea binocular vision endocrine gland homeostasis hormone impulse myopia tympanic membrane**

    seeing with two eyes
    short sight
    part of the inner ear
    ear drum
    chemical messenger
    short burst of electric current
    ductless gland
    'fight or flight' hormone
    regulates the internal organs
    maintaining a steady state   [10]

2 The following notes concern hospital patients who have suffered damage to the central nervous system as a result of injury or disease.
Patient 1. Spinal cord completely severed in the thoracic (chest) region. Total loss of voluntary movement in both legs but still shows knee jerk and periodically empties bladder.
Patient 2. Suffered stroke causing damage to the left side of the cerebrum (forebrain). Right side of the body paralysed.
Patient 3. Brain damage sustained in a car accident. Unable to see although both eyes undamaged.
Patient 4. Has tumour causing extensive damage to the cerebellum (hind brain). Able to walk but only with a staggering gait.
Using this information, discuss the role of the nervous system in controlling and co-ordinating body activities.   [10]

(AEB: O(A) level Biology of Man)

The knee-jerk reflex   To demonstrate this reflex, sit with one leg crossed over the other so that the lower part of the leg hangs free. If the knee is tapped below the knee-cap, the lower part of the leg will jerk forward.

3 Complete the following table of the differences between typical motor and sensory neurones.

	Motor neurone	Sensory neurone
(a) Is the cell body at the end of the cell or part way along?		
(b) Is the cell body situated in the CNS or in a ganglion?		
(c) Is the function to convey impulses towards or away from the CNS?		
(d) Does the neurone receive impulses from a sense organ?		
(e) Does the neurone convey impulses to muscles or glands?		

4 (a) Describe how to demonstrate the knee-jerk reflex.

(b) Using information from the figure, describe the knee-jerk reflex by completing the text below:

Tapping the . . . . stretches the . . . . muscle, and this stimulates the . . . . endings of the . . . . to produce an . . . . This travels along the . . . . fibre to the . . . . where, in the . . . . matter, it crosses a . . . . to a . . . . neurone. It travels along the motor . . . . to the thigh . . . . The impulse makes the thigh muscle contract and the lower leg jerks forwards.

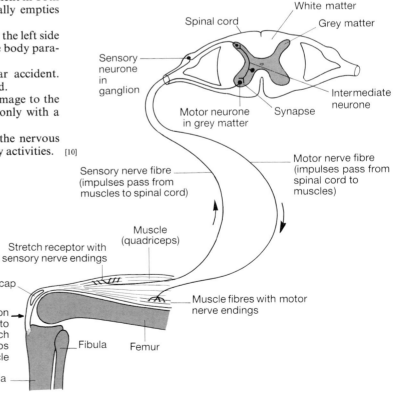

5 Study the figure below and answer the following questions:

(a) The teeth numbered 1 to 8 can be classified into four types.
(i) Name them.
(ii) Say which teeth belong to which type. [8]
(b) Give one reason why this skull could not be that of a young child. [1]
(c) Part 9 is the roof of the mouth. What is it also called? [1]
(d) Part 10: To which part of the face do these holes connect? [1]
(e) Part 11: What passes through this hole (foramen magnum)? [1]
(f) Part 12: Name the vertebra which articulates with the skull here. [1]
(g) Part 13: Which bone articulates with the skull at this joint? [1]
(h) Part 14: Name the sense organ to which this hole leads. [1]

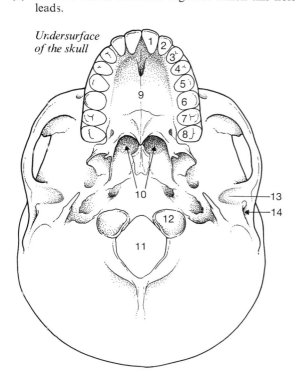

Undersurface of the skull

6 (a) Draw a large diagram of a vertical section through an eye. [6]
(b) Label on the diagram the following structures:
(i) retina (ii) cornea (iii) iris
(iv) muscle which moves the eyeball [4]
(c) Explain the functions of each of the structures (i), (ii), (iii) and (iv) listed in part (b). [7]
(d) A person looking into the distance focuses his eye on a near object, for example this examination paper. State the changes which occur to the eye so that the near object may be seen clearly. [8]

(AEB: Human Biology)

7 (a) Draw a large clearly labelled diagram of a section through the ear. [8]
(b) Explain concisely how sound waves striking the ear drum lead to nerve impulses being transmitted along the auditory nerve. [6]
(c) Explain why an infection in the Eustachian tube may lead to temporary deafness. [2]

(AEB: O(A) level Human Biology)

SECTION 5
Human Development

Genes

A **gene** is a segment of a chromosome which contains the code for a particular characteristic, for example eye colour or blood group. A **chromosome** is a chain of thousands of genes. The 46 chromosomes in the nucleus of each body cell contains the coded instructions for the growth and development of a complete human being. The instructions are coded in **DNA – deoxyribonucleic acid** – the chemical substance of which genes are made.

Genes are switched on and off   Although each cell possesses all a person's genes, it will only use some of them, for example, genes for eye colour will only be active in the cells of the iris. Genes function at the precise moment when they are needed, and then stop, but how a gene is switched on and off is not known.

Structure of DNA

Each chromosome consists of a long, thin, thread of DNA surrounded by a protein coat. The thread is highly coiled. When it is uncoiled, DNA is like a twisted ladder, **Fig 1**.

◆ The sides of the ladder are formed from alternate **sugar** and **phosphate** molecules.

◆ The rungs of the ladder are formed from pairs (**base pairs**) of **nucleotides**, **Fig 2**. There are four nucleotides and they always pair up so that:
     adenine is with **thymine** (**AT** or **TA**);
     cytosine is with **guanine** (**CG** or **GC**).

The segment of DNA which makes the gene consists of thousands of base pairs and each gene is a code for making one kind of protein. The order in which the base pairs are arranged governs the order in which the amino acids are arranged to form a protein molecule: **Fig 3**.

Figure 1 Part of a DNA molecule

Figure 2 Part of a DNA molecule showing the base pairs

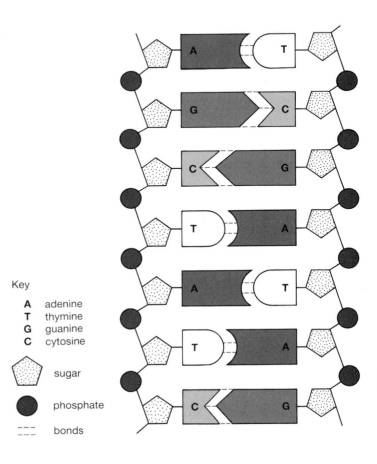

Key

A	adenine
T	thymine
G	guanine
C	cytosine

sugar

phosphate

bonds

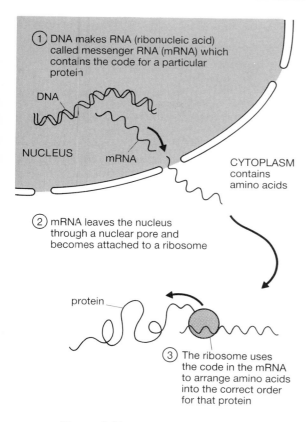

① DNA makes RNA (ribonucleic acid) called messenger RNA (mRNA) which contains the code for a particular protein

DNA

NUCLEUS

mRNA

CYTOPLASM contains amino acids

② mRNA leaves the nucleus through a nuclear pore and becomes attached to a ribosome

protein

③ The ribosome uses the code in the mRNA to arrange amino acids into the correct order for that protein

Figure 3 How a gene makes a protein

How a gene produces a characteristic

Parents pass on to their children, through the genes, the ability to make proteins – a great variety of proteins. Not all genes in a particular cell will become active – only those that give rise to proteins the cell needs. When a protein molecule has been made it becomes either:

◆ **protein** which helps to form the **structure** of cells. The particular genes which become active in a cell determine its shape and size, eg some genes are responsible for heart muscle, others for gland tissue, etc.

◆ an **enzyme** – there are about 2000 different enzymes in a cell, each with its own effect on the cell's activities. If even one of these is missing or fails to function properly, it can have a dramatic effect on development and health, eg PKU, p. 149.

◆ a **special protein** – manufactured by certain cells to produce hormones, antibodies, fibrinogen, blood group factors, etc.

Replication of DNA

When a cell divides into two, it produces a set of chromosomes identical to its own set. In each chromosome, the double strand of DNA uncoils, and a new strand is built along both lengths, from sugar and phosphate molecules and from base pairs (**Fig 4**).

Figure 4 Replication of DNA (only part of the molecule is shown)

① The DNA molecule uncoils

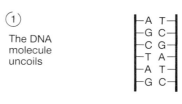

② The two strands separate

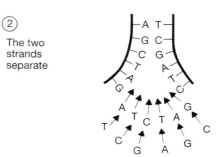

③ New base pairs are built up

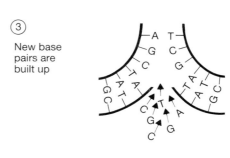

④ There are now two identical copies of the original DNA

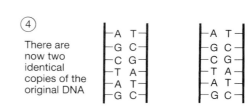

FURTHER WORK

1 Draw diagrams to show how DNA replicates.

2 Read *The Double Helix* by J D Watson (Weidenfeld and Nicolson).

Give a straightforward account of the discovery of DNA. Mention in your account the complicated inter-personal relationships between the scientists involved.

QUESTIONS

1a What is a gene?
b How many genes does a chromosome contain?
c Name the chemical substance in which genetic instructions are coded.
d What is meant by 'genes are switched on and off'?

2 (i) Describe the structure of DNA.
(ii) Draw part of a DNA molecule showing the base pairs.

3 Describe how a gene produces a characteristic.

4 Describe how a gene makes a protein.

Genetics

Genetics is the study of inheritance – the study of the effects of genes on growth and development. Children inherit genes from their parents and this is why they resemble them, their grandparents and other relatives.

Inherited characteristics Any one person has many distinguishing features – characteristics – in shape, height, appearance, behaviour etc. Those characteristics which are passed on from parent to child by the genes are said to be inherited.

Genotype and phenotype The genes which a person possesses are called the **genotype**. The way a person looks – the visible characteristics – is called the **phenotype**.

Genes always occur in pairs

Two sets of matching chromosomes are inherited – one from the father and one from the mother, **Fig 1**. Therefore two sets of genes are inherited which match together in pairs, each member of a pair occupying exactly the same position on their respective chromosomes and affecting the same characteristic.

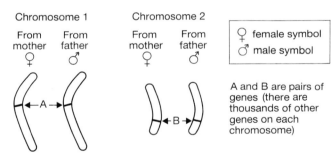

Figure 1 Genes occur in pairs.

Alleles Although both genes of a pair affect the same characteristic, they may vary in their effect, for example, the gene for hair colour, may give rise to brown, black, blonde or red hair. Alternative forms of the same gene are called **alleles**. Alleles occupy the same position on each of a pair of chromosomes and they control the same characteristic.

Homozygous and heterozygous If both genes of a pair have the same effect, for example, they both give rise to black hair, they are called **homozygous**. If they have different effects, for example, one is for black hair and one for blonde hair, they are called **heterozygous**. Individuals which are **pure-bred** for a particular characteristic are homozygous. **Hybrids** are heterozygous.

Dominant and recessive

Genes can be dominant (strong) or recessive (weak). Strong genes mask the presence of weak genes. For example, if a child inherits a gene for dark hair from the father and a gene for red hair from the mother, the child's hair will be dark because the gene for dark hair is dominant to that for red hair.

> **Dominant genes** produce the same effect whether two are present or only one.
> **Recessive genes** do not have an effect when they are with a dominant gene.

Carriers The possession of a gene which does not have an effect makes a person a **carrier** for that gene, eg the child mentioned above will be a **carrier** for red hair. The gene may be passed on in due course to future generations, and will have an effect if it pairs up with a similar recessive gene.

Characteristics with dominant and recessive genes

Most characteristics are controlled by several pairs of genes, but some are due to a single pair of genes including those listed below.

Characteristic	Dominant	Recessive
Hair type	woolly	straight
Hair colour	black	blonde
Eye colour	brown	blue
Blood group	A and B	O
Rhesus factor	Rh positive	Rh negative
Tongue rolling	roller	non-roller

Examples of inheritance

The inheritance of characteristics depends on the combined effects of the genes from both parents. The way they combine to produce characteristics follows certain patterns. This can be shown in its simplest form by the inheritance of the ability, or inability, to roll the tongue.

Tongue rolling Can you roll your tongue so that the sides curl up? Check in a mirror. Some people can, others cannot. The ability to roll the tongue is due to a dominant gene – which can be called capital **T** (capital letters are used for dominant characteristics.) The recessive gene for non-rolling can be called small **t** (small letters are used for recessive characteristics.)

The genotype of a roller will be either:
TT (homozygous dominant), or
Tt (heterozygous).
The genotype of a non-roller will be:
tt (recessive homozygous).
Mating between parents of various genotypes will have different results.

Example When a non-roller (**tt**) mates with a roller, the roller can be either (**i**) homozygous (**TT**), or (**ii**) heterozygous (**Tt**).

(i) tt x TT

Genotype of parents
Each cell of the parent contains a pair of genes which affect tongue rolling

Gametes (eggs and sperm)
When these are formed, the genes separate and each gamete has only one of the genes.

Fertilisation
It is a matter of chance as to which gametes form a fertilised egg.

Children
The four possible ways in which the gametes can unite will, in this case, all have the same result - **Tt** - which will make all the children of these parents rollers

(ii) tt x Tt

Genotype of parents

The **chess board** is another method of showing the ways in which it is possible for genes to unite. The gametes from one parent are put at the side, and those from the other parent at the top. The genes are then brought together in the boxes.

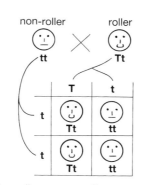

Children of these parents could be either rollers or non-rollers, with a 50% chance of being either.

ABO blood groups
Usually, the variations – alleles – of a gene exist in two contrasting forms, for example, tongue rolling and non-rolling. But there can be more variations than two, an example being the alleles for blood group.

The blood group alleles exist in three variations known as A, B and O, although only two are present in an individual.
A and B are dominant to O.
A and B are **co-dominant** (have equal dominance) when they are together.
The chessboard diagram below shows the various ways in which the alleles can be combined in pairs.

	A	B	O
A	AA	AB	AO
B	AB	BB	BO
O	AO	BO	OO

Genotype AA or AO will be blood group A.
Genotype AB will be blood group AB.
Genotype BB or BO will be blood group B.
Genotype OO will be blood group O.

Example When the mother is blood group A and the father blood group O, what blood group will the children have?
The genotype of the mother can be AA or AO.
The genotype of the father is OO.

(i) If the mother is AA:

	O	O
A	AO	AO
A	AO	AO

All the children will have an AO genotype and therefore be blood group A.

(ii) If the mother is AO:

	O	O
A	AO	AO
O	OO	OO

The children will have a 50% (or 1 in 2) chance of being group A or group O.

FURTHER WORK

1 When the mother has blood group A and the father group O: (**i**) What is the genotype of the father? (**ii**) What are the two possible genotypes of the mother? (**iii**) If the mother is genotype AA, what will be the genotype and blood group of the children? (**iv**) If the mother is genotype AO, what percentage chance does a child have of being group O?

2 Explain, with diagrams, why a child whose blood group is O: (**i**) could have parents who both had blood group A, (**ii**) could not have parents who both had blood group AB.

3 If the mother is Rhesus negative (homozygous recessive) and the father Rhesus positive (heterozygous), what chance does the baby have of being Rh + ? Use diagrams to explain your answer, working them out on a similar basis to either of those given for rollers. When can this condition be dangerous and why? (see p. 38.)

QUESTIONS

1a What is the study of inheritance called?
b Why do children resemble their parents?
c Give the difference between genotype and phenotype.

2a Why do genes occur in pairs?
b What are alleles?
c Describe the difference between homozygous and heterozygous.

3a Give the name for genes which are: (**i**) strong, (**ii**) weak.
b Describe an example of the way in which strong genes mask the presence of weak genes.

c Make a list of characteristics due to a single pair of genes, giving the dominant and recessive effects.

4 Will children inherit the ability to roll the tongue when one parent is a 'roller' and the other parent a 'non-roller'? Use diagrams to explain your answer.

5a (**i**) How many different alleles for blood group are there? Name them. (**ii**) How many alleles does each person possess?
b List the six different blood groups genotypes.
c Name the genotypes responsible for each blood group.

More about genetics

Inheritance of sex

Every cell in the human body except eggs and sperm contains 23 pairs of chromosomes. In 22 of these pairs, the two chromosomes look alike. The 23rd pair are the sex chromosomes: one of the sex chromosomes is called X, and the other is called Y. The Y chromosome has one part missing and therefore differs in shape from the X chromosome.

Females are **XX** because they have two X chromosomes in each cell. When the eggs are formed, each will contain one X chromosome.

Males are **XY** because they have one X and one Y chromosome in each cell. When the sperm are formed, half will contain an X chromosome and the other half will contain a Y chromosome.

During fertilisation an egg with its X chromosome has an equal chance of uniting with a sperm containing an X or a Y chromosome – to produce XX (a girl) or XY (a boy). Consequently the numbers of boys and girls born are more or less equal.

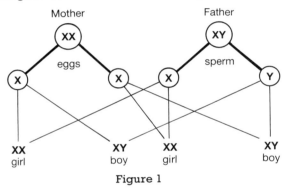

Figure 1

Mutations

A **mutation** is a change in the genetic code. It alters the instructions for making protein and this results in changed characteristics.

Mutations are infrequent and the cells or embryos which contain them usually do not survive. Occasionally cells containing a mutation survive and the mutation is passed on from one generation to the next. Such mutations are usually harmful, but in rare cases can be beneficial. When beneficial, they improve the individual's chance of survival and contribute to evolution. When harmful, they cause disease or deformity. The mutation rate can be increased by radiation (ionising radiation) and by some chemicals.

Gene mutations When the structure of a gene becomes changed, it results in a changed characteristic. If the mutation occurs when eggs or sperm are being formed, it may be transmitted to the offspring who will then have a characteristic not possessed by the parents. If a mutation takes place in a body cell, the variation will occur in all the cells which descend from it.

Mutations occasionally occur in viruses, for example, the influenza virus. This may give rise to a new strain of flu virus to which people have no immunity.

Chromosome disorders These occur when the chromosomes fail to divide properly during cell division. If this happens when eggs or sperm are being formed, it can produce an individual with more, or less, chromosomes than is normal. For example, a person with Down's syndrome has 47 chromosomes instead of the normal 46.

Inherited diseases

A few diseases can be inherited because they are passed on from one generation to the next by genes. When the disease is caused by a:

♦ **dominant gene**, any person who inherits this gene will develop the disease, and there will be a 1 in 2 chance of passing on the gene to any offspring, eg Huntington's chorea.

♦ **recessive gene**, the disease will only develop when the offspring receives two similar genes, one from each parent, eg phenylketonuria (p. 148), sickle cell anaemia (p. 37), cystic fibrosis.

♦ **sex-linked recessive gene** – a gene on the X chromosome – the sex of the child is an important factor in inheritance, eg haemophilia, red–green colour blindness

Cystic fibrosis is a serious disease of the lungs and pancreas. Abnormally thick mucus is produced which blocks the air passages in the lungs, is very difficult to cough up and easily becomes infected. The pancreas also becomes blocked by sticky mucus and fails to produce digestive juices in adequate amounts.

Huntington's chorea The brain gradually loses its ability to function with loss of mental powers and control of movements. The first symptoms usually appear between 20 and 40 years of age, and by that time offspring may have been produced with a one-in-two chance of inheriting the disease.

Down's syndrome (mongolism) Children with this condition develop very slowly and do not reach full adult size or mental ability.

Muscular dystrophy is a wasting disease of the muscles. In most cases it is slow but progressive.

Haemophilia This is a condition which may cause severe bleeding from minor wounds. The blood is unable to clot properly because one of the factors (Factor VIII) necessary for clotting is missing.

Haemophilia is an inherited sex-linked recessive disease transmitted on the X chromosome by mothers to their sons. Boys and men with haemophilia bleed freely from even the smallest injury or knock. Bleeding can be external or internal (bruising). It also follows dental and general surgery unless Factor VIII is given beforehand.

Genetic explanation The gene for Factor VIII lies on the X chromosome and not on the Y chromosome, so females (XX) possess two genes – one on each chromosome – and males (XY) have one. **H** represents the gene for Factor VIII, and **h** represents no gene for Factor VIII:

The genotype of a female could be:
  HH – no haemophilia, or
  Hh – no haemophilia but will be a carrier with a 50% chance of passing the **h** gene to her offspring.

The genotype of a male could be
  H – no haemophilia, or
  h – haemophilia.

Figure 2 Inheritance of haemophilia

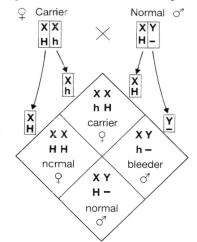

Note: only females can be carriers;
only males get this disease

Detecting inherited disease in unborn children

When there is a chance that the child in the womb may have an inherited disease, a test such as **amniocentesis** (using foetal cells from amniotic fluid) or **chorionic villus sampling** (using placental cells) may be carried out to discover:
◆ the number of chromosomes – important in detecting Down's syndrome.
◆ the sex of the child – important when there is a risk that a male child may inherit muscular dystophy or haemophilia.
◆ the amount of alpha-feto-protein (AFP) in the amniotic fluid – a high level indicates spina bifida or other severe defects of the nervous system.

Genetic counselling Counselling is given to people when there is a chance of their offspring developing a disorder which:
  affects one or both of the parents.
  affected an earlier child.
  affected the grandparents or near relatives.
Advice is given as to the chance of offspring or other relatives being affected. If conception has taken place, and the child is likely to inherit a particular disease, tests may be discussed and, when indicated, abortion may be offered.

Genetic fingerprints

The DNA (deoxyribonucleic acid) in the cells is unique to each person in the same way that fingerprints are unique. DNA found in the white blood cells or semen can be used for identification of criminals such as rapists.

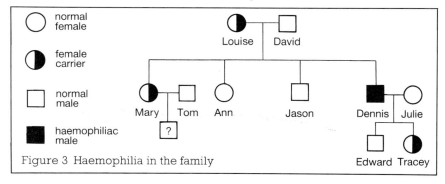

Figure 3 Haemophilia in the family

QUESTIONS

1a (i) What are the sex chromosomes called? (ii) Name the sex chromosomes present in: females, males.
  b Why are the numbers of boys and girls born more or less equal?
2a What is a mutation?
  b What is known to increase the mutation rate?
  c What is the difference in effect of a mutation which takes place when eggs or sperm are being formed and one which happens in a body cell?
  d What may be the result of a mutation in a flu virus.

3a When do chromosome disorders occur, and what can be the effect?
  b Give examples of diseases caused by a: (i) dominant gene, (ii) recessive gene, (iii) sex-linked gene.
  c Describe haemophilia.
  d How is haemophilia inherited?
  e Give the genetic explanation of haemophilia.
4a (i) Name two tests for inherited disease. (ii) What can be discovered by these tests?
  b When is genetic counselling given?
5 Why are white blood cells or semen able to be used for identification purposes?

FURTHER WORK

1 Study **Fig 3.** (i) Give the genotypes of Mary, Ann, Jason and Dennis. Which one is haemophilic and which is a carrier? (ii) What is haemophilia? How is it treated? (iii) Mary and Tom are expecting their first child. Why might they ask for genetic counselling? Why might Mary undergo amniocentesis? Describe amniocentesis. When is it carried out?

2 (i) Using colour vision test cards, carry out a survey of colour blindness in your class. (ii) Investigate the inheritance of colour vision in a family of a person with colour blindness.

Everybody is different

There are 4500 million people on this earth, but no two people are exactly alike. They differ in appearance, personality, behaviour, physiology and lifestyle. These differences are due to the combined effects throughout life of:

◆ **genes** – each child inherits a unique set of genes (except identical twins),
◆ **environment** – the surrounding conditions.

Effects of environment

Environment is the word used to sum up the conditions in which we spend our lives. This includes the food available, climatic conditions, infections and accidents, and the people with whom we mix. The environment is continuously changing, and its effects on any individual will also change throughout life.

Some aspects of the environment which help to make people different are discussed below.

Love and companionship Everyone (whether adult or child) wants to be loved, and needs the companionship of other people and their time and interest. Children learn to love and be friendly, and those brought up in a home without love may find it difficult to make long-lasting friendships and close relationships when they become adults.

Security Security (feeling safe) – knowing there is always someone who cares and a place where you belong – gives confidence. Insecurity can lead to lack of confidence, nervousness, aggression, or tension. An insecure person may be less likely to make friends and have a happy, contented life. Contentment, or the lack of it, can also affect health.

Shelter Shelter is required against the cold, heat, damp and wind. Poor housing is unpleasant to live in and can be the cause of ill-health.

Space Humans are territorial animals – they need space of their own – somewhere which belongs to them where they can do what they like. Overcrowding is a cause of stress, and may lead to violence, vandalism, and child neglect.

Discipline

Children require a certain amount of discipline to make them pleasant people to live with.

◆ The **right kind of discipline** for a child is firm, kind, reasonable and consistent.
◆ **Lack of discipline** is often harmful. It is likely to result in a 'spoilt' child – one who is uncooperative, greedy, selfish and rude.
◆ **Excessive discipline** is also harmful. It prevents a close and loving relationship between parent and child, and can limit the full development of the child's personality.

Throughout childhood, children should gradually be developing **self-discipline**, that is, control over their own behaviour. This will enable them to live and to work more easily with other people.

A clear set of rules for children A clear set of rules both at home and at school gives children security. If there are no rules, a child will not know whether he is doing right or wrong, and this can lead to insecurity and, sometimes, antisocial behaviour.

Society's rules

All societies need to have commonly accepted rules for adults. For example, cars drive on the right or on the left side of the road but not on both. When there are no rules, there is chaos – and the weakest are the losers.

Testing the rules When children are growing up they tend to challenge rules – of parents, of school, and of society. If the rules are not clear, this may lead individuals to 'test' them until they come up against a barrier. The barrier may be:

◆ Physical handicap resulting from reckless behaviour, eg causing road accidents.
◆ Ill-health or self-destruction due to activities such as drug-taking or alcoholism.
◆ The penalties imposed by society for breaking its rules. Rules laid down by the State are called **laws**, and failure to observe them can result in punishment including:
    loss of freedom – prison,
    restriction of freedom – probation, community service.

The long childhood

Humans have a very long childhood – much longer than that of any other animal. This gives time for learning the skills needed for survival:

◆ language,
◆ use of tools,
◆ social skills needed for group living,
◆ acquiring knowledge in and out of school.

The period of dependence has become longer, partly because of the increased amount of knowledge and skills required for a technological society. In Britain, the age at which children could legally leave school has been raised from:
    12 to 14 in 1918
    14 to 15 in 1944
    15 to 16 in 1972
Children mature sexually before they mature socially – that is – before they are ready to live independently from their parents.

Technical skills Life in a modern society is complicated and people need a number of skills to enable them to cope successfully. These include:
a large vocabulary,
the ability to read,
the ability to write,
training for a job,
skills needed to use machinery and equipment,
a knowledge of the environment,
traffic sense,
the ability to communicate with foreigners,
education for leisure.

Social skills These skills enable people to live together more easily and they include:
consideration for others,
the ability to talk easily with people,
knowing how to share, take turns and accept rules,
having standards of cleanliness acceptable to other people,
eating in a manner which does not offend others,
knowing how to behave sexually,
knowing how to make rules with others, or alter them, in a changing situation.

Variations

Variations – differences between individuals – due to inherited genes can be **continuous** or **discontinuous**:

Continuous variations eg weight, height, foot length. These:
◆ show continuous gradation from one extreme to the other without any break, **Fig 1** (when a sufficient number of people are measured);
◆ are produced by the combined effects of many genes;
◆ are affected by environmental conditions.

A characteristic showing continuous variation usually has a frequency distribution similar to that shown in **Fig 1** – most of the individuals fall into the middle range, with smaller numbers at either end. A line joining the centres of the tops of the columns produces a bell-shaped curve called a **normal distribution curve**. A normal distribution curve is unlikely to be symmetrical.

Discontinuous variations eg blood group, finger prints, tongue rolling, sex of the individual. These:
◆ show clearly defined differences with no intermediate stages between them, **Fig 2** (no matter how many people are surveyed);
◆ are usually controlled by one or two genes;
◆ are usually unaffected by environmental conditions.

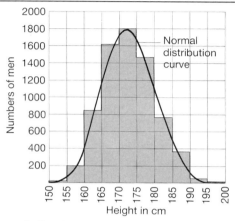

Figure 1 Continuous variation: A histogram showing the distribution of heights of a large number of adult men living in England

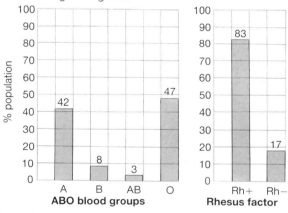

Figure 2 Discontinuous variation: Bar charts of ABO blood groups and Rhesus factor of a large number of people living in the UK

QUESTIONS

1a What are differences between people due to? (Name two causes.)
b What does the word 'environment' sum up?
2a What effect may the lack of love have on a child's development?
b (i) What is meant by 'security'? (ii) How may insecurity affect a child's development?
c Why is space important to humans?
d (i) Why do children require a certain amount of discipline (ii) What can be the effect of lack of discipline?
e (i) What is the right kind of discipline for a child? (ii) How can excessive discipline harm a child?
f What is meant by self-discipline?

3a What is the effect on children of:
(i) a clear set of rules, (ii) no rules?
b Describe three barriers which a person 'testing the rules' may come up against.
4a List four skills for survival which a long childhood gives time to learn.
b List some technical skills for life in a modern society.
c List some social skills which enable people to live easily together.
5a (i) Name two forms of variation. (ii) Give examples of each.
b Compare three main differences between continuous and discontinuous variation.

FURTHER WORK

1 List some of the rules of the society in which you live. What is the effect on other people of the breaking of each of the rules listed? Are there any rules you think should be changed or added?

2 (i) Draw a histogram to show the variation in hand span (maximum distance between tips of thumb and little finger) for a given age group, eg the members of your class.
(ii) Use the same group to make a bar chart showing variation in ability to roll the tongue (see p. 129). Are the variations (i) and (ii) continuous or discontinous?

3 Complete Exercise 2, p. 166.

Male reproductive system

The male reproductive system has three functions:

◆ to make hormones,
◆ to make sperm (spermatozoa),
◆ to eject sperm into the female vagina.

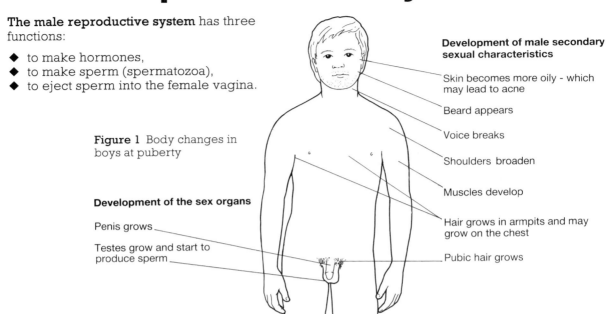

Development of male secondary sexual characteristics

Skin becomes more oily - which may lead to acne

Beard appears

Voice breaks

Shoulders broaden

Muscles develop

Hair grows in armpits and may grow on the chest

Pubic hair grows

Figure 1 Body changes in boys at puberty

Development of the sex organs

Penis grows

Testes grow and start to produce sperm

Puberty in boys

Puberty is the stage during which the sex organs mature. In males this is usually between the age of eleven and fifteen. The testes start to produce sex hormones which cause:

◆ changes in the shape and size of the body,
◆ growth of hair on face and body,
◆ the sex organs to grow and function,
◆ deepening of the voice,
◆ changes in behaviour and attitudes.

Penis

Most of the time, the penis is soft and hangs downwards. It can also enlarge, become stiff and hard, and stand out from the body – this is called an **erection**. The penis becomes erect when the three columns of erectile tissue within it fill with blood. All boys, even babies, have erections, but they become more frequent during puberty.

Circumcision This is the removal of the foreskin by surgery. It is rarely necessary for medical reasons, although it is widely carried out amongst some religious groups. The foreskin will therefore be absent in males who have been circumcised.

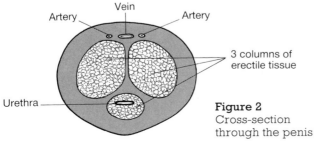

Vein

Artery

Artery

3 columns of erectile tissue

Urethra

Figure 2 Cross-section through the penis

Production of sperm

When the testes have developed they begin to produce sperm and do so continuously throughout life. The sperm are stored close by in a coiled tube called the epididymis. They cannot be stored indefinitely, and after a while they either:

◆ disintegrate and the particles are removed in the blood stream, or
◆ are pushed down the erect penis and out of the body in fluid called semen. This may happen at night, during sleep, and is often called a 'wet dream'.

Semen is the name given to the thick, milky-white fluid which is released from the penis. Besides containing sperm it also contains fluid from the seminal vesicles and prostate gland.

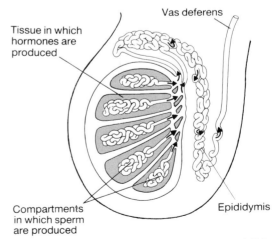

Vas deferens

Tissue in which hormones are produced

Compartments in which sperm are produced

Epididymis

Figure 3 Section through a testicle (testis + epididymis) showing that it consists of a number of compartments in which special cells divide continuously to produce sperm

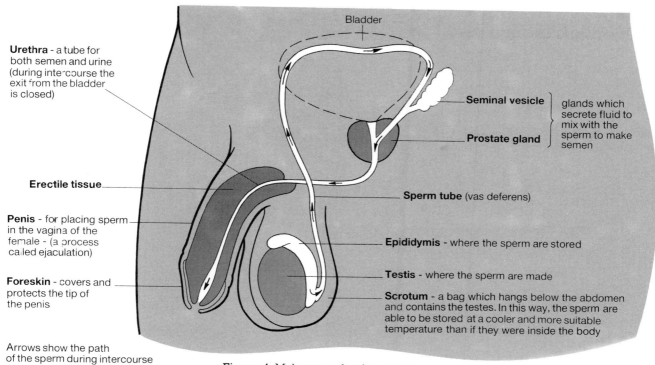

Urethra - a tube for both semen and urine (during intercourse the exit from the bladder is closed)

Bladder

Seminal vesicle

Prostate gland

glands which secrete fluid to mix with the sperm to make semen

Erectile tissue

Penis - for placing sperm in the vagina of the female - (a process called ejaculation)

Foreskin - covers and protects the tip of the penis

Sperm tube (vas deferens)

Epididymis - where the sperm are stored

Testis - where the sperm are made

Scrotum - a bag which hangs below the abdomen and contains the testes. In this way, the sperm are able to be stored at a cooler and more suitable temperature than if they were inside the body

Arrows show the path of the sperm during intercourse

Figure 4 Male reproductive system

Enlarged prostate

The prostate gland surrounds the urethra at the outlet from the bladder. From middle age onwards the prostate gland enlarges. This may cause the frequent desire to urinate, delay in urinating, a thin stream of urine, and dribbling. Treatment to correct the condition is by an operation to remove part of the prostate gland.

A Front view

Figure 5 Diagrams of the male reproductive system

QUESTIONS

1 Name three functions of the male reproductive system.

2a (i) Within what age range does puberty usually take place in boys?
(ii) Give five effects of the male sex hormones.

b Name seven male secondary sexual characteristics.

c Name two changes which take place to the male sex organs as they develop.

3a Draw a section through a testis.

b What are produced in the testes? Give two answers.

c Where are sperm stored?

d What is the advantage to sperm of being stored below the abdomen rather than inside it?

e What happens to the sperm after they have been stored for a while?

f What is semen and what does it contain?

4a What is the function of the penis?

b Describe an erection.

c What makes the penis erect?

d Draw a cross-section through the penis.

e What is the function of the foreskin?

f What is circumcision?

5 (i) When does the prostate gland enlarge? (ii) What effect may this have? (iii) What treatment corrects the condition?

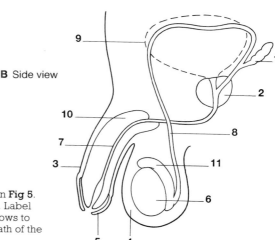

B Side view

FURTHER WORK

Copy both diagrams shown in **Fig 5**. Label the parts 1–9 in **Fig 5A**. Label parts 1–11 in **Fig 5B**. Add arrows to both diagrams to show the path of the sperm during intercourse.

Female reproductive system

The female reproductive system is situated in the lower part of the abdominal cavity and its functions are to:

◆ make hormones,
◆ produce eggs,
◆ receive sperm,
◆ protect and feed the unborn child,
◆ give birth.

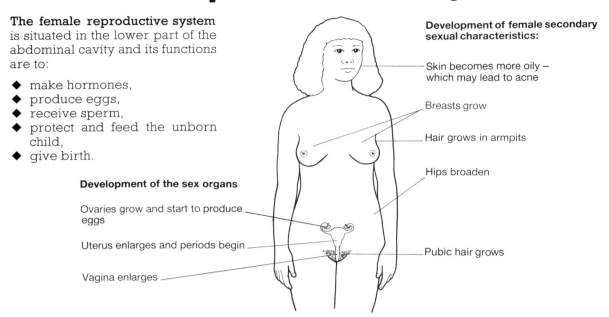

Development of female secondary sexual characteristics:

Skin becomes more oily – which may lead to acne

Breasts grow

Hair grows in armpits

Hips broaden

Pubic hair grows

Development of the sex organs

Ovaries grow and start to produce eggs

Uterus enlarges and periods begin

Vagina enlarges

Figure 1 Body changes in girls at puberty

Puberty in girls

During puberty, usually at the age of twelve or thirteen, the ovaries start to produce female sex hormones which cause:

◆ changes in the shape and size of the body,
◆ growth of body hair,
◆ the sex organs to grow and function,
◆ changes in behaviour and attitudes.

Ovaries

At birth a female has about a million immature eggs in the ovaries, and no more are produced. Less than 500 of these eggs complete their development, at the rate of one egg each month from puberty to the menopause – a span of 30–40 years. The rest of the eggs gradually disappear from birth onwards.

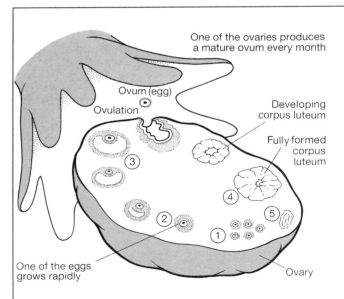

One of the ovaries produces a mature ovum every month

Ovum (egg)

Ovulation

Developing corpus luteum

Fully formed corpus luteum

One of the eggs grows rapidly

Ovary

Figure 2 Section through an ovary to show the different stages of egg development

Development of the egg With each typical menstrual cycle of twenty-eight days (p. 136):
1. From day one, several eggs start to grow, each egg being surrounded by a layer of cells called a **follicle**.
2. On day six, one of these eggs and its follicle grows rapidly and the rest degenerate.
3. About day fourteen, the follicle ruptures and the egg is released – this process is called **ovulation**.
4. The follicle wall thickens and becomes filled with yellowish matter and it turns into the **corpus luteum**.
5. If the egg is fertilised, the corpus luteum will remain until the end of the pregnancy. If the egg is not fertilised, the corpus luteum begins to degenerate about four days before the next menstrual cycle begins.

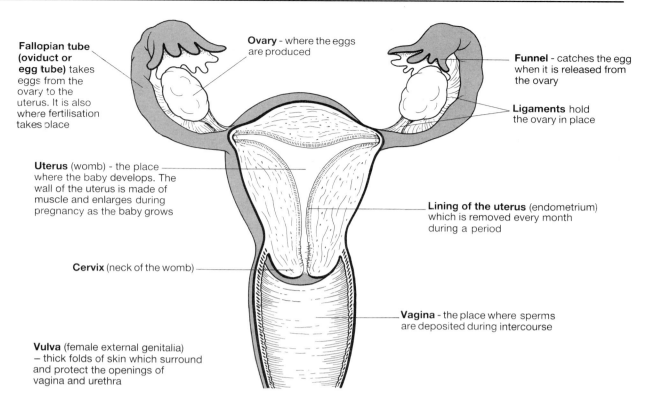

Fallopian tube (oviduct or egg tube) takes eggs from the ovary to the uterus. It is also where fertilisation takes place

Ovary - where the eggs are produced

Funnel - catches the egg when it is released from the ovary

Ligaments hold the ovary in place

Uterus (womb) - the place where the baby develops. The wall of the uterus is made of muscle and enlarges during pregnancy as the baby grows

Lining of the uterus (endometrium) which is removed every month during a period

Cervix (neck of the womb)

Vagina - the place where sperms are deposited during intercourse

Vulva (female external genitalia) – thick folds of skin which surround and protect the openings of vagina and urethra

Figure 3 Female reproductive system

Hysterectomy

Hysterectomy is an operation to remove the uterus. It is carried out because of:
- **fibroids** – lumps of fibrous tissue (benign growths) which enlarge, resulting in excessive bleeding and pain.
- **cancer** which is too advanced for treatment in other ways.

Cervical cancer

This is a common type of cancer in women. It can be detected in the early stages by a **cervical smear** test. A small amount of tissue – a smear – is scraped from the surface of the cervix and examined for abnormal cells. If cervical cancer is treated early, the uterus will not need to be removed.

QUESTIONS

1 Name five functions of the female reproductive system.

2a (i) At what age does puberty usually take place in girls?
(ii) Name four effects of the female sex hormones.
  b Name five female secondary sexual characteristics.
  c Name three changes which take place in the female sex organs as they develop.

3a Draw a section through the ovary.
  b How many eggs are present in the ovaries at birth?
  c How many eggs complete their development?
  d Development of the egg: describe what happens with each menstrual cycle.

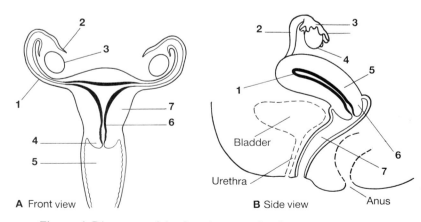

A Front view

B Side view

Bladder

Urethra

Anus

Figure 4 Diagrams of the female reproductive system

FURTHER WORK

1 Copy both diagrams in **Fig 4**. Label parts 1–7 in **Fig 4A**. Label parts 1–7 in **Fig 4B**.

2 Describe the position of the female reproductive organs in the body, and their relationship to bones, muscles, and the organs of digestion and excretion.

Menstrual cycle

The menstrual cycle is a regular series of changes which take place in the female reproductive system to prepare for fertilisation and pregnancy. The cycle is controlled by hormones from the hypothalamus, pituitary gland and ovaries, and takes, on average, about 28 days to complete. During the menstrual cycle, the uterus lining goes through four stages: **Fig 1**.

Stage 1, Menstruation (a period)   The lining of the uterus comes away from the wall, bit by bit, and is removed from the body in a flow of blood.

Stage 2. Repair phase   A new lining is built up on the uterus wall. At the same time, an egg completes its development in the ovary, and is released at about day 14.

Stage 3. Receptive phase   The uterus is in the right state to receive a fertilized egg. If the egg has been fertilised, it will embed itself into the lining of uterus wall and pregnancy will begin.

Stage 4. Pre-menstrual phase   If the egg is not fertilised, the uterus lining begins to break down.

Variations in the menstrual cycle

At puberty   Sometime between the ages of 10 and 17, girls begin to menstruate – have periods – and this shows that menstrual cycles have started. The periods are likely to be irregular and scanty at first, and it is not uncommon for the interval between the first and second period to be as long as a year, but gradually they become more regular.

After puberty   Cycles are usually more or less regular, but they can vary considerably, even in the same woman, in:
◆ **length of the period** – which can last from 3 to 7 days.
◆ **length of time** between one period and the next – it is normal for it to vary between 21 and 35 days.
◆ **the amount of blood lost** – the average total blood loss during a period is 30 cm³, but it can be as much as 180 cm³. Excessive menstrual bleeding is called **menorrhagia** and requires medical advice.

Absence of periods
◆ Periods stop during pregnancy and for several months afterwards.
◆ Periods may also stop for a while during illness, poor feeding or emotional upsets. Absence of periods in women of child-bearing age is called **amenorrhoea**. This condition needs medical advice if more than two periods are missed.
◆ **Menopause** At some time, generally between the ages of 45 and 55, the menstrual cycle ceases and periods stop permanently.

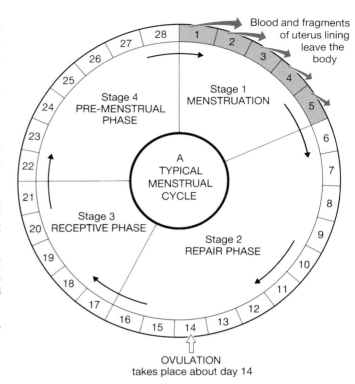

Figure 1 A typical menstrual cycle. It is usual to regard the first day of the cycle as the day when bleeding begins.

Premenstrual tension (PMT)

This is the name given to the changes which occur regularly in many healthy women in the few days before menstruation. The symptoms can be mild or severe and may include irritability, tiredness, bloatedness, headaches, weight gain due to fluid retention, and sore breasts. PMT is partly due to hormone changes which are taking place at this time.

Treatment   The effects may be eased by:
◆ regular exercise,
◆ plenty of sleep,
◆ comfortable clothes,
◆ cutting down on fluid and salt,
◆ medicines, eg pyridoxine (vitamin B₆),
◆ diurectics to increase the loss of fluid from the body via the kidneys.

If PMT is very severe or continues to be a problem, then expert help can be obtained through the family doctor or a Well Woman Clinic. It may be possible to treat the symptoms with hormones.

The menstrual cycle is controlled by the hypothalamus in the brain which acts as a 'menstrual clock'. It receives information about conditions in all parts of the body both from the nervous system and from the blood as it flows through the brain.

When the conditions are right, the hypothalamus releases appropriate hormones. These in their turn control production of the hormones FSH and LH by the pituitary gland.

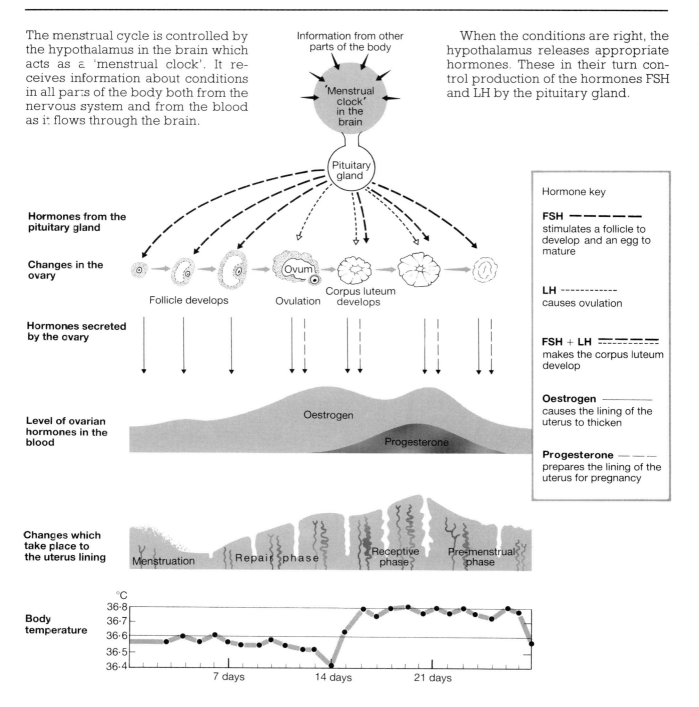

Information from other parts of the body

'Menstrual clock' in the brain

Pituitary gland

Hormones from the pituitary gland

Changes in the ovary

Ovum

Follicle develops   Ovulation   Corpus luteum develops

Hormones secreted by the ovary

Level of ovarian hormones in the blood

Oestrogen

Progesterone

Changes which take place to the uterus lining

Menstruation   Repair phase   Receptive phase   Pre-menstrual phase

Body temperature

°C
36·8
36·7
36·6
36·5
36·4

7 days   14 days   21 days

Hormone key

FSH — — —
stimulates a follicle to develop and an egg to mature

LH - - - - -
causes ovulation

FSH + LH ≈≈≈
makes the corpus luteum develop

Oestrogen ———
causes the lining of the uterus to thicken

Progesterone — — —
prepares the lining of the uterus for pregnancy

Figure 2 Details of the menstrual cycle and the hormones which control it.

QUESTIONS

1a What is the menstrual cycle?
 b Draw a diagram of a typical menstrual cycle.
 c Describe the four stages of the menstrual cycle.
2a Between what ages does menstruation begin?
 b Describe three ways in which cycles vary.
 c Name three possible causes for absence of periods.

3a Describe pre-menstrual tension.
 b How may the effects of PMT be eased?
4a Which part of the brain acts as a menstrual clock?
 b Name two hormones produced by the pituitary gland which affect the ovaries, and give the effect of each.
 c Name two hormones secreted by the ovaries which affect the uterus, and give the effect of each.

FURTHER WORK

1 Study **Fig 2**, then describe the diagram in your own words.
2 Complete Exercise 3, p. 166.

Conception

Conception takes place when an egg is fertilised by a sperm and becomes implanted in the uterus wall.

Ovulation

An egg (ovum) is released each month from one of the ovaries and it moves slowly along the Fallopian tube towards the uterus due to:

peristalsis – rhythmic squeezing movements of the Fallopian tube,

cilia which line the tube and sweep the ovum in the right direction.

The journey from ovary to uterus takes about seven days.

Sexual intercourse (coitus; copulation)

Before intercourse, the man's penis enlarges and becomes hard and erect and is able to penetrate the vagina of the woman. Sperm stored in the testicles are rapidly squeezed along the vas deferens and through the urethra. On the way they are mixed with fluid from the seminal vesicles and prostate gland to make a thick sticky fluid – **semen** – which is ejaculated from the penis into the vagina.

Sperm become active   During intercourse about 300 million sperm are placed inside the vagina and are then able to swim around because:

◆ Fluid from the prostate gland enables the sperm to become active.

◆ Fluid from the seminal vesicles provides food for energy. The sperm swim in all directions and some may find their way through the cervix, into the uterus and along the Fallopian tubes.

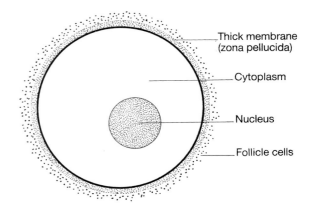

Figure 1 Egg (ovum)

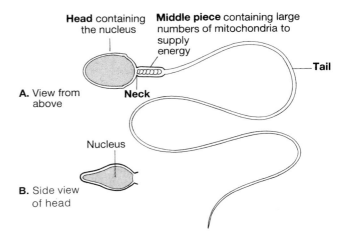

Figure 2 Sperm (spermatozoon)

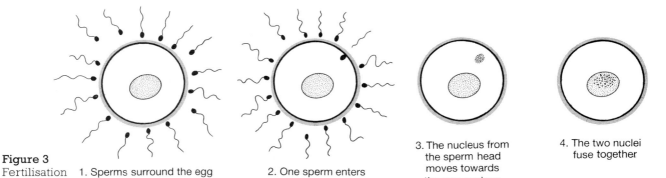

Figure 3
Fertilisation   1. Sperms surround the egg   2. One sperm enters   3. The nucleus from the sperm head moves towards the egg nucleus   4. The two nuclei fuse together

Fertilisation

Fertilisation is the fusion of a sperm with an egg, and it takes place in the Fallopian tube. Although several sperm may reach the egg, only one will penetrate the membrane which surrounds it. The membrane immediately changes and forms a barrier to the entry of other sperm.

The head of the sperm (the male nucleus) moves through the cytoplasm towards the nucleus of the egg and the two fuse (join) together. The fertilised egg (**zygote**) now starts to divide, first into two cells, then into four, and so on, as it continues on its journey along the Fallopian tube. By the time it reaches the uterus it is a hollow ball of cells and called an **embryo**.

Implantation

The embryo becomes embedded in the lining of the uterus wall about six days after conception. The mother then supplies it with food and oxygen so that it can grow and develop into a baby.

Pre-conception care

Because the first few weeks after conception are most important for the developing baby, a woman who is hoping to conceive should:
- have a good, nutritious diet,
- not be overweight,
- give up smoking and drinking,
- not take any drugs or medicines because all can be harmful.

Infertility

Infertility – being unable to conceive – affects about 10% of couples. These are some of the known causes:
- Too few sperm are being produced.
- The sperm are not sufficiently active.
- The ovaries are not producing eggs.
- The Fallopian tubes are blocked.
- Mucus in the cervix is too thick – so the sperm are unable to enter.
- The pituitary gland is producing too much prolactin, causing impotence in men and infertility in women. (**Impotence** – inability to have sexual intercourse.)

Fertility drugs Women who are infertile because they do not ovulate may be given fertility drugs. They contain hormones, and there may be difficulty in adjusting the dose to suit a particular person. This sometimes causes several eggs to be released at once, resulting in multiple births.

'Test-tube babies' (in vitro fertilisation) A test-tube baby is one where fertilisation takes place outside the mother's body, using the couple's own egg and sperm. When the fertilised egg is a few days old it is implanted into the uterus, and development proceeds in the normal way.

Artificial insemination This is a method of treating infertility where the male partner is infertile. Sperm from a donor (another male) is collected, and then inserted into the uterus at the time of ovulation.

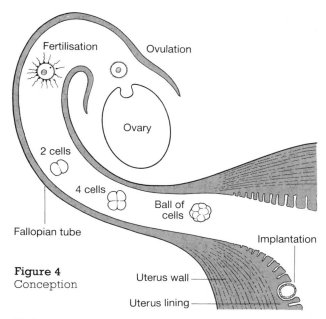

Figure 4
Conception

Twins

There are two types of twins depending on whether they come from one fertilised egg or two.

Non-identical twins (fraternal twins) result when two eggs are released at the same time (both from the same ovary, or one from each) and each egg is fertilised by a different sperm. The twins may or may not be of the same sex, and are no more alike than other brothers or sisters in the same family.

Identical twins develop when a fertilised egg splits into two at an early stage of development and each develops into an individual. The twins are of the same sex and, as they have the same genes, are very similar in appearance.

Siamese twins are identical twins who failed to separate completely.

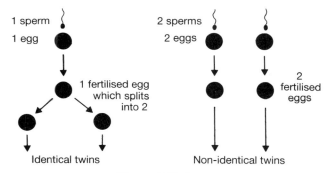

Figure 5 Twins

QUESTIONS

1a What is meant by conception?
 b Draw a diagram of: (i) an egg, (ii) a sperm.

2a How is an ovum moved along the Fallopian tube?
 b Where does fertilisation take place?
 c How do sperm get from the vagina to the Fallopian tubes?
 d (i) What is fertilisation? (ii) Draw diagrams to show this process.

3a What happens to the egg after it has been fertilised?
 b Describe implantation.

4 What is meant by pre-conception care?

5a Give six causes of infertility.
 b (i) What do fertility drugs contain?
    (ii) Why may they result in multiple births?
 c What is meant by a 'test-tube baby'?

6a Draw diagrams to show the different types of twins by the fertilisation of one egg or two.
 b Which type of twins are always of the same sex?

FURTHER WORK

Draw and label a diagram to illustrate conception.

141

Contraception

Contraception is the deliberate prevention of pregnancy.

It is natural for two people who love each other to want to have intercourse (make love; have 'sex'). But if they do not want a baby, they need to know how to prevent conception. Conception takes place when an egg is fertilised by a sperm and becomes implanted in the wall of the uterus, so any method of contraception will aim to prevent this from happening (contra = against; ception = conceiving).

Which method?

Deciding which method of contraception to use depends on a number of factors including:
◆ individual preference,
◆ religious beliefs,
◆ age,
◆ whether a short- or long-term method is required.

Obtaining advice   Advice on contraception and family planning is provided free by the National Health Service. It can be obtained by people of all ages, married or single, male or female, from:
◆ **Family Planning Clinics,**
◆ **Doctors (GPs).** Most will give advice.

Abstention – 'saying No'

When couples do not have intercourse there is no chance of pregnancy and therefore no need for any other method of contraception. However loving the relationship, many couples may feel that they should abstain from intercourse (not have 'sex') unless they want children. This method of contraception is completely reliable.

Rhythm method

This method relies on calculating the **fertile period** of the menstrual cycle. The rest of the cycle is known as the **safe period**, and intercourse should only take place during this time.

Fertile period   The days in the menstrual cycle during which intercourse could result in fertilisation. Calculation of the fertile period is based on these facts:
◆ Ovulation takes place about two weeks before the next menstrual cycle begins.
◆ The egg remains fertile for at least two days.
◆ Sperm can survive for up to five days inside the Fallopian tubes.

Safe period   The days in the menstrual cycle when intercourse is unlikely to result in fertilisation. There are several methods of working out the safe period.
◆ **Temperature method** – relies on the measurement of normal changes in body temperature that occur with ovulation: p. 139.
◆ **Mucus method (Billings method)** – relies on detecting changes in cervical mucus which occur with ovulation.
◆ **Calendar method** – the safe period is calculated in advance by using records of the last six or more cycles.

The rhythm method of contraception is unreliable because it is difficult to be sure of the date of ovulation and therefore when the woman is, and is not, fertile – even for women who consider that their periods are regular.

'Morning after' (post-coital) contraception

These methods of contraception are for emergency use only. They may be recommended by a doctor when intercourse has taken place and there is the risk of an unwanted pregnancy which could lead to a later abortion.
◆ **'Morning after' pills** contain hormones and need to be taken within 2–3 days following intercourse.
◆ A **coil** fitted within five days of intercourse usually prevents pregnancy.

Figure 1 Methods of contraception for men

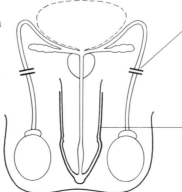

Withdrawal ('being careful'; coitus interruptus)
The penis is withdrawn from the vagina before semen is ejaculated.
● A very unreliable method of birth control because a little semen can leak from the erect penis before the main amount is released.

Male sterilisation*(vasectomy)
A simple operation in which the vas deferens (sperm duct) on each side is cut or blocked, to prevent semen from containing sperm.
● A permanent method of birth control which is almost 100% reliable. It does not affect the hormone function of the testes – p.114.

Condom; sheath
A thin rubber covering fitted over the erect penis just before intercourse prevents sperm from being deposited in the vagina
● Very reliable if properly used so that no semen comes into contact with the vaginal area. Spermicide placed in the vagina gives extra protection.

* Method which requires medical advice or treatment from a doctor or Family Planning Clinic

Unwanted babies

It is estimated that in Britain more than 100 000 unwanted babies are born every year. Many more are deliberately aborted (**abortion** means the loss of a child from the womb before it has grown enough to survive on its own).

Many of the unwanted pregnancies happen to girls and young women because either they have been given wrong advice or have ignored sound advice. A girl who does not wish to become pregnant should remember the following:

◆ Pregnancy can result from first intercourse.
◆ Pregnancy can occur even if the penis does not enter the vagina (sperm can swim).

◆ Pregnancy sometimes occurs when intercourse takes place during a period.
◆ Pregnancy can occur when the woman does not 'come' (have an orgasm).
◆ Intercourse in any position can result in pregnancy.
◆ 'Withdrawal' (being careful') can result in pregnancy.
◆ Douching (washing out the vagina) will never prevent pregnancy, however soon after intercourse.
◆ Breast-feeding does not prevent pregnancy, although it may make it less likely.

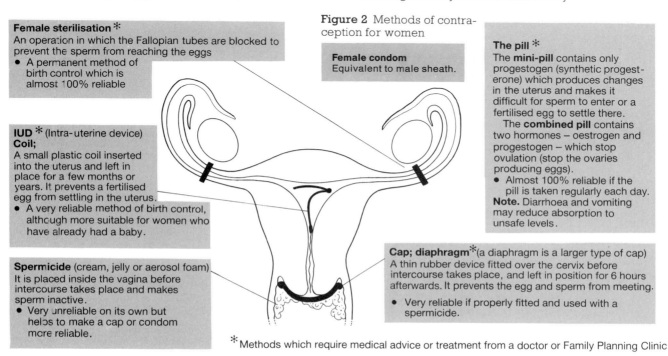

Figure 2 Methods of contraception for women

Female sterilisation *
An operation in which the Fallopian tubes are blocked to prevent the sperm from reaching the eggs
● A permanent method of birth control which is almost 100% reliable

Female condom
Equivalent to male sheath.

The pill *
The **mini-pill** contains only progestogen (synthetic progesterone) which produces changes in the uterus and makes it difficult for sperm to enter or a fertilised egg to settle there.
  The **combined pill** contains two hormones – oestrogen and progestogen – which stop ovulation (stop the ovaries producing eggs).
● Almost 100% reliable if the pill is taken regularly each day.
Note. Diarrhoea and vomiting may reduce absorption to unsafe levels.

IUD * (Intra-uterine device)
Coil;
A small plastic coil inserted into the uterus and left in place for a few months or years. It prevents a fertilised egg from settling in the uterus.
● A very reliable method of birth control, although more suitable for women who have already had a baby.

Spermicide (cream, jelly or aerosol foam)
It is placed inside the vagina before intercourse takes place and makes sperm inactive.
● Very unreliable on its own but helps to make a cap or condom more reliable.

Cap; diaphragm *(a diaphragm is a larger type of cap)
A thin rubber device fitted over the cervix before intercourse takes place, and left in position for 6 hours afterwards. It prevents the egg and sperm from meeting.
● Very reliable if properly fitted and used with a spermicide.

*Methods which require medical advice or treatment from a doctor or Family Planning Clinic

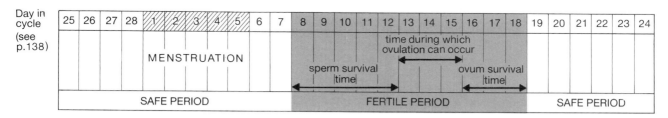

| Day in cycle (see p.138) | 25 | 26 | 27 | 28 | 1 | 2 | 3 | 4 | 5 | 6 | 7 | 8 | 9 | 10 | 11 | 12 | 13 | 14 | 15 | 16 | 17 | 18 | 19 | 20 | 21 | 22 | 23 | 24 |

Figure 3 The safe period and the fertile period in a typical 28-day cycle

QUESTIONS

1 Complete the table to include the following methods of contraception: abstention, rhythm method, withdrawal, vasectomy, condom, mini-pill, combined pill, female sterilisation, coil, cap, spermicide.

Method	Description	How reliable

2a An asterisk marks those methods of contraception which require medical advice or treatment from a doctor or Family Planning Clinic. List them.
  b List eight pieces of sound advice for the prevention of unwanted pregnancy.
  c (i) When does ovulation occur? (ii) For how long do eggs remain fertile. (iii) For how long can sperm survive?
  d Draw a diagram to show the fertile period and the safe period in a typical 28-day cycle.

3 Name two methods of 'morning after' contraception.

FURTHER WORK

Draw a diagram of the female reproductive system. Label ovary, Fallopian tube, uterus, cervix, vagina, and indicate a method of contraception applicable to each.

After conception

It takes about nine months for a fertilised egg to grow and develop into a fully formed baby. During this time, the mother provides it with food, breathes for it, excretes its waste materials, keeps it warm, and protects it from damage and disease.

The fertilised egg not only produces the embryo but also gives rise to structures for the support of the baby – placenta, umbilical cord and amnion. After the baby has been born, these structures leave the uterus as the **afterbirth**.

Growth and development after conception

At 1 month After developing for a month, a human embryo looks rather like the embryo of a fish or frog (tadpole embryo). It is possible to see a tail and parts which look as though they might develop into gills.

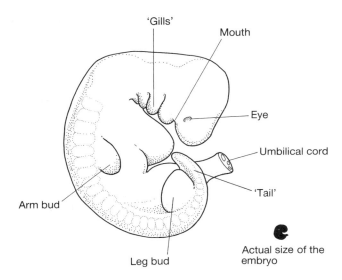

Figure 1 Embryo one month after conception

At 2 months The embryo has now grown to look more human and at this stage it becomes called a **foetus** (or **fetus**). The main structures of the body are more or less in place and the heart is beating.

At 3 months During the third month, the nerves and muscles develop rapidly. By the end of the month the foetus will be able to swallow, frown, clench its fists, turn its head, and kick. It is now about the size of a mouse and weighs about 50 g.

At 5 months The mother can feel movements made by the baby. Very fine hairs cover the baby's skin and the sex organs have developed sufficiently to be able to tell, from an ultrasound scan, whether the baby is a boy or a girl. At this stage the foetus weighs about 350 g.

At 7 months Development is almost complete. The baby will spend the rest of the time in the womb growing larger and stronger. Fat becomes stored as a layer under the skin – and makes the baby look plump. During the next two months the weight will be doubled, and the length increases three times.

Miscarriage A miscarriage (spontaneous abortion) occurs when the baby comes out of the womb accidentally and too early to survive on its own. The first sign of a miscarriage is bleeding from the vagina, sometimes with pain.

Premature babies Any baby weighing less than $2\frac{1}{2}$ kg at birth is called premature. These small, weak babies often have difficulties with breathing, sucking, and keeping warm. It is usual for a premature baby to be kept in the controlled environment of an incubator where the temperature remains constant, to which oxygen can be supplied to help with breathing, and where it can be fed through a tube or dropper until it has the strength to suck.

Inside the womb

The baby develops within a 'bag of waters' – amniotic fluid – and is kept at a constant temperature of about 37°C.

Development of the placenta As soon as the embryo has become implanted in the uterus, the placenta starts to develop. About twelve weeks later, it is a thick, disc-like structure firmly attached to the uterus wall. It continues to grow to keep pace with the developing baby to become about 15 cm (6 in) across and weigh about 500 g (1 lb). Identical twins share the same placenta, but non-identical twins each develop their own.

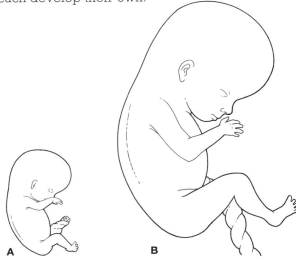

Figure 2 Actual size of the foetus at: A. two months, B. three months

144

Exchange through the placenta Blood from the baby flows continuously to and from the placenta through the umbilical cord. In the placenta, the baby's blood comes very close to the mother's blood, but they do not mix. However, they are close enough for substances to be exchanged:

◆ **Food** and **oxygen** pass from mother to baby,
◆ **Carbon dioxide** and other waste products pass from baby to mother.
◆ **Antibodies** from the mother pass to the baby and help to protect it.
◆ Other substances which may be in the mother's blood can also cross to the baby's blood:

    Medicines. It is advisable that no medicines are taken in early pregnancy unless a doctor considers it vital for the health of the mother or the child.

    Alcohol. It is advised that only small quantities are taken during pregnancy.

    Chemicals in smoke (p. 188).

    Viruses, eg german measles virus (p. 146).

Foetal blood The red blood cells made by the foetus contain a foetal form of haemoglobin which is better at picking up oxygen than the usual type of haemoglobin. During the first few months after birth, foetal haemoglobin is replaced by the usual type.

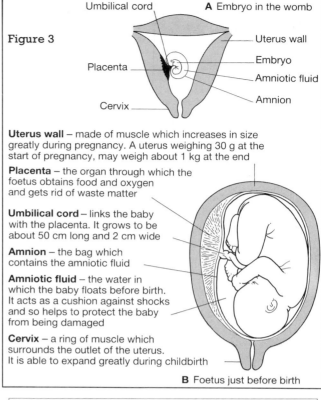

Figure 3

A Embryo in the womb

Uterus wall – made of muscle which increases in size greatly during pregnancy. A uterus weighing 30 g at the start of pregnancy, may weigh about 1 kg at the end

Placenta – the organ through which the foetus obtains food and oxygen and gets rid of waste matter

Umbilical cord – links the baby with the placenta. It grows to be about 50 cm long and 2 cm wide

Amnion – the bag which contains the amniotic fluid

Amniotic fluid – the water in which the baby floats before birth. It acts as a cushion against shocks and so helps to protect the baby from being damaged

Cervix – a ring of muscle which surrounds the outlet of the uterus. It is able to expand greatly during childbirth

B Foetus just before birth

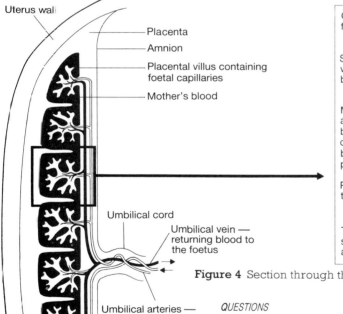

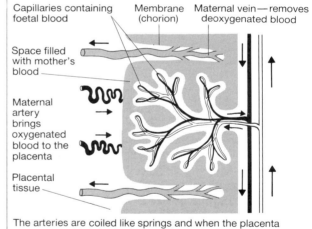

The arteries are coiled like springs and when the placenta separates at birth the broken arteries spring back, coil tightly and stop loss of blood from the mother

Figure 4 Section through the placenta to show the foetal and maternal circulations

QUESTIONS

1a (i) Draw a diagram of an embryo one month after conception. (ii) Describe this stage.
  b The fertilised egg gives rise to three structures in addition to the embryo. Name these.
2a Draw and describe the foetus at: (i) 2 months, (ii) 3 months.
  b Describe development at: (i) 5 months, (ii) from 7 months onwards.
  c What is meant by miscarriage?
  d When is a baby described as premature?
  e Name three difficulties premature babies often have. For each, say how they can be overcome in an incubator.

3a Describe briefly – uterus wall, umbilical cord, amnion, amniotic fluid, cervix.
  b (i) What is the placenta? (ii) Describe its development.
  c What substances are exchanged between mother and baby in the placenta?
4a Draw a diagram of the placenta and blood vessels in the umbilical cord.
  b Explain the difference between foetal haemoglobin and the usual type.

FURTHER WORK

Draw and label diagrams of the: (i) embryo in the womb, (ii) the foetus just before birth.

Antenatal care

Signs of pregnancy

For a woman whose periods are regular and who has had sexual intercourse recently, the first sign is usually a missed period.

By the time a second period has been missed, other signs of pregnancy may be noticeable – feelings of nausea, enlarged and tender breasts, and more frequent passing of urine.

Pregnancy tests A pregnancy test measures the amount of HCG hormone (p. 117) in the urine. This rises soon after pregnancy starts, is measured in the early morning, and an answer may be obtained within two hours. It is best to wait at least two weeks after the first missed period because a pregnancy test before this time may give a false result. It should also be remembered that, like every other test, a pregnancy test is not 100% reliable.

Antenatal clinics

Pregnant women are advised to visit a clinic regularly to have;
◆ the mother's state of health checked,
◆ the baby's development monitored,
◆ early medical treatment if necessary,
◆ the opportunity to obtain parentcraft advice and the chance to ask questions.

Checks made on the mother

Weight check Apart from the first few months, a pregnant woman gains, on average, about 450 g (1 lb) in weight per week. In total she puts on about 12 kg (2 stone). The increased weight is due to the baby plus the greatly enlarged uterus, the placenta, umbilical cord and amniotic fluid. In addition, extra fat may be stored in the layer under the skin to be used in milk production after the baby is born.

If the mother puts on too much weight, she will be advised to diet.

Blood tests A small sample of blood is taken from the mother to test for:
◆ **Haemoglobin** – a shortage of haemoglobin is called **anaemia** (p. 36). The amount of oxygen the blood can carry is reduced and results in tiredness and weakness. Iron and folic acid (p.66) are essential for the production of haemoglobin, so the usual treatment is to take iron-folate tablets. During pregnancy the demands for iron-folate increase as the foetus grows.
◆ **Blood group.** This is essential information:
  if, in an emergency, a blood transfusion should be needed.
  to prevent rhesus-damaged babies (p. 38).

◆ **German measles antibodies** if the mother does not have these antibodies she will not be immune to the disease. Should she catch german measles in the early months of pregnancy the virus may kill the baby or leave it deaf, blind, mentally handicapped, or with heart disease.

Urine tests At every visit to the clinic a sample of urine is tested for:
◆ **sugar** (glucose) – if present it may indicate diabetes.
◆ **protein** (albumin) – if present it may indicate: infection of the kidneys or bladder, or toxaemia of pregnancy.
It is not very likely that any of these substances will be present. If they are, further tests will be made so that early treatment can be given if needed.

Vaginal examination On the first visit to the antenatal clinic, the mother's vagina is examined:
◆ **to check that there is no infection**, for example, thrush.
◆ **to obtain a cervical smear** (p. 137).
Towards the end of pregnancy, the vagina is checked to make sure that the outlet will be big enough for the baby's head to pass through.

Blood pressure The mother's blood pressure is checked at every visit to the clinic, as high blood pressure may be a sign of toxaemia of pregnancy. This condition requires rest, often in hospital.

Toxaemia of pregnancy (pre-eclampsia) This condition occurs only during late pregnancy, and disappears as soon as the pregnancy is over. The patient has:
◆ swollen ankles,
◆ excessive weight gain,
◆ high blood pressure,
◆ protein in the urine.
Should the condition be allowed to continue, the mother may develop a type of epilepsy (eclampsia), and this can be fatal to both the baby and the mother. Fortunately, because of modern antenatal care, eclampsia rarely occurs nowadays.

Placental hormones The placenta produces hormones which can be detected in the mother's blood. In the last eight weeks of pregnancy, her blood may be tested for **oestrogen** to check that the placenta is functioning normally and can keep the baby well supplied with food and oxygen.

Checks made on the baby

Examination of the uterus By gently pressing the outside of the abdomen, it is possible for the doctor to get some idea of the baby's size and position in the uterus. Towards the end of pregnancy, it is important to know if the baby is in the best position to be born, that is, with the head downwards and facing the mother's back. Should the baby be in the breech position (p. 149), the doctor will try to turn it so that the head points downwards.

Baby's heartbeat In the second half of pregnancy, the baby's heartbeat can be heard through a stethoscope placed on the mother's abdomen. It will be beating between 120 and 160 times per minute, which is much faster than the mother's heart rate.

Ultrasound scanning Ultrasound (sound at a higher frequency than can be heard by the human ear) is used to produce pictures of the baby in the uterus. Information is obtained about the baby's size, age, sex, and position; also about the position of the placenta and whether twins are present.

A. Section through skull and chest

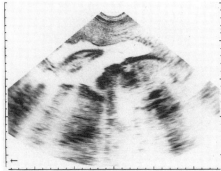

B. Section through the foetal pelvis

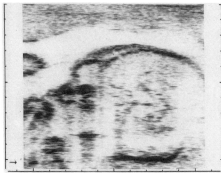

C. Section through foetal skull and face

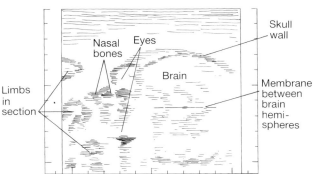

James Paget Hospital, Great Yarmouth

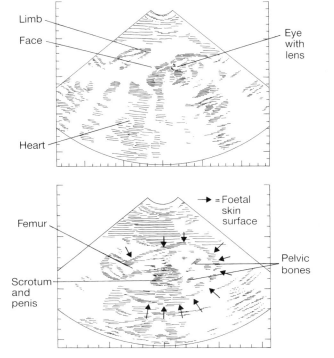

Figure 1 Ultrasound scans of a male foetus of 22 weeks

QUESTIONS

1a Give four signs of pregnancy.
 b What does a pregnancy test measure?
 c Give four reasons for attending an antenatal clinic.

2a Describe weight gain in pregnancy.
 b List six reasons for increase in weight during pregnancy.
 c List three things that the blood of a pregnant woman is tested for, and say why each is important.
 d Name the two substances that urine is tested for, and say why each is important.

3a (i) Why is the vagina examined at the first visit to the antenatal clinic?
 (ii) Why is it checked towards the end of pregnancy? Give two reasons.
 b Why is blood pressure checked at every visit?
 c (i) When may toxaemia of pregnancy occur?
 (ii) Give four signs of this condition.
 (iii) Why is it dangerous?
 d When and why may the mother's blood be tested for oestrogen?

4a What information is obtained from examination of the mother's abdomen?
 b How is it possible to tell the difference between the heartbeats of the baby and of the mother?
 c (i) What is ultrasound? (ii) What can it be used for? (iii) What information can be obtained?

FURTHER WORK

1 Invite a local midwife to talk to the class about antenatal care in the district.

2 Complete Exercise 4, p. 166

Birth

The estimated date of delivery (EDD) – the date on which the child is most likely to be born – is calculated by adding 40 weeks to the first day of the mother's last period. (Pregnancy lasts, on average, about 38 weeks from the date of fertilisation and this is most likely to have happened about 2 weeks after the last period began.)

Labour

As the mother goes through the process of giving birth she is said to be 'in labour'. Towards the end of the pregnancy, the baby moves into the correct position to be born with its head pointing downwards: **Fig 1**.

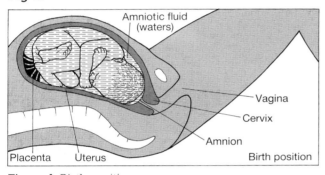

Figure 1 Birth position

Stage 1. Dilation

One or more of the following signs indicate that labour has started:

◆ **A show** This is a small discharge of blood and mucus which has come away from the cervix where it formed a plug.

◆ **The breaking of the waters** The **amnion** – the bag containing amniotic fluid in which the baby has been developing – breaks and the fluid is released.

◆ **Regular and strong contractions occur** These contractions of the uterus wall start slowly, perhaps one every 20–30 minutes. They then become stronger, regular and more frequent.

During the first stage of labour, contractions by muscles in the uterus wall gradually dilate the cervix. The amnion may burst when labour starts, or it will do so at some time later on. The first stage is the longest stage of labour, taking usually between 4 and 12 hours. It comes to an end when the cervix has opened wide enough for the baby's head to pass through: **Fig 2**.

Stage 2. Delivery

The uterus, cervix and vagina have now become one continuous **birth canal**. The uterus wall is contracting strongly and, as it does so, it pushes the baby head first through the birth canal. The moment when the baby's head emerges from the vagina is called **crowning: Fig 3**. The midwife may now clear

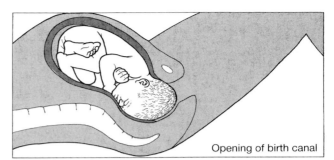

Figure 2 Opening of the birth canal

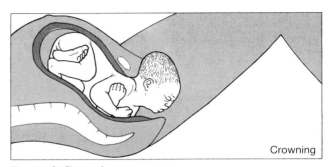

Figure 3 Crowning

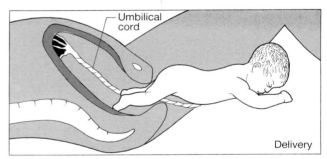

Figure 4 Delivery

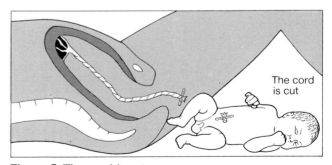

Figure 5 The cord is cut

mucus from the nose and mouth and the baby may start to breathe, and even cry. The midwife now eases the shoulders through the birth canal and the baby slides out into the world: **Fig 4**. Once the baby is breathing, the umbilical cord is clamped in two places to prevent bleeding and the cord between them is cut through: **Fig 5**. This separates the baby from the mother.

When the baby first appears, the skin is a bluish colour. As soon as breathing starts, the skin quickly turns pink as the increased supplies of oxygen are collected by the red blood cells – their haemoglobin (dark red) becomes oxyhaemoglobin (bright red).

Stage 3. Afterbirth

Contractions of the uterus continue until the placenta (**afterbirth**) has become separated from the wall of the uterus and has been pushed out through the vagina: **Fig 6**. Labour is then completed.

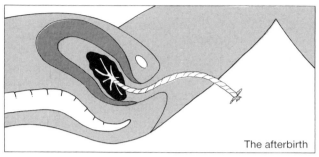

The afterbirth

Figure 6 The afterbirth

Other ways of being born

Breech birth – when the baby comes out feet or bottom first. It is usually much more difficult.

Forceps delivery – special forceps are placed by the doctor over the baby's head to ease the baby gently through the birth canal. A forceps delivery may be necessary when the contractions are not strong enough to push the baby out, or when the baby is lying in an awkward position. The baby's head may look a little bruised afterwards but it soon returns to normal.

Caesarian section (a Caesar) – an operation to remove the baby from the uterus. It is carried out when the birth canal is too narrow, or the health of the mother or baby makes immediate delivery necessary. The mother is given a general anaesthetic or epidural anaesthetic and an incision is made through the abdominal wall and into the uterus so that the baby can be removed. The umbilical cord is cut, the placenta is then removed, and the uterus and abdominal wall are stitched up.

Induction – the process of labour is started artificially. It may be possible to do this by breaking the waters. The mother may also be given the hormone **oxytocin** through a 'drip' in her arm. Oxytocin stimulates the uterus to start contracting. The birth may be induced when the baby is very overdue (late), or when the health of the mother or baby is at risk.

Pain relief

Labour is usually painful, but there are a number of ways in which the pain can be relieved.

Relaxation and breathing exercises (taught in antenatal classes) help to relax the mother's muscles and this makes labour easier. They work well for many women, especially during the first stage of labour.

Gas-and-oxygen may be offered to the mother during the second stage of labour. A gas such as nitrous oxide (laughing gas) is mixed with oxygen and the mother inhales the mixture through a mouthpiece when the contractions are very strong.

Pethidine is a powerful pain-reliever. An injection of pethidine may be given if the contractions become very uncomfortable.

Epidural anaesthetic is injected into the space around the lower part of the spinal cord to block the sensory nerves which relay pain from the lower abdomen. No labour pains can now be felt, but the mother remains fully conscious.

Postnatal care

Postnatal care is the care given to the mother and baby after the birth has taken place (post=after; natal=birth).

The mother

The uterus   The enlarged uterus shrinks rapidly in the days following the birth, and this is speeded up by breast-feeding. Eventually the uterus will be almost as small as it was before the baby was conceived. Bleeding continues from the place in the uterus where the placenta was attached until the wound is healed. This may take up to a month.

Stretched muscles   Pregnancy greatly stretches the muscles of the abdomen and afterwards they are very loose and floppy. The muscles of the pelvic floor (between the tops of the legs) are also stretched and weakened during delivery. All these muscles will gradually improve and tighten. Special postnatal exercises will help them to regain their shape and tone.

Restarting the menstrual cycle   The time at which periods start again varies considerably and may take six months or longer after the birth. It is possible to become pregnant before periods return. It is also possible to become pregnant whilst still breast-feeding, although breast-feeding makes conception less likely.

Baby blues and postnatal depression   During the week following the birth, commonly between the third and fifth day, it is quite usual for the mother to feel miserable and depressed without knowing why. This period of mild depression is often called the 'baby blues'. Reasons for it include:
◆ **Hormones** which controlled pregnancy and childbirth have not yet settled back into their normal pattern of activity and they are making the mother feel 'out of sorts'.
◆ **Tiredness** – due to disturbed nights and busy days.
◆ **Reaction** to the excitement of the birth: Now it is all over, life seems to be nothing but a constant round of feeding, changing nappies and washing.
The mother can be helped by understanding that these feelings are quite common in new mothers, by letting her family know how she feels, and by asking the midwife for advice.

More severe 'baby blues' are often called **postnatal depression** which usually needs medical advice.

Breast feeding

During pregnancy, the breasts enlarge and the glandular tissue within them develops so that it is ready to supply food for the baby. Towards the end of pregnancy, the breasts start to secrete small amounts of a yellow, watery fluid called **colostrum** and the baby feeds on this for the first few days. Besides containing water, colostrum is rich in protein, and it also contains **antibodies** to protect the baby against disease.

Structure of the breasts   Each breast contains about 15–20 sections in which milk is produced from milk glands. Each section has a duct which opens on the surface of the nipple; the milk therefore comes from about 20 tiny openings. The dark area around the nipple is called the **areola**.

The size of the breasts before pregnancy depends on the amount of fat tissue and not the number of milk-producing glands. So women with small breasts should be able to breast-feed just as well as those with larger breasts.

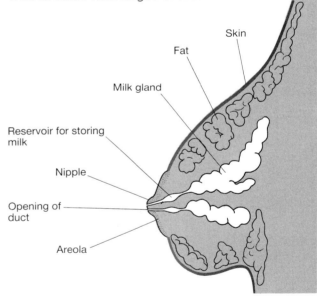

Figure 1 Structure of the breast

Lactation   After the baby has been born, the hormone **prolactin** stimulates the milk glands and about three days later milk is produced (see p. 70). The baby is now ready for much larger quantities of food and may want to feed ten or twelve times in 24 hours. This also helps to establish a good supply of milk, because the more the baby sucks, the more the breasts are stimulated to produce milk. The baby soon settles into a pattern of wanting to be fed about six times a day. Gradually, the interval between the feeds in the night gets longer so that by the age of three months, the night feed is usually given up altogether.

The baby

Examination of the baby All newborn babies are given a routine examination in which the doctor examines the skin, listens to the heart, checks the mouth for cleft palate, and counts the fingers and toes to see if an extra one is present. Other checks include testing the movement of the hip joints for **congenital dislocation of the hip**. If a dislocated hip is discovered, the baby will require hospital treatment to prevent the development of a permanent limp.

Blood test When the baby is a few days old, a few drops of blood from its heel are tested for:

- **Phenylketonuria (PKU)** This is an inherited condition which affects about 1 child in 10 000–20 000. It is due to the absence of the enzyme which deals with phenylalanine – a substance (an amino acid) present in milk and other foods. Consequently, phenylalanine acumulates to toxic levels, and this damages the brain. The child becomes mentally handicapped and stunted growth.
  Treatment If this condition is discovered early enough, the child will develop normally on a special diet which lacks phenylalanine.
- **Thyroid deficiency (hypothyroidism)** The object is to check that the thyroid gland is producing **thyroid hormone**, which is needed for normal growth and development, A baby who lacks thyroid hormone develops into a cretin – undersized and mentally handicapped.
  Treatment This condition can be prevented by giving the child doses of the hormone from an early age.

Umbilical cord The stump of the umbilical cord attached to the baby dries, and shrivels and drops off about a week, leaving the **umbilicus** (**navel** or belly button).

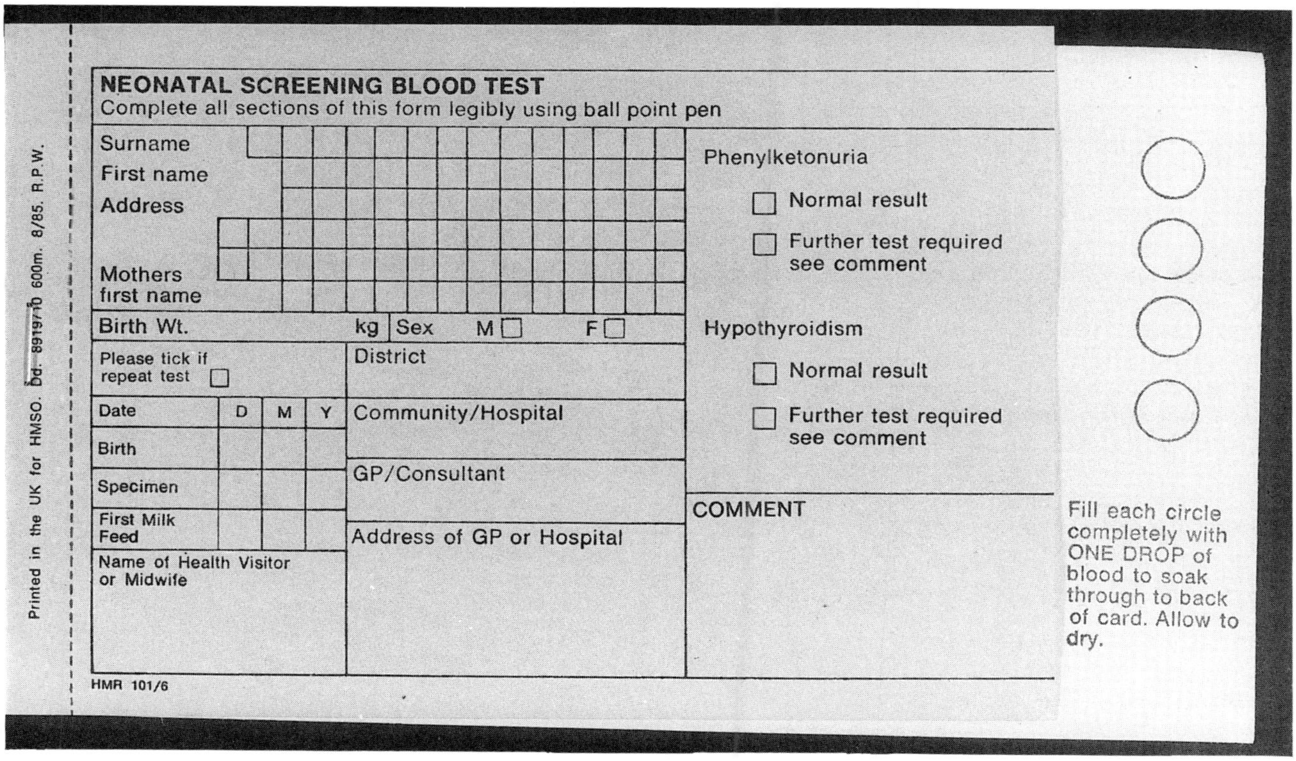
Printed in the UK for HMSO. Dd. 8919710 600m. 8/85. R.P.W.

NEONATAL SCREENING BLOOD TEST
Complete all sections of this form legibly using ball point pen

Surname
First name
Address
Mothers first name
Birth Wt. kg Sex M ☐ F ☐
Please tick if repeat test ☐
District
Date D M Y
Birth
Specimen
First Milk Feed
Community/Hospital
GP/Consultant
Address of GP or Hospital
Name of Health Visitor or Midwife

Phenylketonuria
☐ Normal result
☐ Further test required see comment

Hypothyroidism
☐ Normal result
☐ Further test required see comment

COMMENT

Fill each circle completely with ONE DROP of blood to soak through to back of card. Allow to dry.

HMR 101/6

Figure 2 Blood test card

QUESTIONS

1a Describe the change in the uterus following the birth.
b Name the two sets of muscles which were stretched by pregnancy. What helps them to regain their shape?
c When does the menstrual cycle restart?

2a Give three reasons for the 'baby blues' during the week following the birth.
b What is the difference between the 'baby blues' and postnatal depression?

3a Draw and label a diagram to show the structure of the breasts.
b (i) Name the fluid produced by the breasts towards the end of pregnancy. (ii) What does this fluid contain?
c When is milk produced?

4a Why is movement of the hip joints of new-born babies checked?
b How is the navel formed?

FURTHER WORK

1 Study Fig 2. (i) What does neonatal mean? (ii) What two conditions are being investigated? (iii) Why are these tests carried out? (iv) What would happen to the child if these conditions were not diagnosed and treated?

2 Complete Exercise 6, p. 167.

Newborn babies

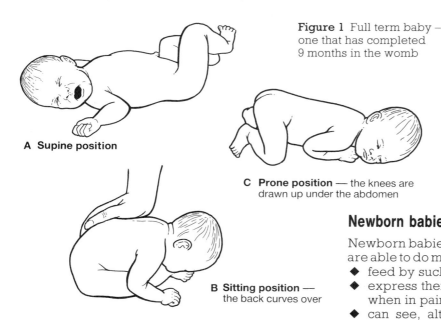

Figure 1 Full term baby – one that has completed 9 months in the womb

A Supine position

C Prone position — the knees are drawn up under the abdomen

D When lifted — the head falls backwards

B Sitting position — the back curves over

Changes at birth

When the baby emerges from the womb, changes rapidly take place to enable the child to live a separate existence from its mother.
- It has to start breathing almost immediately.
- It responds to light, sound, touch and pain.
- It has to deal with the germs to which it becomes exposed.
- The kidneys begin to function on their own.
- The digestive system starts to function on its own.
- The baby can stretch and move unhindered.
- Changes in circulation take place because oxygen arrives from the lungs and not the placenta.

The change to air breathing

At birth, the baby has to get its oxygen supplies from the air by breathing, and no longer from the mother's blood. This change involves re-routing the blood and expansion of the lungs. The following stages are involved:
- The process starts as the placenta begins to separate from the uterus wall:
- The umbilical artery then contracts and stops blood from flowing to the placenta.
- Blood continues to flow through the umbilical vein until most of the baby's blood has returned from the placenta to the baby. When pulsating movements in the umbilical cord cease, the cord is clamped and cut.
- Blood then circulates through the lungs.
- The fall in oxygen and the rise in carbon dioxide stimulates the baby to gasp in air.
- The lungs expand and breathing begins.
- The foramen ovale and ductus arteriosus close.

Newborn babies

Newborn babies sleep for most of the time, but they are able to do many other things. For example, they:
- feed by sucking.
- express their feelings – they cry when hungry, when in pain or if lonely.
- can see, although not clearly – they blink at nearby movements and shut their eyes when a bright light is suddenly turned on.
- can hear – they are startled by loud noises.
- are sensitive to smell – they turn the head away from an unpleasant smell.
- have a certain amount of muscle control – they can make jerky movements.
- have a certain amount of co-ordination between the senses – they turn their eyes towards a source of a noise.
- have started to learn.

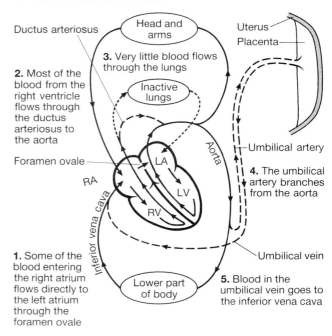

Ductus arteriosus

Head and arms

Uterus
Placenta

3. Very little blood flows through the lungs

2. Most of the blood from the right ventricle flows through the ductus arteriosus to the aorta

Inactive lungs

Foramen ovale

RA

LA

Aorta

Umbilical artery

4. The umbilical artery branches from the aorta

LV

RV

Inferior vena cava

1. Some of the blood entering the right atrium flows directly to the left atrium through the foramen ovale

Lower part of body

Umbilical vein

5. Blood in the umbilical vein goes to the inferior vena cava

Figure 2
Foetal circulation

– – – Blood vessels which close at birth

····· Blood vessels which open at birth

Maintaining the body temperature Full term babies are born with a store of fat – **brown fat** – in a layer under the skin which:
◆ acts as an insulating layer to help keep the baby warm,
◆ can be used as fuel to supply extra heat when necessary.
Nevertheless, newborn babies have difficulty in keeping warm and for the first month of life should be kept in a room temperature of around 20°C, day and night. The baby gradually becomes able to keep himself warm but the temperature of the room in which he sleeps should be kept at about 20°C for the first few months. (Hypothermia – p. 165)

Reflex actions Young babies display a number of automatic movements – reflex actions – which mainly disappear within three months and are replaced by actions the baby has to learn. Examples are shown in **Fig 3**.

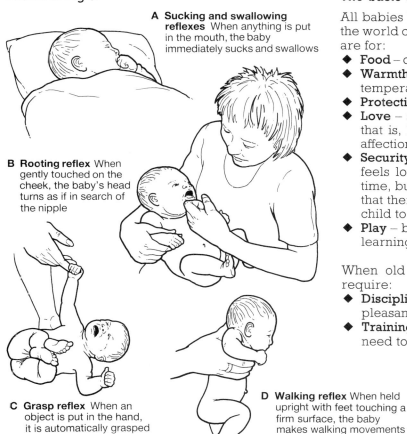

A **Sucking and swallowing reflexes** When anything is put in the mouth, the baby immediately sucks and swallows

B **Rooting reflex** When gently touched on the cheek, the baby's head turns as if in search of the nipple

C **Grasp reflex** When an object is put in the hand, it is automatically grasped

D **Walking reflex** When held upright with feet touching a firm surface, the baby makes walking movements

Figure 3 Reflex actions

Premature babies

A premature baby is one which is born before it is expected, perhaps as early as the seventh month. Any baby weighing less than 2.5 kg (5½ lb) is also called premature, even if it was born at full term.

Premature babies are very small and weak and need special care. Frequently they have difficulties with breathing, sucking and keeping warm, and need to be kept in an incubator for the first few days or weeks. The incubator acts as a half-way house between the womb and the outside world. the baby is kept isolated, protected and in a controlled environment. The temperature is kept constant, so is the humidity. The baby can be fed through a tube or dropper until he has the strength to suck. If necessary, extra oxygen can be supplied to help with breathing.

The basic needs of a child

All babies have the same needs, whatever part of the world or type of home in which they live. These are for:
◆ **Food** – of the right type and in the right amounts.
◆ **Warmth** – sufficient for the baby to keep its body temperature at about 37°C.
◆ **Protection** – from illness and injury.
◆ **Love** – so that the child can learn how to love, that is, how to make the long-lasting bonds of affection with others that are deeply rewarding.
◆ **Security** – to make the child feel safe. Everyone feels lonely, rejected and afraid from time to time, but knowing that people care for him and that there is a place where he belongs, helps a child to develop normally.
◆ **Play** – because while they are playing they are learning.

When old enough to understand, children also require:
◆ **Discipline** – which is firm but kind to make them pleasant people to live with.
◆ **Training** – to help them acquire the skills they need to gradually become independent.

QUESTIONS

1a Describe seven changes which take place at birth to enable the child to live separately from its mother.

2a List some of the things that newborn babies can do.
b Describe a newborn baby: (i) in the sitting position, (ii) in the prone position, (iii) when being lifted.

3a Name two uses of brown fat in babies.
b What is the reason for recommending that newborn babies should be kept in a room temperature of about 20°C?

4 Describe four reflex actions shown by newborn babies.

5a Give six basic needs of a baby.
b Give two other requirements when the children are old enough to understand.

FURTHER WORK

1 Use **Fig 3** to draw two diagrams:
(i) **Foetal circulation** (exclude those blood vessels which open after birth);
(ii) **Circulation after birth** (exclude those blood vessels which close at birth)..

2 For each of the basic needs of a child listed above, suggest two ways in which it contributes to healthy development.

3 Complete Exercise 5, p. 166.

Physical growth

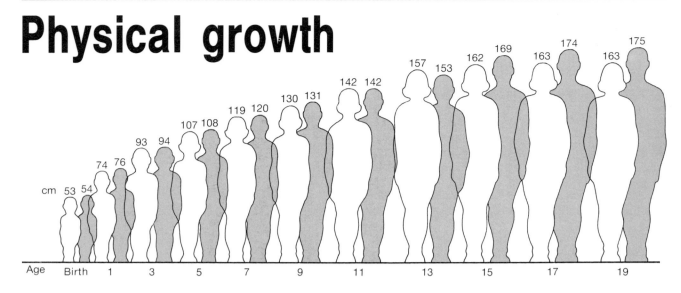

Figure 1 Average height of boys and girls

Growth can be measured as increase in height and weight. Generally, as a child grows taller he also becomes heavier, but not always, because weight also depends on how fat or thin the child is.

Average growth rates

When the average rate of growth for height or weight is plotted on a graph, the growth curve shows the following phases:
◆ Rapid growth during the first year.
◆ Slow, steady growth during childhood.
◆ A sharp increase during puberty.
◆ A slow increase during the latter part of adolescence until growth in height ceases at 16–17 years.

To find the average growth rate in a group being studied, children of the same age are measured for height and weight, then:
◆ The heights of all the children are added together, and the total is divided by the number of children. This gives the average height for that age group.
◆ The average weight for that age is calculated in the same way as for average height.

Individual variation

The measurements of children of the same age can vary greatly and spread over a wide range on either side of the average. Three factors responsible for the variation are
genes
food
illness.
Severe illness usually slows down growth, and the younger the child the greater is the risk of illness having a permanent effect. If the growth rate is only temporarily slowed down, the child will afterwards adapt with a period of 'catch-up' growth.

How tall will a child grow? Maximum height mainly depends on the genes inherited from the parents. If both parents are small, the child is likely to resemble them. On the other hand, poor feeding can result in a child never growing to its full potential height.

Sex differences At birth, on average boys are slightly heavier and longer than girls, and they remain so during childhood. The growth spurt at puberty occurs about $2\frac{1}{2}$ years earlier in girls than in boys, and growth is completed at an earlier age. On average, girls are 15 cm shorter than boys when they have finished growing.

QUESTIONS

1a Draw the average growth curve and show the four phases of growth.
 b Describe how to find the average growth rate in a group of children.
 c Give three factors responsible for variation in growth of children of the same age.

2a On what does the maximum height to which a child can grow mainly depend?
 b List three differences between the average rates of growth of boys and girls.

FURTHER WORK

1 Use the information on **Fig 1** to draw graphs to show average height of: (i) boys, (ii) girls. Note on your graph the four growth phases.
2 Use the information on **Fig 2** to complete this chart.

Median weight of boys and girls in kg

Age	1	2	3	4	5	6	7	8	9	10	11	12	13	14	15	16	17	18	19
Boys																			
Girls																			

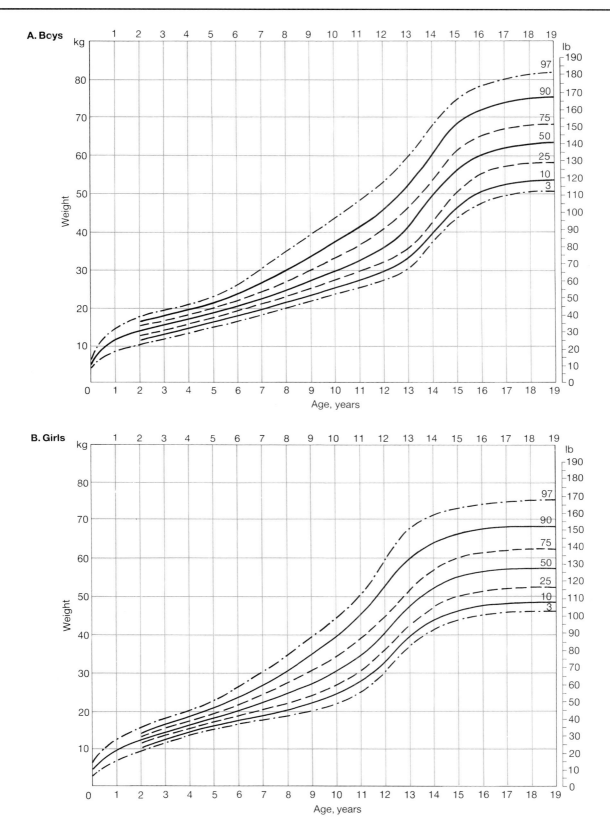

A. Boys

B. Girls

Figure 2 Percentile graphs to show the normal range in weight of boys and girls. The 50th percentile is the **median** – it represents the middle of the range. The 97th percentile is close to the top of the range; in any typical group of 100 children, there would be 96 who weighed less, and 3 who weighed more. The 10th percentile is near to the bottom of the range; in any typical groups of children, 90 would weigh more and 9 weigh less

A child may move from one percentile to another as he/she gets older due to change in diet or activities, illness, recovery, or emotional stress.

Development 0–18 months

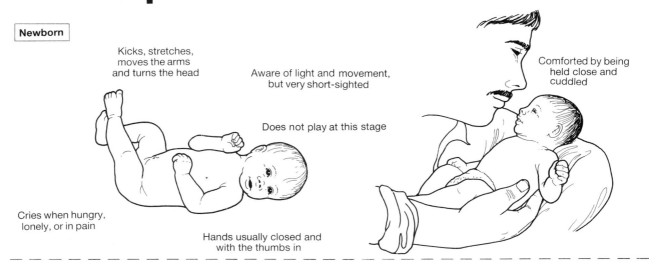

Kicks, stretches, moves the arms and turns the head

Aware of light and movement, but very short-sighted

Does not play at this stage

Comforted by being held close and cuddled

Cries when hungry, lonely, or in pain

Hands usually closed and with the thumbs in

3 months

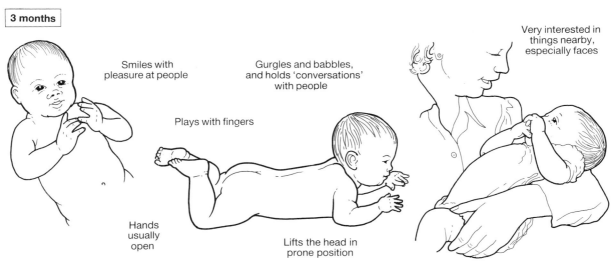

Smiles with pleasure at people

Gurgles and babbles, and holds 'conversations' with people

Very interested in things nearby, especially faces

Plays with fingers

Hands usually open

Lifts the head in prone position

6 months

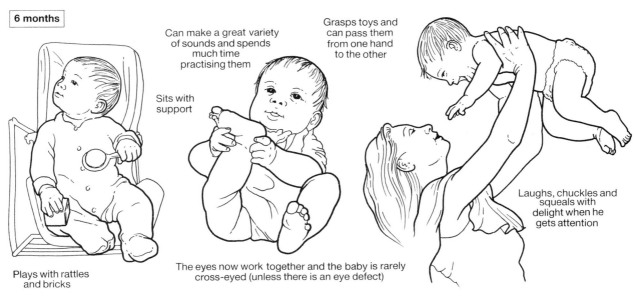

Can make a great variety of sounds and spends much time practising them

Grasps toys and can pass them from one hand to the other

Sits with support

Laughs, chuckles and squeals with delight when he gets attention

Plays with rattles and bricks

The eyes now work together and the baby is rarely cross-eyed (unless there is an eye defect)

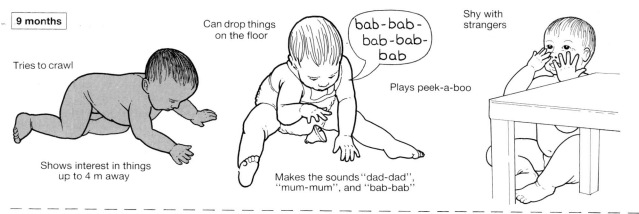

9 months

Tries to crawl

Can drop things on the floor

bab-bab-bab-bab-bab

Shy with strangers

Plays peek-a-boo

Shows interest in things up to 4 m away

Makes the sounds "dad-dad", "mum-mum", and "bab-bab"

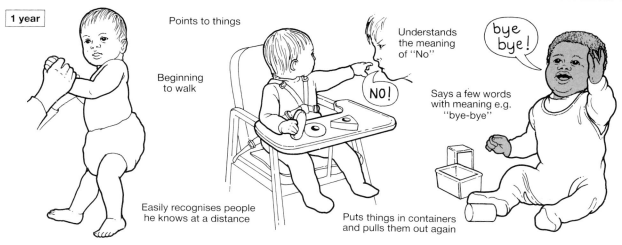

1 year

Points to things

Understands the meaning of "No"

bye bye!

Beginning to walk

Says a few words with meaning e.g. "bye-bye"

NO!

Easily recognises people he knows at a distance

Puts things in containers and pulls them out again

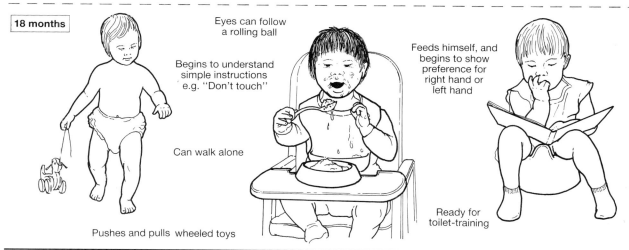

18 months

Eyes can follow a rolling ball

Feeds himself, and begins to show preference for right hand or left hand

Begins to understand simple instructions e.g. "Don't touch"

Can walk alone

Pushes and pulls wheeled toys

Ready for toilet-training

QUESTION

Study the illustrations and text on these two pages. Make a table to the pattern shown below and complete it by placing the correct information in the appropriate column for each age group.

	A Body movements	B Hands	C Eyes	D Communi- cation and speech	E Behaviour	F Play
Newborn 3 months 6 months 9 months 1 year 18 months						

FURTHER WORK

The information in this topic gives the average age at which each stage of development takes place. But each child is an individual, and the age at which normal children sit up, walk, talk, etc, varies greatly. From your own observations of children aged up to two years, describe how their development compares with the information given here.

Development 2–5 years

2 years

The 'NO' stage – often says 'No' when told to do something, and may have temper tantrums

Please get down

No!

Climbs on furniture to look out of window

Holds pencil and scribbles

Me draw

Can make a simple sentence of 2–3 words

Plays near other children but not with them

Can see as far as an adult can see

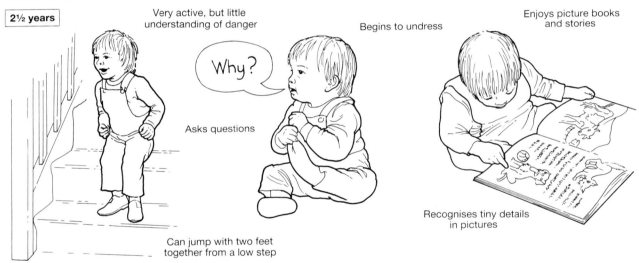

2½ years

Very active, but little understanding of danger

Can jump with two feet together from a low step

Asks questions

Why?

Begins to undress

Enjoys picture books and stories

Recognises tiny details in pictures

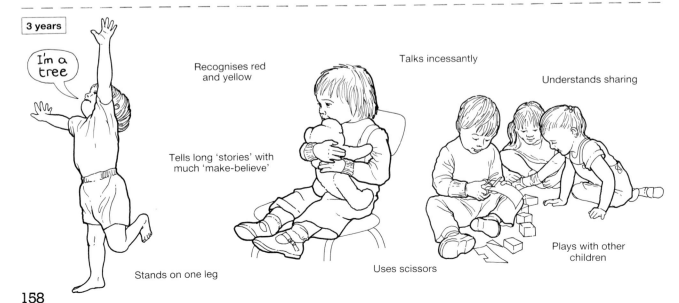

3 years

I'm a tree

Recognises red and yellow

Tells long 'stories' with much 'make-believe'

Stands on one leg

Talks incessantly

Uses scissors

Understands sharing

Plays with other children

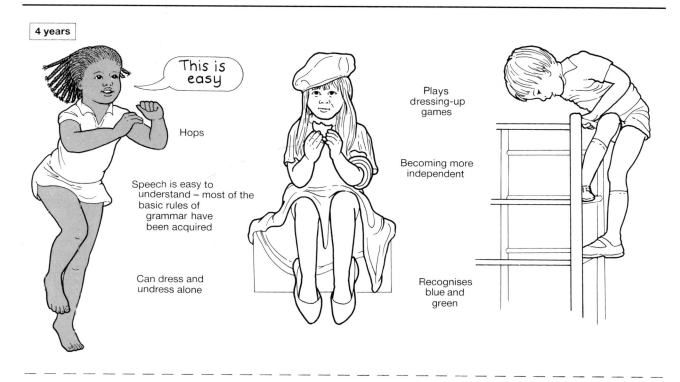

4 years

This is easy

Hops

Speech is easy to understand – most of the basic rules of grammar have been acquired

Can dress and undress alone

Plays dressing-up games

Becoming more independent

Recognises blue and green

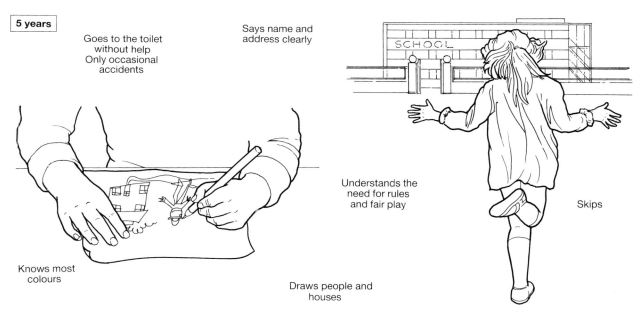

5 years

Goes to the toilet without help
Only occasional accidents

Says name and address clearly

Knows most colours

Draws people and houses

Understands the need for rules and fair play

Skips

SCHOOL

QUESTION

Study the illustrations and text on these two pages. Make a table to the pattern shown below and complete it by placing the correct information in the appropriate column for each age group.

	A Body movements	B Hands	C Eyes	D Communi-ation and speech	E Behaviour	F Play
2 years 2½ years 3 years 4 years 5 years						

FURTHER WORK

The information in this topic gives the average age at which each stage of development takes place. But each child is an individual, and the age at which normal children sit up, walk, talk etc, varies greatly. From your own observations of children aged between 2 and 5 years, describe how their development compares with the information given here.

More about growth and development

Throughout life there is continuous change to the tissues and organs as the body grows and develops and ages. The changes are most obvious during childhood and adolescence, and much slower in adults.

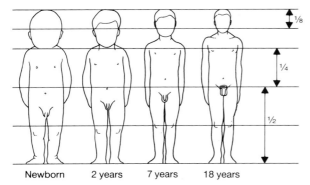

Figure 1 Proportions change with growth

Proportions change with growth

As a child grows, the different parts of the body both increase in size and alter in shape. This has the effect of changing the proportions of the body as the child gets older. For example, at birth, the legs are about three-eighths of the total length of the body, but by the age of 16 years they are about a half.

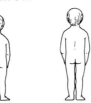

| Babies have bow-legs | At 3 years knock-knees often develop | By 6 years the legs have usually straightened | During puberty the feet grow rapidly, then the legs |

Figure 2 Growth and development of the legs

Growth of the skeleton

At birth the skeleton consists mainly of cartilage. As growth proceeds, most of the cartilage becomes replaced by bone, a process known as **ossification** – which is not completed until the late teens. Because ossification proceeds in a regular pattern, it is possible to estimate the age of a child from examination of the skeleton, or just the wrist and hand: **Fig 3A**.

The **fontanelles**, **Fig 3B**, are the 'soft spots' in a baby's skull – the areas between the bones which are covered by a tough but flexible membrane. They allow the skull to alter shape slightly during childbirth as the head is pushed through the birth canal. The fontanelles disappear as the skull bones enlarge and join together, the posterior fontanelle by the age of 2 months, and the anterior fontanelle by about 18 months.

Figure 3 Growth of the skeleton
  A. Bones in the hand as shown by X-ray

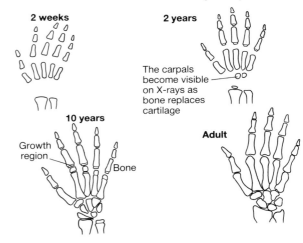

B. Fontanelles

Figure 4 The changing shape of the backbone. The shape changes as growth proceeds and can be most clearly seen in side view.

Newborn

Curve in the neck region develops as the baby becomes able to lift its head

Lumbar curve develops when the baby begins to stand

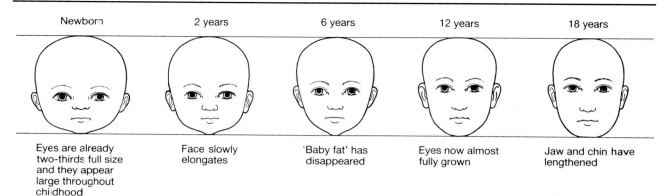

Newborn	2 years	6 years	12 years	18 years
Eyes are already two-thirds full size and they appear large throughout childhood	Face slowly elongates	'Baby fat' has disappeared	Eyes now almost fully grown	Jaw and chin have lengthened

Figure 5 Changes in the shape of the face

Tissues and organs

Different tissues and organs vary in their rate of growth and each has its own growth pattern, for example:

Brain At birth, the brain is already a quarter of the adult size and it has all the nerve cells it will ever possess. By the end of the first year the brain is three-quarters of the adult size. Full adult size is reached by the age of 17, although it is almost complete by 7–8 years.

Brain growth after birth is due to increase in:
- size of the cells,
- number of fibres (dendrites and axons) as cross-connections are formed between the cells,
- development of myelin sheaths around the axons

Lymphoid tissue This type of tissue is found in lymph nodes (glands), thymus, tonsils and adenoids, and one of its functions is to produce antibodies. The amount of lymphoid tissue increases rapidly until the child is about 12 years old, and then decreases to adult level. It has this pattern because childhood is the time when the body is rapidly acquiring immunity to a large number of infectious diseases and needs to make antibodies in larger amounts.

Reproductive organs These show little change until the beginning of puberty, when rapid growth takes place and continues throughout adolescence.

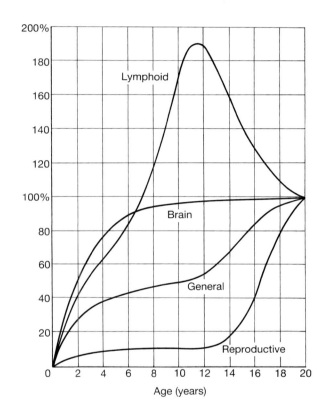

Figure 6 Graph to show the variation in the rate of growth of different parts of the body.

QUESTIONS

1a Why do the proportions of the body change with growth?
 b Describe the changes to the shape of the legs as they grow and develop.
2a How does the skeleton change with growth?
 b What are the fontanelles, and what happens to them?
3 Use diagrams to describe the changes which take place to: (i) the backbone, (ii) the face.

4a (i) Copy the graph from **Fig 6** which shows the rate of growth of the brain. (ii) Describe the graph. (iii) What is brain growth after birth due to?
 b (i) Copy the graph from **Fig 6** which shows the rate of growth of lymphoid tissue. (ii) Explain the graph.
 c (i) Copy the graph from **Fig 6** which shows the rate of growth of the reproductive organs. (ii) Explain the graph.

FURTHER WORK

1 Find the height and weight of a group of boys, and of a group of girls, of approximately the same age. How do the averages for the groups compare with the information given in **Figs 2A** and **2B**, p. 155. Give reasons to account for any differences.

2 Measure the members of the class to find the average measurements for: (i) head circumference, (ii) hand span. Find the average differences between males and females.

Males and females

Up to about 9 years of age, boys and girls who are dressed alike look very much the same, and it is often difficult to say which is which from their appearance. However, differences in behaviour may be noticeable by the age of three months onwards.

Boys *tend* **to be more:**
◆ active and energetic,
◆ aggressive,
◆ competitive,
◆ keen to explore.

Girls *tend* **to be:**
◆ earlier in learning to walk, talk, and control the bladder,
◆ better with words, particularly when younger,
◆ more interested in people.

Males are more at risk

Although modern medicines and improved living conditions have lengthened the life span for both men and women, the expected life span for men is still shorter than for women (p. 204).
◆ Male infants have more complications at birth and during the following weeks (perinatal and postnatal complications).
◆ Throughout life, men are more likely to suffer from some diseases, eg heart attacks.
◆ Men tend to have riskier occupations, eg deep sea fishing, mining.
◆ Young men tend to choose riskier interests, eg motor cycles, mountain climbing.

Cause of the differences in behaviour

At one time it was taken for granted that **genetic factors** were responsible for differences in behaviour. They were thought to be the underlying cause of the differences in interests, emotions, attitudes and achievements of males and females. Nowadays, some people argue that these differences are the result of training – that parents and teachers have one set of expectations for boys and a different set for girls, and that the children respond accordingly. These are **environmental factors**.

As happens in other aspects of development, the differences in behaviour are most likely to be due to the interactions of genetic and environmental factors. Some cultures prefer to emphasise the male and female differences, and others to minimise them.

Genetic factors   The genes a child inherits are responsible for:
◆ the sex of the individual,
◆ the functioning of the sex organs,
◆ the rate of growth and development.

Environmental factors   The way children are brought up encourages or discourages differences. For example:
◆ The type of clothes boys and girls are dressed in differs
◆ The colours they are expected to wear differ.
◆ Boys are expected to be braver than girls.
◆ Girls are allowed to cling to mother.
◆ Girls are nursed and cuddled more than boys. There is some evidence to show that this is so – but whether it comes about because it is the wish of the parent or of the baby is not known.
◆ Boys and girls may be given different types of education and opportunities.

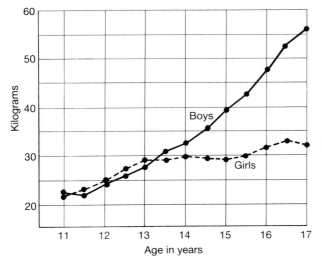

Figure 1 Strength of arm thrust   Arm thrust can be measured by a measuring instrument called a dynamometer. The instrument is held in front of the chest with one hand on each end. The thrust is produced by pressing the hands towards each other and so causing the dynamometer to be compressed and to indicate the force being exerted.

Differing physical abilities

During childhood, there is little difference in strength between boys and girls. But at puberty, physical changes take place which result in males becoming generally stronger than females and capable of greater athletic performance. For example:

◆ **Muscles** – males develop relatively larger muscles and females develop more fat. More muscle and less fat gives greater speed and strength of movement: **Fig 1**.

◆ **Heart** – males develop a larger heart which allows more blood to be pumped with each heart-beat. The **heart rate** lowers at adolescence for both sexes, but drops more for males than females.

◆ **Blood** – males develop more red cells and a greater haemoglobin content per unit of blood than females.

◆ **Metabolic rate** – males develop a higher metabolic rate and use more food to supply the increased energy needs.

◆ **Lungs** – the larger lungs of males allows greater quantities of oxygen to be obtained and carbon dioxide excreted (a greater vital capacity – p. 54).

◆ **Arms** – the greater arm length and smaller carrying angle (**Fig 2**) of males helps them to throw objects harder and further or hit them with greater force.

◆ **Pelvis** – the wider pelvis of females, **Fig 4**, p. 5, results in a more acute angle at the joint between pelvis and femur. This is a disadvantage when running.

◆ **Flexibility** – females have more flexible muscles and joints.

◆ **Body fat** – the increased amount of body fat in the average female gives greater insulation from heat loss and added bouyancy when swimming. The disadvantage is that it is extra weight to carry.

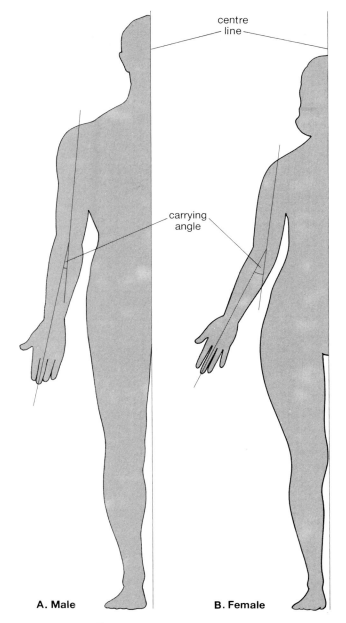

A. Male **B. Female**

Figure 2 Carrying angles

p. 54

QUESTIONS

1a What differences may be noticeable in behaviour of boys and girls?
 b Name two factors which could be responsible for these differences.
 c What are genes responsible for?
 d Give examples of environmental factors which encourage or discourage differences between boys and girls.

2a At what stage do boys generally become stronger than girls?
 b List the physical changes which result in males becoming generally stronger than females.

3 Give reasons why males are considered to be more at risk than females.

4a How is arm thrust measured?
 b Describe how the strength of arm thrust changes between the ages of 11 and 17.

5 Draw diagrams to show typical male and female carrying angles.

FURTHER WORK

1 Discuss: 'Is being a genius inherited?'

2 Males tend to dominate games of all types, from darts and chess to football and track events. Obtain evidence from the Guinness Book of Records to support this statement. In your opinion, is this due to greater physical ability, mental ability, interest, attitudes or training?

Ageing

Ageing is a natural process and results in gradual changes in the various tissues and organs which prevent them from functioning as efficiently as they did because of:

◆ cell loss – of those cells which, when damaged or worn out, are not renewed, eg nerve cells, teeth,

◆ inaccurate repair of tissues,

◆ accumulation of unwanted matter in the tissues, eg cholesterol in blood vessels,

◆ reduced immunity.

Normal processes of ageing

Skin As a person grows older, wrinkles develop because the skin becomes less elastic and loses the thin underlying layer of fat. Skin also becomes drier and more fragile.

Hair Hair on the head usually turns grey and becomes finer and thinner. It may be lost altogether from the top of the head, especially in men, although this does happen to a few women. There is also a tendency for women over 60 to develop facial hair.

Weakening of the bones (osteoporosis) Calcium and protein are lost from the bones and they break more easily. This condition is most common in post-menopausal women. It may be possible to delay the condition by a diet rich in calcium and vitamins, and by hormone replacement therapy (HRT, p. 117).

Height It is usual to lose height, mainly because the intervertebral discs become thinner, and also if the posture becomes bent.

Posture The bent posture shown by some old people may be due to a health problem (eg Parkinson's disease; osteoporosis), to habit, or to painful conditions such as backache, aching joints and sore feet.

Joints They gradually stiffen and movements become more difficult. When the weight-bearing joints are damaged by arthritis, movement may also be painful.

Muscles Muscles gradually weaken and lose their power, and greater effort is required to perform the same task. For this reason, very energetic sports such as football are replaced by golf and bowls. Movements become slower due to the combined effects of muscle weakness and stiff joints. Poorer co-ordination may make movements unsteady.

Hardening of the arteries (arteriosclerosis) This condition reduces the blood supply to the various organs. A poor blood supply to the brain can result in a stroke, or gradually increasing confusion. A poor blood supply to the heart may result in angina or a heart attack. A poor blood supply to the leg may result in cramp of the calf muscles on walking, or in gangrene (death of tissue) of the toes.

Breathlessness The amount of air that can be breathed in and out by the lungs steadily falls, thus reducing the supply of oxygen and the removal of carbon dioxide. With some people, even slight exertion results in breathlessness – a condition that develops earlier and faster in smokers.

Tendency to slower mental function Although the number of brain cells decreases throughout life, this does not necessarily have a marked effect as there are many millions of brain cells left. It may become more difficult to remember recent events than to recall those which happened many years ago, but older people are often very creative, particularly in literature, music and art.

Sight With increasing age, the lens loses its elasticity, causing difficulty in focusing on close objects. The change to the lens becomes obvious when a person whose sight has been normal has to hold a paper at arm's length in order to read it – and this often happens in middle age. Short-sighted people often find their sight improving with age because they can now see distant objects more clearly.

Hearing It is quite common for older people to notice that they are gradually becoming deaf. Loud sounds and low sounds can be heard but other people's speech is difficult to understand. This is because the high-pitched sounds of the consonants – l, t, d etc – cannot be distinguished. Shouting at a person with this form of deafness does not help, but speaking slowly and clearly does. Much deafness, however, is caused by wax in the ears.

Sense of smell There is a tendency for the sense of smell to decrease with age. When this happens the person will not be able to detect such things as escaping gas, bad food, or smelly conditions in themselves and the house. They also lose some of their sense of taste as this mainly depends on the sense of smell.

Rate of ageing

Some very old people remain energetic, mentally active and enjoy life, whilst sometimes other much younger people are 'old for their years'. The rate at which people 'age' depends on many factors including:

inherited genes,
attitude to life,
state of **health**.

To help delay the effects of ageing   Older people are advised to:

◆ **Keep physically active** for 'What you don't use you lose':

Muscles deteriorate if they are not used – true for any age group, physical activity also exercises the heart and circulation.

◆ **Keep mentally active** – a brain that is not used deteriorates.

◆ **Have a well balanced diet** in order to keep healthy.

◆ **Avoid becoming overweight**   Obesity makes many disorders more likely, eg high blood pressure, heart disease, diabetes, osteo-arthritis. It may also be the cause of difficulty in walking or climbing stairs.

◆ **Take care of the feet**   Much pain and lack of mobility can be avoided by preventing or treating corns, bunions, hammer toes, callouses and long toe nails.

◆ **Be interested in other people** – it helps to prevent boredom and loneliness.

Difficulty in keeping warm   Slower movement means that less heat is generated by the muscles. Also the body's temperature-regulating mechanism may not work as efficiently. Old people are subject to **hypothermia** – low body heat – which is a special hazard of old age. Old people may be less aware of the cold and therefore may not wear enough clothes or heat the house sufficiently.

Section 5   EXERCISES

1 Match each of the terms with the correct statement in the list below.

(a) **allelles   cervix   chromsome   DNA   fertilisation gene   genetics   haemophilia   mutation   ovulation**

    code for a characteristic
    the study of inheritance
    alternative forms of a gene
    deoxyribonucleic acid
    a change in the genetic code
    release of an egg
    fusion of egg and sperm
    a chain of genes
    neck of womb
    condition causing severe bleeding from minor wounds [10]

(b) **conception   epididymis   fallopian tube fontanelle   foetus   hypothermia   osteoporosis prostate   scrotum   zygote**

    fertilised egg
    implantation of fertilised egg
    where fertilisation takes place
    unborn baby
    weakening of bones
    low body heat
    contains testes
    gland surrounding urethra
    where sperm are stored
    area between bones in a baby's skull [10]

2 The heights of the 30 pupils in a biology class were measured and the results are shown in the table below.

Pupil	Height (cm)	Pupil	Height (cm)	Pupil	Height (cm)
1	150	11	152	21	140
2	150	12	138	22	144
3	148	13	144	23	146
4	150	14	146	24	148
5	146	15	148	25	150
6	150	16	150	26	152
7	152	17	152	27	154
8	144	18	154	28	156
9	148	19	160	29	158
10	150	20	138	30	160

(a) (i) Complete the table below to show how many pupils there are at the various heights. [2]

Height in cm	138	140	142	144	146	148	150	152	154	158	160
Number of pupils											

(ii) Use graph paper to make a bar graph of the results. [3]

(b) Name the kind of variation shown by your bar graph. [1]

(NEA: GCSE Biology Specimen)

3 State the function of each of the following hormones in the female reproductive system:

(a) follicle-stimulating hormone (FSH)
(b) luteinising hormone (LH)
(c) oestrogen
(d) oxytocin
(e) progesterone
(f) prolactin

4 (a) On investigating the energy **loss** by a human the following results were recorded:

Heat loss from body = 9800 kilojoules in 24 hours
Energy loss in urine = 380 kilojoules in 24 hours

Energy **release** in the same 24-hour period by the oxidation of ingested food:

From oxidation of carbohydrates = 3540 kilojoules
From oxidation of fats   = 2390 kilojoules
From oxidation of proteins   = 1880 kilojoules

(i) By how much does the energy utilised exceed the energy available from the food ingested? [2]
(ii) The energy deficit is made available from food reserves. Name **two** food reserve materials and for each state **one** organ in which it is stored in humans. [4]
(iii) Energy release occurs in all cells of the body. In which cell organelle does this process occur? [1]
(iv) Which organ, because of its many chemical activities, releases very large quantities of heat? [1]

(b) The table shows the energy, protein and calcium requirements for 24 hours of various subjects.

	Energy (kilojoules)	Protein (g per kg body mass)	Calcium (g)
Child 6–12 years	7150	2.8	1.2
Child 12–18 years	11 500	2.5	1.3
Moderately active man	14 600	1.0	1.0
Nursing mother	12 550	2.3	2.1

(i) Explain why the moderately active man requires almost twice as much energy as a child of 6–12 years. [2]
(ii) Explain why the children and the nursing mother require betwen two and three times as much protein as the man. [3]
(iii) Explain why the nursing mother requires nearly twice as much calcium as the children and the man. [2]
(iv) What is the most likely effect on the nursing mother if she does not have a sufficient intake of calcium in her diet? [2]

(c) Some tissues of the body can release energy in the absence of oxygen.
(i) In which tissues and under what conditions can this type of respiration occur? [2]
(ii) Which substance is the end product of this type of respiration? [1]

(AEB: O-level Human Biology)

5 The temperature of the human foetus while in the uterus is about 0.5°C above that of its mother. At birth it emerges into a relatively cool, dry atmosphere and immediately encounters a problem of temperature control.

(a) (i) Suggest an explanation for the fact that the temperature of the foetus may be above that of its mother.
(ii) Suggest how the temperature of the foetus is normally controlled. [5]

(b) Explain how the following help the new-born baby to control its temperature.
(i) From about the fifth month of pregnancy onwards, a layer of subcutaneous fat is developed by the foetus.
(ii) At birth there is a sudden constriction of the peripheral blood vessels. [5]

(c) A premature baby is less able to control its body temperature and must be kept in an incubator.
(i) A constant temperature is maintained within the incubator and, to do this, it is provided with a thermostat (this is a switch which is operated by a change in temperature) and an electric heater. Using this information as an example, explain the term *negative feedback*.
(ii) Suggest **two** functions of the hood which covers the incubator.   [6]

(d) If the baby is more than a few weeks premature, its suckling reflex is undeveloped and it must be fed directly through the plastic tube inserted via its nostril into its stomach.
(i) Explain what is meant by a reflex action.
(ii) What advantage is there in suckling being a reflex rather than a voluntary action?
(iii) Whichever way the baby is fed, its diet must contain substantial quantities of carbohydrate and protein. State **one** function of each of these substances within the body of a new-born baby.   [6]

(AEB: O(A) level Biology of Man)

6 (a) The diagram represents a family pedigree showing the
inheritance of *phenylketonuria* which is controlled by a single pair of alleles, **A** and **a**.

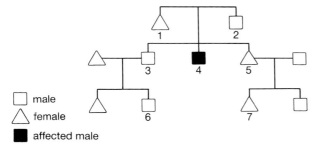

☐ male
△ female
■ affected male

(i) Is the allele for phenylketonuria dominant or recessive?   [1]
(ii) State with reasons the genotype of each of individuals **1, 2** and **4**.   [4]
(iii) What are the possible genotypes of each of individuals **3** and **5**?   [2]
(iv) Why would it be genetically inadvisable for cousins **6** and **7** to marry and have children?   [3]
(b) The diagram shows a simplified sequence of chemical reactions which occur in the body.

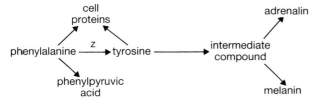

In the disease *phenylketonuria* the reaction labelled **z** does not take place and a build-up of phenylpyruvic acid (a phenylketo-acid) occurs.
(i) What is a gene mutation?   [2]
(ii) A gene mutation has given rise to the inability to carry out reaction **z**. Explain this statement.   [5]
(iii) Infants suffering from *phenylketonuria* often have fair hair and fair complexion. Explain briefly, using information from the diagram, why this is so.   [3]

(AEB: O-level Human Biology)

Health and ill-health

Figure 1 Factors involved in keeping healthy. People who are living in countries where there is no over-riding disaster, such as famine, can do much to keep themselves healthy

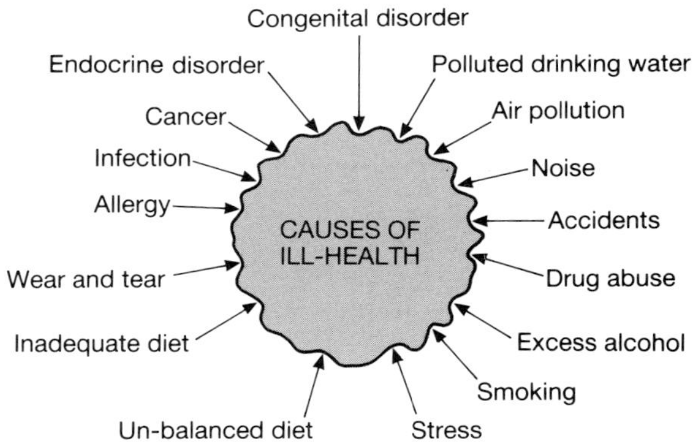

Figure 2 Causes of ill-health

Health is a state of complete mental, physical and social well-being, and not merely the absence of disease or infirmity – this is the definition of health by the World Health Organisation (WHO).

Mental, physical, and social well-being are inter-related, for example:

◆ People who are generally happy and contented with their lives are less likely to be ill.
◆ People in jobs they enjoy are less likely to have days off sick than those who are not..
◆ Bored or discontented people are more likely to complain of ill-health or to have accidents.
◆ Unemployed people tend to have more health problems.

Disease

Disease is present in the body when part of it does not function properly.

Prevention of disease Many common and killing diseases can be prevented by, for example:

◆ clean water and food supplies,
◆ immunisation,
◆ balanced diet,
◆ safety precautions at home, at work and on the roads,
◆ not smoking,
◆ maintaining normal blood pressure.

Healers

Most doctors and other types of healer practise **holistic medicine** ('whole person' medicine) – the whole patient and his personal circumstances are considered even when treating that patient for one particular condition.

Modern medicine Modern (orthodox) medicine involves:

◆ trained and registered doctors, nurses, physio-therapists, etc,
◆ high technology to diagnose and treat disease,
◆ modern drugs,
◆ surgery and general anaesthetics.

Modern medicine has resulted in great advances in the diagnosis and treatment of disease. For example:

blood transfusion,
the use of antibiotics for meningitis, TB and other bacterial diseases,
hormone replacement, eg sugar diabetes, HRT (p. 117),
dialysis for kidney failure,
removing a bowel cancer.

For most illnesses it seems sensible to seek advice first from qualified doctors. If the help or treatment received does not, for some reason or other, seem satisfactory, the patient may decide to consult other types of healer such as those listed on p. 169, preferably with their own doctor's approval.

Medicines

Medicines are taken to:
◆ destroy germs which are causing disease, eg antibiotics to kill bacteria,
◆ prevent disease, eg vaccines,
◆ supply essential substances which the body lacks, eg insulin in diabetes,
◆ correct the body processes when they are not working properly, eg laxatives,
◆ relieve symptoms, eg pain,
◆ prevent pregnancy, eg 'the pill'.

Alternative (complementary or 'fringe') medicine Alternative medicine provides treatment for illness which does not include modern drugs. Examples are:

Acupuncture – based on the ancient Chinese practice of inserting needles into the skin and rotating them to cure a variety of disorders. It is also used with some success in China as an anaesthetic, but not everyone responds. In the UK, a modified form of acupuncture is occasionally used in orthodox medicine, usually for pain relief.

Chiropractice – based on the theory that diseases are caused by pressure on nerves and that they can be cured by manipulating the spine.

'Healing', 'laying on of hands', spiritual healing, spirit healing' The healer transmits healing influences to the troubled person or to the damaged part.

Herbalism the use of plants to treat disease. Many modern medicines contain the same ingredients but in a purified form. Serious side effects from herbal remedies are uncommon, but they do occur.

Homeopathy – based on the theory that if a particular substance can mimic an illness in full dose, it will cure it when given in extreme dilution. For example, belladonna poisoning makes the patient hot and dry, so very greatly diluted belladonna is used in homeopathy to treat fevers. The advantage of this type of treatment is that it has no serious side effects.

Hypnosis – a state of deep trance – is used with occasional success to treat asthma, for some psychiatric disorders caused by emotional problems, and to treat and prevent pain, particularly for complex dental work. It has an established place in orthodox medicine.

Osteopathy – based on the theory that abnormal tensions in joints, particularly of the spine, cause a variety of symptoms which can be relieved by skilled manipulation.

Weighing the benefits against the risks
Medicines have side effects, for example:
◆ An antibiotic taken too often increases the risk of germs arising which are resistant to the antibiotic.
◆ Typhoid vaccine can give brief headache and fever.
◆ Too much insulin causes low blood sugar and a 'hypo' – unconsciousness.
◆ Laxatives taken too often stop the gut muscles from working normally.
◆ Pain relievers can cause drowsiness and are therefore dangerous when taken before driving or operating machinery. They can also cause loss of blood from the stomach.
◆ 'The pill' gives a slight risk of increased blood pressure and thrombosis, so women taking oral contraceptives need regular medical check-ups, and should not smoke.

People more at risk
The following groups of people are more at risk from the effects of medicines:
◆ The very young – they react differently.
◆ The very old because they are more sensitive to many medicines, and because they tend to take many different kinds – with increased chances of drug interaction and unpleasant effects.

◆ The foetus ⎫ when the
◆ Babies who are breast- ⎬ mother takes
feeding ⎭ medicine.
◆ Drivers and machinery operators who take sedatives – particularly when also taken with alcohol.
◆ Those who are already taking other medicines – because of possible drug interactions.

Getting better without medicines
Most minor ailments – colds, coughs, headaches, diarrhoea, etc – will get better with or without medicines. The body just needs time to heal itself. Therefore, only simple remedies, or none at all, are advised for minor ailments.

Placebos
A placebo (pronounced pla-sea-bo) is a harmless substance given in place of medicine. Most of us react favourably when we believe we are being cured. About one third of the normal population will go to sleep more easily if told they have been given a 'sleeping pill', or gain some pain relief after taking a 'pain-reliever' which contains only sugar or starch. Both orthodox medicine and alternative medicine make use of this placebo response.

QUESTIONS

1a Give the meaning of health as defined by the WHO.
b List twelve factors involved in keeping healthy.
c List sixteen possible causes of ill-health.
2a What is meant by disease?
b Give ways in which disease can be prevented.
3a (i) What does Modern medicine involve?
(ii) What is meant by Alternative medicine?
b What is meant by holistic medicine?

c Give a brief description of six types of alternative medicine.
4a When using medicines it is necessary to weigh the benefits against the risks. List six reasons for taking medicines and, for each, give one side effect.
b Which groups of people are more at risk from the effects of medicines?
c Are medicines necessary for minor ailments?
d What is a placebo?

FURTHER WORK

1 Study **Fig 2**. Place the causes of ill-health given in **Fig 2** in three groups:
(i) disease, (ii) environment, (iii) life-style.
2 With reference to the section 'Prevention of disease', for each category, give examples of diseases which could be prevented.

Communication

Humans are social animals, that is, they live in groups or societies. **Communication** is the passing on of information, and this is essential for:

    sorting out problems,
    making rules,
    planning for the future,
    benefiting from history and the experiences of others,
    development of scientific ideas,
    teaching the next generation.

Lack of communication between people leaves them isolated and depressed. The inability to communicate may be due to deafness, strokes, loneliness – particularly amongst the elderly.

    Communication may be non-verbal or verbal.

Non-verbal communication

Non-verbal communication is communication without words. Information can be conveyed in a number of other ways, for example:

Body language
- Posture – fighting position, a tired slump.
- Movement of the head – shake, nod.
- Forehead – surprise, frown.
- Eyes – staring, glancing, looking away.
- Mouth – smile, pout, sneer.
- Arms – waving, salute, pointing, beckoning.
- Legs – crossed, relaxed, kicking.
- Hands – touching, V-sign, clenched fist, clasping and unclasping.

Noise
- Using the voice – laugh, cry, shout.
- Using objects – banging, knocking, music.

Symbols and signs
- Symbols to replace words – male and female symbols on toilet doors, road signs.
- Sign language – useful for deaf people.

Verbal communication

Speech involves putting a series of sounds – words – together in a meaningful way that is understandable to people who have the same language. It is the result of the combined action of:
- **brain** – the speech area,
- **hearing** – children learn to speak by copying the sounds they hear,
- **larynx** – voice box – which produces the sound,
- **throat, mouth, tongue, teeth and lips** – the shape and position of these parts alters the sounds which come from the larynx.

Development of communication

Babies are unable to talk but nevertheless they have non-verbal ways of making other people understand what they want or feel by:
- **tone of voice** – crying with hunger, pain, loneliness; gurgling with contentment,
- **eye-to-eye contact** – showing that they are interested and would like attention,
- **using the hands** – grabbing, pushing,
- **expression on the face** – smile, excitement, misery.

Learning to talk   Young children start to use words to communicate from the age of about one year onwards. They learn to talk by:
- hearing other people talk,
- practising those sounds,
- understanding what each sound means,
- learning new words.

Toddlers often find it easier to use actions rather than words to make other people understand them. As speech becomes easier, fewer actions will be used, but non-verbal communication remains important throughout life.

Figure 1 Examples of body language

Larynx

The larynx (voice box) is at the front of the neck – it is possible to feel the firm cartilage of the larynx. It moves up and down during swallowing.

Structure of the larynx The larynx is situated between the back of the mouth and the upper end of the trachea: **Fig 2**. Its sides are kept rigid by cartilages, it is lined inside with mucous membrane, and is covered with muscles on the outside. Two **vocal cords** within the larynx stretch across the opening from front to back. Most of the time the vocal cords are kept apart, and air flows freely through the V-shaped opening between them.

Making sounds When the cords are brought closer together, air from the lungs is forced between them – making the cords vibrate and produce sound. Sounds vary in:

pitch – the tighter the vocal cords and the closer they come together, the higher the pitch,
volume – the greater the amount of air forced out, the louder the sound.

Dumbness

Children are dumb because they are deaf – they do not know how to make the right sounds because they do not hear sounds which they can copy. Nor can they monitor, by hearing, the noises they make themselves. Their deafness needs to be discovered as early as possible so that speech therapy can help to lessen the handicap.

Speech therapy This is given to deaf children to train them to speak, and to other children with speech impediments. It is also given to adults whose speech has been affected by surgery of the larynx or by damage to the part of the brain which controls speech.

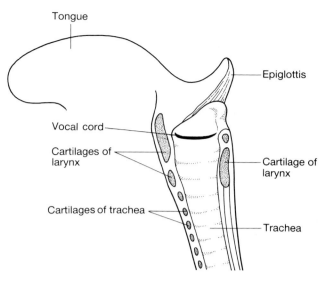

Figure 2 Structure of the larynx – vertical section.

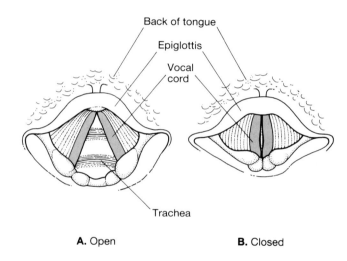

A. Open   **B.** Closed

Figure 3 View of the larynx from the throat

QUESTIONS

1a (i) What is meant by communication?
(ii) Why is it essential?
b What effect does the lack of communication have on people?

2a What is meant by non-verbal communication?
b Give 8 ways in which parts of the body are used in body language.
c Name, or draw, some examples of signs and symbols used for communication.

3a How do babies communicate?
b How do children learn to talk?
c Name the parts of the body involved in verbal communication.

4a Describe the structure of the larynx.
b Describe the vocal cords and how they produce different sounds.
c What makes a child dumb?
d When may adults require speech therapy?

FURTHER WORK

1 Study **Fig 1** and describe how body language is being used to communicate.

2 Use the thumb and fore-finger to:
(i) gently feel the firm cartilage of the larynx, (ii) note how the larynx goes up and down during swallowing, (iii) detect the vibrations when sounds are being made, (iv) feel the variation in movement of larynx between high notes and low notes.

3 Say each letter of the alphabet in turn and note how the mouth is used.

Stress and relaxation

Stress

Stress (mental stress) is psychological pressure caused by situations or people. **Tension** is the body's response to stress, eg feelings of 'uptightness' and agitation.

Occasional stress is a normal part of human life, and a certain amount is stimulating and necessary. Everyday stress may be due to worries about:
◆ exams,
◆ job interviews,
◆ playing in a match,
◆ arriving at an appointment on time,
◆ what to buy for a birthday present,
◆ remembering instructions,
◆ falling out with a friend,
◆ appearing on stage.
It is interesting how easily yesterday's worries may be forgotten as new ones take their place.

Harmful stress Stress becomes harmful when it is continuous, difficult to cope with, and when it disrupts normal life and relationships. Whether a situation gives rise to harmful stress depends on:
◆ the individual's ability to cope with the situation,
◆ the total amount of stress involved – every normal person has a breaking point,
◆ for how long stress continues.
Life events which can be unduly stressful, **Fig 1**, are usually those which occur at times of change or over which we have little control.

Effects of harmful stress Too much stress can be the cause of an anxiety state and/or depression, with fear and marked agitation sufficient to disrupt normal living (p. 102).

People's ability to deal with stress varies widely, depending upon personality, home circumstances, and particular stage of life. But **no one** can easily throw off big problems and everyone gets phases of anxiety, tension and depression throughout life.

Psychosomatic disorders

A psychosomatic disorder is physical illness caused, at least in part, by psychological factors. It is an unconscious process that transforms emotional conflict and anxiety into physical symptoms.

Stress produces feelings of fear and anger, and when these are suppressed they produce emotional conflict and tension. The cause may be unrealised ambitions, reduced income, reduced social position, trouble in the family, marital problems, or any of the factors shown in **Fig 1**. Stress may produce symptoms such as:
  diarrhoea,
  headache,
  breathlessness,
  chest pains,
  abdominal pain,
  skin rash,
  insomnia.

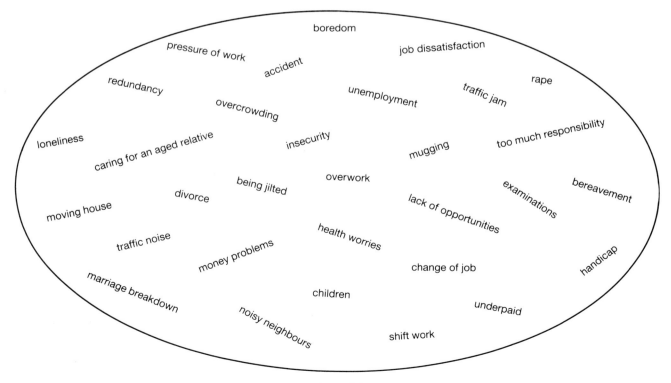

Figure 1 Stressful events

Reactions to bereavement

The death of a close relative, a good friend or a loved animal is always stressful. The closer the relative and the better the friend, the greater the sadness, and it may cause depression.

Bereavement can produce unexpected feelings as well as those of grief;
- **Relief** – when the death follows months or years of illness.
- **Guilt** – at not doing more for the person while still alive.
- **Anger** – that other people did not do more to keep the person alive.

All these feelings are absolutely normal responses.

Relaxation

The body needs to relax after activity – physical or mental. Relaxation can be taken as rest, sleep, or change of occupation, eg a hobby, craft or sport. Relaxation can take many forms: **Fig 2**.

Sleep Sleep is a form of unconsciousness from which it is possible to be woken fairly easily. During sleep:

heart rate slows down,
blood pressure falls,
breathing becomes slower and more regular,
metabolic rate slows down,
temperature falls,
less urine is produced,
nervous system and sense organs are active only to a limited extent (but noise can wake a person up), the skin is sensitive to touch, and dreaming occurs.

The need for sleep The body needs sleep to allow the nervous system to function efficiently. Lack of sleep makes people irritable, unable to concentrate and clumsy. When people are deprived of sleep for several days they may suffer from hallucinations.

The amount of sleep The amount of sleep needed varies enormously from individual to individual. It also varies with age, with an average of sixteen hours for babies to five hours for old people. Good, sound sleep can be encouraged by:
- physical exercise which tires the body,
- a warm, comfortable bed,
- a quiet, darkened room,
- the ability to put worries aside.

Bio-rhythms

All biological activity seems to have set patterns or rhythms:
- Hormone levels rise and fall during the day, eg cortisol is highest at 8–9 am and lowest at midnight.
- Individuals have their own sleep/wake patterns, and become exhausted if these are disturbed by shift work or by air travel – jet lag.
- Periods occur about every 28 days.

Figure 2 Aids to relaxation

QUESTIONS

1a Give some examples of everyday stress.
 b (i) When may stress become harmful?
   (ii) Whether a situation gives rise to harmful stress depends on certain factors. Name three such factors.
 c What can too much stress be the cause of?

2a What is a psychosomatic disorder?
 b Give some examples of symptoms produced by stress.

 c Describe three types of feelings which are normal responses to a bereavement.

3a Give examples of forms of relaxation.
 b Give seven examples of the effects on the body of sleep.
 c Why is sleep needed?
 d How much sleep is needed?

4 Give three examples of bio-rhythms.

FURTHER WORK

1 Select ten events from **Fig 1** which you think would cause the most stress. Place them in order, with the most stressful at the top of the list. Match each item in the list with a suitable relaxation (from those in **Fig 2** or others).

Infectious diseases

Infectious diseases are diseases which spread from one person to another, and, with starvation, are the commonest cause of ill-health world-wide. Diseases of this type are caused by **pathogenic microbes** (patho = disease; genic = causing; microbes = micro-organisms) – usually called **germs**, and they can be bacteria, viruses, protozoa, or microscopic fungi such as yeasts.

Microbes are everywhere. Many are useful (p. 200–1), some live naturally on the skin, or in the mouth, vagina or colon, and only a relatively small number cause disease in humans.

How infection occurs

Infection occurs when germs: enter into the tissues, survive, grow and multiply.

Infectious disease is present when germs in the body:
◆ prevent the tissues in which they are living from functioning normally and/or
◆ produce toxins (poisons) which travel in the blood stream to harm other parts.

Infectious disease is more likely when:
◆ the germs are virulent.
◆ a large dose of germs is received,
◆ the body's resistance is low; the cause may be:
    low level of antibodies,
    poor nutrition,
    an unhealthy environment,
    less resistance to infection in the very young or very old.

Symptoms and signs of infectious disease

The following symptoms and signs may indicate an infectious disease:
fever and/or chills
headache
loss of appetite
hot, dry skin ⎫
furred tongue ⎬ the result of dehydration from
scanty, dark yellow urine ⎪ fever and
thirst ⎭ sweating.

Pattern of infectious disease

Entry of germs – a sufficiently large number manage to get past the body's defences: **Fig 1**.
⇩
Incubation period – the time between the entry of germs and the appearance of symptoms. The incubation period varies with different diseases, eg diphtheria 3 days, measles 10 days, viral hepatitis 1–3 months, leprosy more than a year.
⇩
Infectious stage – the time during which germs can be spread. The patient can be infectious during the incubation period, during the illness itself, and sometimes after it (as a carrier).
⇩
Convalescence – the symptoms disappear and the patient regains strength.

Controlling infectious diseases

Infectious diseases can be controlled and reduced by:
Elimination of the source of the germs This has happened, for example, with the elimination of tuberculosis bacteria from milk, and the successful world-wide campaign to eradicate smallpox.
Increased resistance of the host Resistance of the host is increased by a good state of health, and by immunisation.

Preventing germs from spreading

Germs can be stopped from spreading by:
◆ **Isolation** of the patient so that germs cannot spread to others.
◆ **Quarantine** – isolation of people who have been in contact with the patient because, if they have caught the disease, they may be infectious before symptoms appear.
◆ **Sterilisation** to destroy the germs.
    Most microbes are killed by **sunlight (ultraviolet rays)**, also by **boiling water**, but some bacterial spores can withstand prolonged boiling.

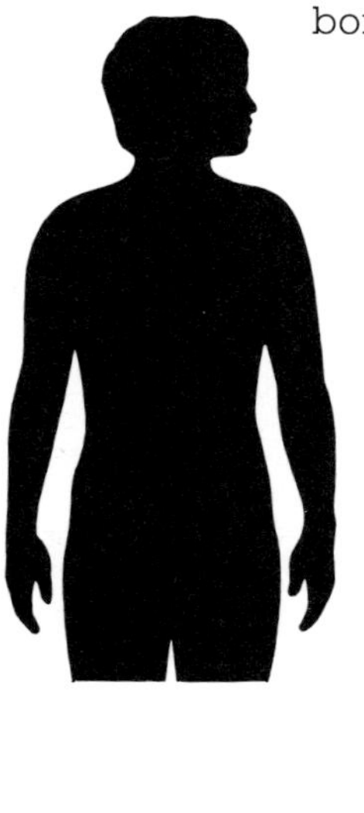

Entry of germs is prevented:
1. *Skin* forms a barrier
2. *Tears* ⎫ contain *lysozyme* –
3. *Saliva* ⎭ an antibacterial enzyme
4. *Mucus* lines the tubes of the
  – respiratory tract;
  – alimentary canal;
  – vagina;
  – urethra.
5. *Blood clots* seal wounds

Germs which get inside are discouraged by:
1. *Gastric juice*
2. *White blood cells*
3. *Antibodies*
4. *Vaginal acidity*
5. *Normal bacteria in the large bowel*

Figure 1 How the body defends itself against infectious diseases

How infectious diseases spread

Germs are transmitted – spread – from one person to another in a number of ways:

Contact   Diseases spread in this way are called **contagious diseases**, and include many skin diseases. Examples of contagious diseases are ringworm, impetigo, herpes, chicken pox, gonorrhoea. Germs pass from an infected person to others by:
♦ **direct contact** – touching the infected person,
♦ **indirect contact** – touching articles which have been in contact with the infected person such as toys, handkerchiefs, towels.

Droplet infection – minute droplets sprayed from an infected person during sneezing, coughing or talking are inhaled by people close by. Also, small droplets which dry rapidly and remain suspended in the air may be carried some distance in the air currents. Diseases of the respiratory tract, eg common cold and influenza, are often spread by droplet infection; also most of the infectious diseases of childhood, eg measles and whooping cough.

Contaminated food and drink   When food or drink is contaminated by germs from an infected person, or flies, or dust and dirt, it may give rise to disease. Diseases of the digestive system are often spread in this way, eg salmonella food poisoning, typhoid, cholera and dysentery.

Vector   Animals which transmit disease are called vectors: **Fig 2**.

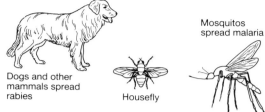

Dogs and other mammals spread rabies

Housefly

Mosquitos spread malaria

Figure 2 Animals which spread infectious diseases

Dust   Some types of germ can survive a long time outside the body in dust, dirt or soil, eg tetanus and anthrax, and may perhaps be moved long distances by wind.

Inadequate sterilisation   Germs can spread from infected patients to others by, for example, inadequate sterilisation of instruments, eg AIDS and hepatitis B (jaundice). Diseases can spread amongst drug addicts in this way.

Carriers   These are people who harbour infectious microbes without ill effects. They may be unaware that they carry germs for typhoid, hepatitis B or AIDS etc, and they do not show any symptoms of the disease.

Sterilisation (contd.)

Disinfectants and **antiseptics** are chemicals which destroy microbes; generally, antiseptics are used on people, and disinfectants are used on things such as bed-linen, equipment, drains etc.

Complete sterilisation can be achieved by compressed steam in an **autoclave**, or by **gamma irradiation**. Any article receiving either of these treatments will be **sterile** or **aseptic**, meaning free from microbes.
♦ **Control of the vector**, for example, of dogs and cats to prevent the spread of rabies, or of mosquitos to prevent malaria.
♦ **Precautions by carriers**   Carriers are little danger to other people provided they take suitable precautions, eg typhoid carriers should wash hands thoroughly and clean under the nails after visiting the toilet, and they should not be employed in the catering industry.
♦ **Treating the patient** with antibiotics or other medicines to destroy germs.

Epidemics

An epidemic occurs when a disease:
   spreads rapidly and
   infects large numbers of people, then
   disappears until the next outbreak.
An epidemic becomes **pandemic** (world wide) if it spreads to many countries throughout the world.

Endemic or sporadic disease

A disease is said to be:
♦ **endemic** if it is always present in a particular part of the world, eg malaria in the tropics.
♦ **sporadic** if it occurs in different places at different times, with no known connection between the outbreaks.

Conditions favourable for epidemics
♦ Little or no immunity amongst the population.
♦ A virulent strain of the disease, eg Hong Kong flu.
♦ Germs that can easily spread.
♦ The population in a poor state of health.

Immunity

Immunity is one of the body's ways of resisting infection. White blood cells and antibodies attack germs they recognise and destroy them. The degree of immunity varies – there may be:

◆ **total immunity** – germs entering the body are destroyed.
◆ **partial immunity** – not enough immunity to prevent the disease, but sufficient to make it less severe.
◆ **no immunity** – if the germs gain entry, infection usually follows.

Active immunity (acquired immunity)   is obtained when the body produces its own antibodies in response to either: ◆ germs – bacteria or viruses,
or: ◆ vaccines.
This type of immunity gives long-term protection, often for many years and, with some diseases, for life, eg German measles, poliomyelitis.

Passive immunity   is obtained by injection of ready-made antibodies (antitoxin). This type of immunity gives only short-term protection but is useful for treating or preventing some infectious diseases, eg tetanus and hepatitis, or preventing Rh factor damage in pregnancy.

Congenital immunity (immunity at birth)   When the baby is in the womb, antibodies cross the placenta from the mother's blood to the baby's blood. Because of this, the baby is born with the same protection against diseases which the mother has had or has been immunised against. If breast-fed, the baby continues to receive antibodies in the milk.

The antibodies survive in the baby for several months and then gradually disappear. This gives time for the baby to grow stronger and more able to withstand infection. By the age of three months, the baby is better able to develop its own antibodies, so this is the recommended time to begin immunisation.

Antigens and antibodies

Antigens   An antigen is any substance which stimulates the production of antibodies. Antigens can be germs, vaccines, pollen, some foods, etc.

Antibodies   An antibody is a substance the body produces in response to an antigen. Each different antigen stimulates the production of the particular type of antibody which will destroy that antigen. Antibodies:
◆ are molecules of protein (immunoglobulins – Ig – mostly gamma globulin).
◆ are found in the blood, tissues and lymph nodes.
◆ are made by white blood cells called lymphocytes. When the lymphocytes have 'learnt' to make a particular type of antibody, this 'memory' may last for many years.
◆ help to destroy germs.

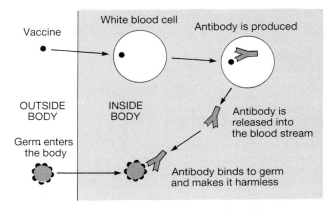

Figure 1 How vaccination protects against infectious diseases

Immunisation (Vaccination; Inoculation)

It is possible to be protected against a number of infectious diseases by immunisation. The body is given a vaccine which results in the production of the appropriate antibodies. Some vaccines are given at intervals, in two or three doses, to build up more and more antibodies on each occasion. A 'booster' dose may also be needed after a time to maintain the immunity.

Vaccines   A vaccine can be a dose of:
◆ dead germs, eg cholera and typhoid, which have been killed by heat or chemicals.
◆ live microbes which can grow and multiply in the body without causing disease. This type of vaccine is known as **live, attenuated vaccine** and contains germs which have been altered so that they are no longer dangerous, eg polio, measles.
◆ **toxoid**, which is a harmless form of the toxin which the disease produces, eg tetanus.

Problems with the immune system

Auto-immune diseases   Some diseases are caused by the body producing antibodies which destroy its own cells – why this happens is not known. One example is hypothyroidism – underactive thyroid – underactive because the body destroys its own thyroid function by an immune reaction.

Allergy   The body becomes sensitive to a substance and over-reacts against it. For example, when:
◆ pollen causes hay-fever,
◆ strawberries, shell-fish or other food cause vomiting and diarrhoea,
◆ wool or other type of clothing causes a rash,
◆ bee stings can cause a violent reaction with swelling of the face, tongue and mouth.

Transplants   Organs or tissues – heart, kidney, liver, skin – removed from one person and transplanted in another, are normally rejected. The new owner's white cells recognise the transplanted tissue as 'foreign' and destroy it, even when the donor and recipient are well matched. To prevent rejection, the patient's immune response is reduced by drugs. The disadvantage of this is that the patient has less resistance to infection.

Disease	Symptoms	Incubation in days	Infectious stage	Other information	Immunisation
BACTERIAL INFECTIONS					
Diphtheria	A white layer forms on the throat which may block the airway; it produces poison which damages heart and nervous system.	2–5	Usually for about 2 weeks after onset.	Uncommon. It can occur in children who have not been immunised.	Vaccines against diphtheria, whooping cough and tetanus are often given together as **triple vaccine** (DPT vaccine). Three injections are needed between the age of 3 and 12 months. **Booster doses** of vaccine for diphtheria and tetanus are given at 5 years and again between 15 and 19 years. Further doses of tetanus vaccine may be given at 5-yearly intervals.
Whooping cough (Pertussis)	Long bouts of coughing which may end with a 'whoop' and vomiting.	7–12	A few weeks before onset to 4 weeks after onset.	Whooping cough vaccine prevents the disease or makes it much less severe.	
Tetanus (Lockjaw)	Muscles of the neck, back and limbs tighten and the jaw may lock.	4–21	Cannot be passed directly from one person to another.	Germs exist in soil and enter the body through cuts and scratches.	
Tuberculosis (TB)	Usually coughing and damage to lungs. Swollen glands in the neck.	28–42	Variable.	Most people who are infected by TB germs do not develop TB, but they develop natural immunity to TB.	Vaccination of young children and teenagers who are at risk of infection.
Typhoid (Salmonella typhi)	Fever, constipation, dry cough.	about 14	Variable. A few people become permanent carriers.	Can be prevented by proper sewage disposal, clean water supply, clean food handling.	Two injections of vaccine with an interval between them of not less than 7 days. A booster dose required every 1–3 years.
Cholera	Violent diarrhoea, dehydration and collapse.	1–5	A few days after recovery.		Immunisation every 6 months for those exposed to risk of infection.
VIRUS INFECTIONS					
Poliomyelitis (Polio)	Infection of the spinal cord which may result in paralysis.	3–21	From 2 days after infection to 6 weeks or longer after onset.	Immunisation has almost eliminated this disease from Britain.	Polio vaccine is given by mouth. Three doses are required and are given at the same time as DPT vaccine. Booster doses are given at 5 years and again between 15 and 19 years.
Measles	Fever, severe cold, cough. 4–5 days later a red rash appears on face and spreads downwards.	10–15	From onset of cold symptoms to 5 days after rash appears.	More serious in infancy than in older children.	A single dose of combined measles, mumps and rubella vaccine (MMR vaccine) is given at 15 months. Rubella vaccine is offered to all girls between the age of 11 and 13 years who have not already had German measles.
Mumps	Painful swellings near the jaw on one or both sides.	12–18 usually about 18	Until the swelling goes down.	Mumps in males over the age of 11 may affect a testis but rarely results in sterility.	
German measles (Rubella)	A mild disease with a red rash and usually with swollen glands.	10–21	From onset to end of rash.	Dangerous to the baby in the first 4 months of pregnancy. (See p. 146.)	
Chicken pox (Varicella)	Small red spots which turn to blisters then scabs.	10–21	2 days before the spots appear until a week after.	A mild disease in children. More severe in adults. The same virus causes **shingles**.	
Rabies (Hydrophobia – fear of water)	Fever, delirium, convulsions, paralysis. The throat muscles tighten so that it is impossible even to drink.	Variable, usually 1–2 months	Rabies can only be caught from the saliva of an animal with rabies after being licked, scratched or bitten.	Rabies can infect all mammals – foxes, bats etc, but is only a serious risk to people if domestic animals are infected – hence the need for quarantine of dogs and cats entering the country.	A course of six injections – no longer painful – starting immediately after possible infection (active immunity). Passive immunity can be obtained by an injection of gamma globulin.

Figure 2 Infectious diseases

QUESTIONS

1a (i) What is meant by immunity?
  (ii) How does it vary?
b Copy the table on the right and fill in the differences between active and passive immunity:
c (i) What is congenital immunity?
  (ii) How is it obtained?
  (iii) How long does it last?

2a What is the difference between antibody and antigen?
b Describe antibodies.
c Use labelled diagrams to show how an antibody can destroy germs.

	Active immunity	Passive immunity
How is immunity obtained?		
Short-term or long-term protection?		
Examples of diseases		

3a Give two other words which mean immunisation.
b Describe three types of vaccine.

4a Give a time-table for immunisation against diphtheria, measles, polio, rubella, tetanus, mumps, whooping cough.
b Which vaccine is given orally?
c Why are dogs and cats entering the country put into quarantine?

FURTHER WORK

1 Describe three problems of the immune system.

2 What advice would be given to a person who has been scratched by a dog in a country where rabies is endemic?

177

Infections of the sex organs

The sex organs can be infected by various microbes. Such infections may be known as **venereal diseases** (VD) or **sexually transmitted diseases** (STD) because they are usually, but not always, spread from one person to another by sexual intercourse. These diseases are usually more common in those with many casual sexual partners.

Warning symptoms of infection

One or more of the following may indicate infection of the sex organs:
◆ Unusual discharge from the vagina – a different colour, strange smell, or thicker.
◆ Discharge from the penis.
◆ Sore or blister near the vagina, penis or anus.
◆ Rash or irritation around the vagina, penis or anus.
◆ Pain or burning feeling when passing urine.
◆ Passing urine more often than usual.
◆ Pain during intercourse.

Medical advice If the symptoms listed above occur it is important to visit a doctor or a special clinic so that:
◆ the infection can be diagnosed,
◆ correct treatment given,
◆ when necessary, sexual partners can be traced and advised to have treatment to prevent the disease from spreading.

Absence of symptoms in a sexual partner **does not mean absence of infection** because:
◆ an infection takes time to develop,
◆ some people do not develop symptoms anyway, eg many women with gonorrhoea do not get symptoms, and most men with herpes do not have sores.

Clinics Clinics specialising in diseases of the sex organs may be labelled:
◆ Genito-urinary (G-U) clinic,
◆ Special Clinic,
◆ STD Clinic.

Types of infection

Non-specific genital infections These are the most common infections of the sex organs and they can be caught in other ways besides having sexual intercourse with an infected partner.
Infection of the
◆ urethra is called **urethritis** (NSU – non-specific urethritis),
◆ vagina is called **vaginitis**,
◆ bladder is called **cystitis** (p. 92)
Cause *Chlamydia* (microbes similar to bacteria) are often the cause, but other germs may also be responsible. **Pelvic Inflammatory Disease (PID)** can result if *Chlamydia* is left untreated. This is a serious infection in women as it can make a woman infertile (unable to have a child).

Thrush Although thrush usually occurs without any sexual contact, it is mentioned in this section because it is also possible to catch thrush from someone else during sexual intercourse.
Cause – *Candida*, a yeast, which commonly occurs on the skin and causes no harm there. It sometimes causes an infection – thrush – in the mouth, vagina or penis. It may also develop in those with undiagnosed or poorly-controlled diabetes – therefore the urine of people with thrush should be tested for sugar.

Trichomoniasis ('Trich' or 'Tv') This is a common infection of the vagina.
Cause – *Trichomonas vaginalis*, a small parasite (a protozoan) which infects the vagina and urethra.

Genital warts These are warts which appear anywhere on the genitals.
Cause – a virus similar to that which produces the common skin warts.

Figure 1 Sexually transmitted microbes. Some are shown with white blood cells, which are 10 μm approx. in diameter

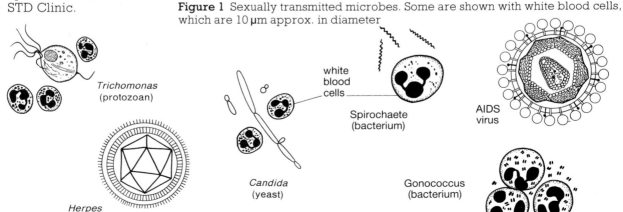

Trichomonas (protozoan)

white blood cells

Spirochaete (bacterium)

AIDS virus

Herpes (virus)

Candida (yeast)

Gonococcus (bacterium)

Genital herpes   This infection produces sores on or around the genital area.

Cause – *Herpes simplex* – a different strain of the same virus which produces 'cold sores' around the mouth. This infection is accompanied by flu-like symptoms – headache, fever, etc.

Gonorrhoea ('the clap')   Every year over 50 000 cases of gonorrhoea are reported in the UK – over half of them people under 24 years old.

Cause – bacteria (Gonococcus) which can only live in warm moist areas of the genital region. It is easily spread by casual sex because about 50% of women who get gonorrhoea, and 10% of men, do not have any symptoms. This infection spreads only through sexual intercourse.

Syphilis ('the pox')   Although nowadays uncommon, this is one of the most dangerous sexual infections if left untreated. It can spread to other parts of the body and be the cause of blindness, heart disease, deafness, insanity and death. A pregnant woman with untreated syphilis can pass on the infection and the baby may be born diseased or dead.

Cause – bacteria (spirochaetes) which are spread only by sexual intercourse.

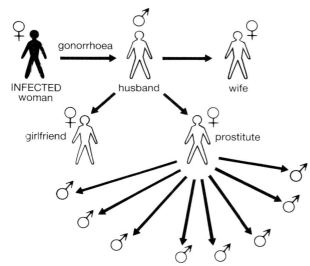

Figure 2 Perils of promiscuity (promiscuous – having a number of sexual partners)

Hepatitis B   (hepar = liver; itis = inflammation). One of the ways in which this type of hepatitis spreads is through sexual contact.

Cause – a virus which is spread by the body fluids such as blood, saliva, urine and genital secretions of an infected person. A vaccine has been developed against hepatitis B.

AIDS – Acquired Immune Deficiency Syndrome

This disease reduces the efficiency of the white cells and resistance to infection, so a person with AIDS easily becomes infected with many kinds of germ. The AIDS patient tends to get enlarged lymph nodes and also a particular kind of cancer which affects the skin.

Although AIDS is not a disease of the sex organs, it is included in this topic as it is usually transmitted sexually.

Cause – a virus called HIV (human immunopathic virus). Only a proportion of people infected with HIV virus develop AIDS within five years, but they are able to pass the infection on.

How AIDS spreads
AIDS is caught:
◆ by having sexual intercourse with someone who has the virus. HIV passes from one partner to the other in men's semen and women's vaginal fluid (including menstrual blood).
◆ by coming into contact with infected blood, hence the disease in drug addicts. It has also been transmitted to people with haemophilia who were transfused with infected blood before routine screening for the virus was introduced – haemophiliacs need frequent blood transfusions containing Factor VIII to prevent bleeding (p. 131).
◆ by a child in the womb from an infected mother.

AIDS is not caught:
◆ by shaking hands, embracing, touching or even kissing someone with AIDS.
◆ from dirty cups or lavatory seats – the virus is very delicate and dies quickly outside the body.

QUESTIONS

1a Give the meaning of: STD, VD, G-U, PID, 'Trich', AIDS.
 b List the warning symptoms of infection of the sex organs.
 c Why is it important to visit a doctor or clinic if infection of the sex organs is suspected?
 d Why does absence of symptoms not mean absence of infection?
2a (i) What are the most common infections of the sex organs?
 (ii) Name three sites of infection.
 (iii) Name the germ which is often the cause.

 b When may PID develop, and why may it be serious?
3a What is the difference between genital warts and genital herpes?
 b Why is syphilis considered a dangerous infection?
 c What is the cause of gonorrhoea, and how is it spread?
4a (i) What causes AIDS?
 (ii) Why can an AIDS patient easily become infected with many kinds of germ?
 b Describe two ways in which AIDS can be caught.
 c How is AIDS not caught?

FURTHER WORK

1 Draw a diagram, similar to **Fig 2** to show how AIDS can spread.

2 Describe, with diagrams, some microbes which are sexually transmitted.

Parasites

A **parasite** is a creature which lives on or in another living creature – the **host** – and benefits by obtaining food and/or shelter. Some parasites have little effect on the host, some cause serious disease, and some kill the host.

Human parasites

Parasites which live in or on humans include:

bacteria ⎫
viruses ⎬ when they cause disease
protozoa ⎭ they are called **germs** (p. 174).

fungi – ringworm (a fungus) ⎫ These parasites pass easily from person to
worms – threadworms ⎬ person in the right conditions. They do not
insects – fleas, lice ⎬ do much harm, apart
mites – itch mites ⎭ from causing irritation, but they are unpleasant and disturb sleep.

Fleas These small wingless insects live in clothing next to the skin, and lay eggs in crevices of buildings, furniture, bedding or wherever there is dirt. The type of flea which lives on humans does not carry disease but, after feeding on blood, it leaves small red spots on the skin which irritate.

Control Cleanliness is important for the eradication (removal) of fleas. They do not live for long on clean people, or in clothes which are regularly washed. The eggs will not survive for long in clean buildings or bedding.

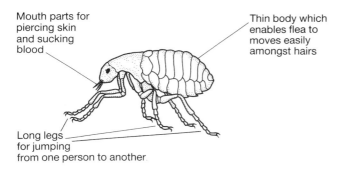

Mouth parts for piercing skin and sucking blood

Thin body which enables flea to moves easily amongst hairs

Long legs for jumping from one person to another.

Figure 1 Flea

Lice They are tiny wingless insects (each is called a **louse**). They are able to crawl around fairly rapidly and several times a day pierce the skin of their host for a meal of blood, leaving little red bite marks which itch. The eggs are called **nits** and they are more easy to see than adult lice. Nits look like tiny white specks and each is firmly cemented to a hair.

The most common type of louse – the **head louse** – lives amongst the hairs of the head and looks rather like dandruff which moves. It spreads easily by crawling directly from head to head, or a comb, brush, hat or headscarf borrowed from an infected person.

Control Washing the hair does not get rid of lice. A special lotion needs to be applied, and the whole family needs to be treated at the same time.

Pubic louse This species lives amongst the pubic hair and is more 'crab'-shaped. It is a sexually transmitted infection.

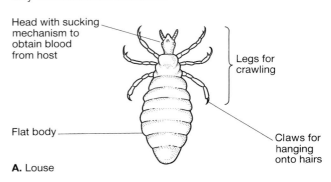

Head with sucking mechanism to obtain blood from host

Legs for crawling

Flat body

Claws for hanging onto hairs

A. Louse

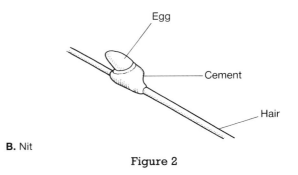

Egg

Cement

Hair

B. Nit

Figure 2

Threadworms They look like small pieces of white thread about 1 cm long which wriggle. They live in the large bowel and feed on the contents. The worms cause itching around the anus, especially in the evenings, when female worms crawl out to lay eggs – about 10 000 of them, and then die. The eggs stick to the skin and clothes or are caught up in the finger nails when scratching, or get into the house dust. The eggs only hatch if they enter the mouth and pass down to the large bowel. The worms cannot multiply in the bowel, so the number of worms depends on the number of eggs which are eaten.

Control Medicine taken by mouth kills the worms, and general cleanliness prevents re-infection.

Figure 3 Threadworm

Itch mites (scabies) Itch mites are very small and spend most of their life in burrows in the outer layer of the skin – the epidermis. They feed on the skin and lay eggs in the burrows.

The presence of itch mites causes **scabies** – an irritating rash which develops 3–4 weeks after infection. It looks like a scaly area with pimples and it may be possible to see the burrows. Scabies most commonly occurs between the fingers, and at the wrists, elbows, buttocks and armpits. Scabies spreads by direct skin contact – the mites crawl from one person to another. For this reason, scabies spreads easily between members of the same family, especially when they share a bed.

Control A lotion (benzyl benzoate) applied daily for three days with a paintbrush from the neck downwards will kill the mites. All the family should be treated.

The itch mite has a simple body as most of its life is spent in tunnels in the epidermis

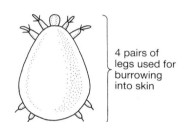

4 pairs of legs used for burrowing into skin

Figure 4 Itch mite

Roundworms (*Ascaris*) The pale yellow worms are 20–35 cm long and they live in the small intestine. The male and female breed inside and produce eggs which are removed in the faeces. The eggs develop when eaten by the same person or by someone else.

Control A medicine will remove the worms. A high standard of personal hygiene will prevent re-infection.

Ringworm This is not a worm but a fungus which infects the skin and grows outwards from the point of infection to form a ring. When it infects the scalp, a patch of hair is lost. When it infects the feet it is called **athlete's foot** – and does not necessarily form rings. It grows well in the damp, warm conditions between the toes where it makes the skin turn white and peel off. If a nail becomes infected it will become thickened and irregular.

Ringworm spreads by touching infected skin or towels, bathmats etc which have been in contact with the infection.

Control An anti-fungal cream or powder can be applied to the infected area or an anti-fungal drug can be taken by mouth.

Bed bugs They are small wingless insects which live in bedding and cracks and crevices in the room, and lay their eggs there. They come out at night to suck blood from sleeping humans and cause intense irritation of the skin. The bugs also give off a most unpleasant smell.

Control Bed bugs are killed by insecticide spray.

The whole body is covered with fine hairs to which dust and dirt containing germs can cling

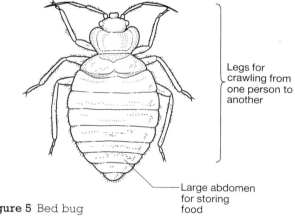

Legs for crawling from one person to another

Large abdomen for storing food

Figure 5 Bed bug

QUESTIONS

1 Copy and complete the chart on the right.

2 Draw and label diagrams of a: (i) flea, (ii) louse, (iii) nit, (iv) threadworm, (v) itch mite, (vi) bed bug.

FURTHER WORK
Hookworm (*Ankylostoma*) is a common parasite in hot countries. Describe (i) its life-cycle, (ii) mode of infection, (iii) the damage it causes, (iv) the resulting illness.

Parasite	Description	How they spread	Where eggs are laid	Control
Fleas				
Lice				
Threadworms				
Itch mites				
Bed bugs				

Parasites with two hosts

Some human parasites require another animal to complete their life cycles and survive. The parasites mentioned here are not important health problems in Britain, but they are common in warmer parts of the world and are the cause of much disease.

Tapeworms

Tapeworms live in the intestine of humans (the human host) and feed on digested food, absorbing it through the whole length of the worm, which may be up to several metres long.

Prevention
◆ Inspection of meat for tapeworm cysts by Environmental Health Officers.
◆ Thorough cooking of meat destroys any cysts.

Treatment
◆ Medicine is taken to dislodge the head of the tapeworm so that the whole worm can be expelled with the faeces.

Figure 1 The two hosts of the tapeworm

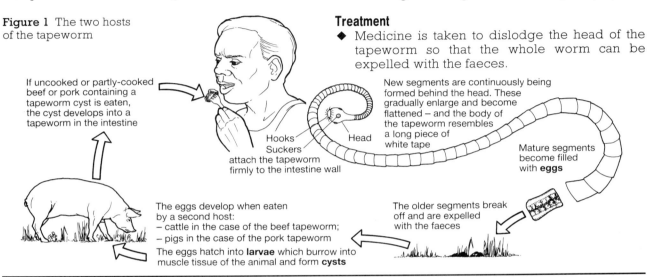

If uncooked or partly-cooked beef or pork containing a tapeworm cyst is eaten, the cyst develops into a tapeworm in the intestine

Hooks
Suckers
attach the tapeworm firmly to the intestine wall

Head

New segments are continuously being formed behind the head. These gradually enlarge and become flattened – and the body of the tapeworm resembles a long piece of white tape

Mature segments become filled with **eggs**

The eggs develop when eaten by a second host:
– cattle in the case of the beef tapeworm;
– pigs in the case of the pork tapeworm
The eggs hatch into **larvae** which burrow into muscle tissue of the animal and form **cysts**

The older segments break off and are expelled with the faeces

Schistosomiasis (bilharziasis)

(Shis-to-so-my-a-sis; bil-harts-eye-a-sis). This disease is caused by a small fluke – a flatworm – which needs humans, water snails and a hot climate to complete its life cycle.

Prevention
◆ Hygienic disposal of sewage.
◆ Eradication of the snails.
◆ Avoidance of standing or bathing in fresh water in areas where the disease is present.

Treatment
◆ Medicine destroys the parasites in an infected person.

The adult flukes live in the veins of the bladder, liver or intestine, causing disease, and producing eggs which leave the body in urine or faeces

Figure 2 'Catching' schistosomiasis

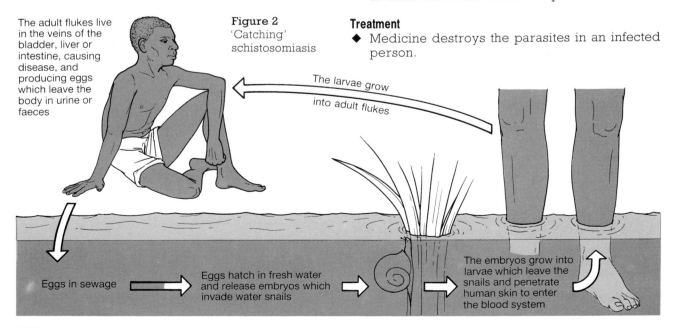

The larvae grow into adult flukes

Eggs in sewage

Eggs hatch in fresh water and release embryos which invade water snails

The embryos grow into larvae which leave the snails and penetrate human skin to enter the blood system

Malaria

Malaria is caused by a protozoan – a single-celled animal – called *Plasmodium*. To complete its life cycle and survive, this parasite needs a human host and also certain species of mosquito. Malaria is one of the commonest serious causes of fever in people in the tropics.

Prevention

◆ Anti-malarial drugs taken once or twice weekly protect against infection.
◆ Mosquito nets and insect repellants protect against mosquito bites.
◆ Insecticides destroy mosquitoes.
◆ Mosquito breeding grounds are destroyed by draining swamps, marshes and stagnant pools.

Treatment

◆ Chloroquine and other drugs destroy the malaria parasites in an infected person.

Figure 3 'Catching' malaria

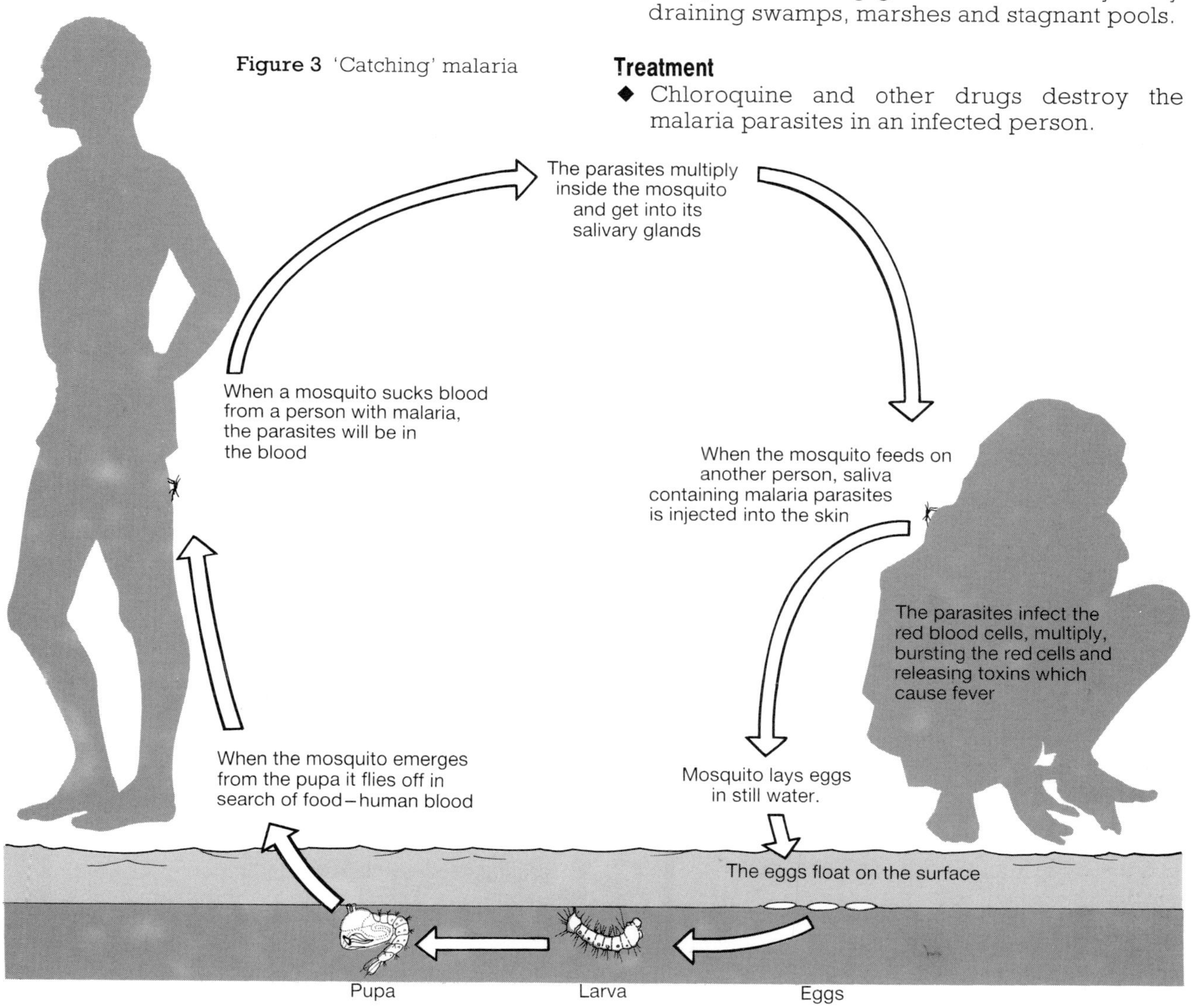

The parasites multiply inside the mosquito and get into its salivary glands

When a mosquito sucks blood from a person with malaria, the parasites will be in the blood

When the mosquito feeds on another person, saliva containing malaria parasites is injected into the skin

The parasites infect the red blood cells, multiply, bursting the red cells and releasing toxins which cause fever

When the mosquito emerges from the pupa it flies off in search of food – human blood

Mosquito lays eggs in still water.

The eggs float on the surface

Pupa   Larva   Eggs

QUESTIONS

1a Describe the structure of a tapeworm by means of a labelled diagram.
 b How does the parasite pass from the human host to a second host?
 c What happens to the eggs when they reach the second host?
 d How does a tapeworm get inside a human?
 e How can tapeworm infection be: (i) prevented, (ii) treated?

2a (i) What is the cause of schistosomiasis? (ii) Name the two hosts required for this parasite to complete its life cycle.

 b How does a person become infected with the parasites?
 c How do the parasites affect the human host?
 d How can schistosomiasis be: (i) prevented, (ii) treated?

3a Name the parasite which causes malaria.
 b How do malaria parasites enter the human body?
 c How can malaria be: (i) prevented, (ii) treated?

FURTHER WORK

1 Draw a simple diagram of the life cycle of the pork tapeworm. Complete your diagram by adding the following words in the right places: egg, larva, cyst, pig, human. Draw simple life cycles for: (i) the schistosomiasis parasite, (ii) the malaria parasite.

2 Complete Exercise 3, p. 194

Social drugs and medicines

Figure 1

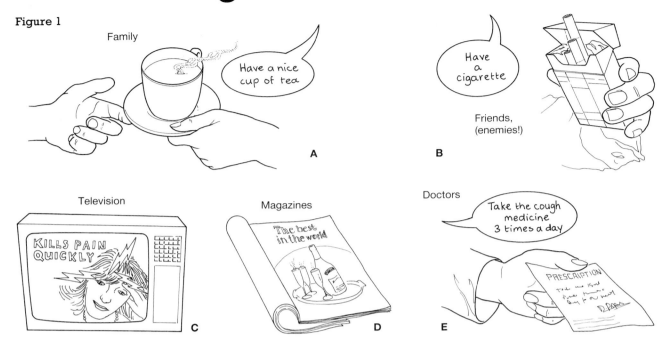

A **drug** is a chemical which alters the way the mind or body works or which is used to treat infection. We all take drugs in one form or another – it is part of our way of life – and we are encouraged to do so by the influences in **Fig 1**.

Three groups of drugs Drugs can be divided into three groups:
◆ Social drugs
◆ Medicines
◆ Illegal drugs (p. 186)

Social drugs

These are drugs which are considered socially acceptable by a large part of the population. They may be taken for pleasure, or because taking them has become a habit, or for some people, because they are addicted to the drug. Drugs of this kind are often provided as a sign of friendship on social occasions: **Fig 1A, B,** and **D**.

Caffeine occurs in tea and coffee. It has a stimulating effect, making a person feel more awake.

Nicotine is the main drug in tobacco and is obtained by smoking cigarettes, chewing tobacco or inhaling snuff. Nicotine is also used on occasions in medicines. Many of the harmful effects of smoking come from other chemicals present in the smoke besides nicotine (p. 188).

Alcohol occurs in many drinks and is dealt with in detail on pp. 190–3.

Medicines

Medicines are drugs which are used to treat or prevent disease. Drugs of this type are in very common use and they fall into two groups:

Over-the-counter medicines These can be bought by anyone from the chemist or from other types of shop, eg aspirin, paracetamol, cough mixture.

Prescription-only medicines These can be obtained only with a doctor's prescription because medical knowledge is required for their safe use. They may:
◆ have harmful side effects,
◆ interact with other drugs which the patient is also taking,
◆ have different effects on different people,
◆ be dangerous if taken in large doses,
◆ be addictive if taken repeatedly.

All drugs can have side effects

Drugs taken for one purpose often have unwanted side effects. The following are examples.

Coffee and **tea** are drunk for pleasure, to be sociable, or to quench the thirst. They may also:
 keep the drinker awake,
 cause palpitations (faster, or irregular heartbeats).

Pain killers numb pain. Some may also:
make reactions slower,
cause sleepiness,
irritate the lining of the stomach.

Cough mixture is taken to stop a dry cough – a cough without sputum. (A wet cough should not be stopped as it is necessary to remove sputum.) Some may also cause:
drowsiness,
nausea.

Tranquillisers reduce tension. They may also cause:
drowsiness,
anxiety when stopped.

Antibiotics are given to treat bacterial infection. They may also cause:
rashes,
diarrhoea.

Medicines and machinery

Drugs which affect the nervous system may cause drowsiness, lack of concentration, blurred vision and slow reactions. They are therefore likely to reduce the ability to drive motor vehicles and to operate machinery. Medicines containing such drugs include:
◆ sleeping drugs, sedatives and tranquillisers,
◆ some cold and cough cures,
◆ most anti-depressants,
◆ drugs used to treat nausea in motion sickness and in pregnancy.
The side effects of these medicines are increased if taken with even a little alcohol.

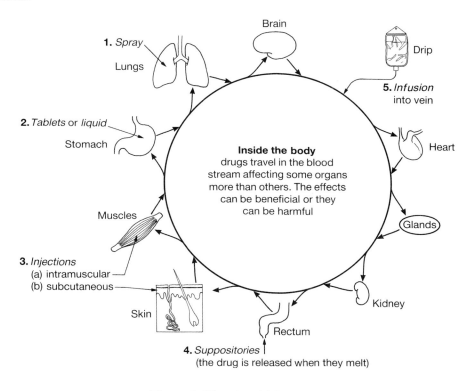

Figure 2 Ways in which drugs enter the body

QUESTIONS

1a What is a drug?
 b Fig 1 shows five ways in which people are encouraged to take drugs. Name the type of drug shown in **A–E**.
 c Name the three groups into which drugs can be divided.
2a What is the difference between social drugs and medicines?
 b Name: (i) three social drugs,
  (ii) two groups of medicines.
3 Study Fig 2.
 a Name five ways in which drugs can enter the body 1–5.

 b Describe what happens when drugs are inside the body.
4 Give five examples of drugs, the purposes for which they are taken, and their possible side effects.
5 (i) Give four ways in which drugs affect the nervous system.
  (ii) List examples of medicines containing such drugs.
  (iii) What increases the side-effects of these medicines?

FURTHER WORK

1 Some medicines impair the ability to operate machinery. Name ten jobs which can be affected when such medicines are taken, eg lorry driving.

2 List the drugs available to you at home in: (i) the kitchen, (ii) the medicine cabinet.

Drug abuse

Drug abuse and drug misuse are terms for the non-medical use of drugs which is considered to be either harmful or socially unacceptable.

In everyday language, the word drug usually refers to substances which are used illegally in order to produce feelings of pleasure in the mind. Some of these drugs, eg morphine, pethidine, are also used as medicines and are of great benefit in relieving anxiety and pain. When drugs are being used purely for pleasure the dose often has to be constantly increased to obtain the desired effect, and there are many serious risks.

Effects of drugs

The effect of a drug depends on:

- whether it is being taken for the first-time or is used regularly,
- the amount of drug taken (rarely known),
- side effects of any impurities,
- interaction with other drugs, eg alcohol,
- the mood of the user,
- the health of the user,
- what the user expects to happen,
- the surroundings,
- the reactions of other people.

Tolerance   Often, when a drug is taken regularly the body adapts to its presence – develops a tolerance – and larger quantities are then required to produce the same effect.

Withdrawal symptoms   These are the body's reaction to the sudden absence of a drug to which it had become adapted. These unpleasant feelings Fig 1 can take weeks or months to disappear because the body has to get used to being without the drug.

Drug dependence (drug addiction)   This term applies to those who:
   have an uncontrolled craving for drugs,
   suffer severe withdrawal effects if they cannot obtain drugs.
   are causing serious harm to themselves, and possibly to others.

Physical dependence occurs when severe symptoms would follow withdrawal of the drug.

Psychological dependence occurs when the person depends on the drug for feelings of well-being.
   Drug dependence can happen with tranquillisers, sleeping pills, alcohol and smoking as well as with illegal drugs such as heroin.

Risks of drug-taking

Addiction   Not all drug-takers become addicts – but some do, particularly those who say 'it won't happen to me' because they will not want to recognise the warning signs.

Links with crime   Drugs are illegal. They are linked with other crimes such as theft, blackmail, prostitution, mugging, murder. Those who supply drugs – pushers – are criminals, and so are those who possess them.

Change in behaviour   Drug-takers are liable to become withdrawn, devious and lazy.

Ill-health and death   Health often suffers from poor feeding, lack of exercise, constipation and wasted muscles – drug-takers often look very thin. Dirty needles used for injections spread diseases such as hepatitis and AIDS. Death from drug-taking is usually through accidental overdose or reduced ability to fight infection, eg pneumonia.

Why do people take drugs?

The habit often starts when a person is offered a drug by someone they know, perhaps at a party. They accept because they:

- think it is exciting, or
- want to know what the effect is like, or
- are afraid to say 'No', or
- are too drunk to know what they are doing.

The habit continues when the person continues to mix with others who take drugs.

How to give up a drug habit

The user must:

- want to come off drugs.
- keep away from his 'friends' – often easier said than done, unless the person moves away from the area for a while.
- get help, if necessary, from a drug clinic, family doctor, priest, parents or other relatives.

Misused drugs

Cannabis comes from the plant *Cannabis sativa* and may be called 'pot', 'dope', 'hash', 'grass' etc. Its most common effects are talkativeness, laughter, relaxation, and an impression of brighter colours and louder sounds. There is little evidence that taking cannabis is particularly harmful in itself – it is regarded as a **soft drug** – but it is illegal and has links with crime and the pushers of hard drugs.

LSD (lysergic acid diethylamide) is a powerful hallucinogen. The user takes a 'trip' to a different 'world' where everything seems more intense. Light, sound, space and distance appear different and this increases the likelihood of accidents. A bad trip can be very frightening and can lead to mental illness.

Opiates This group of drugs include **opium**, **morphine**, **heroin**, **codeine**, **methadone** and **pethidine**. They are produced from the seeds of the opium poppy *Papaver somniferum* or are manufactured from chemically related substances. Their main effect is to reduce pain and they make the drug-taker feel drowsy, warm and content, and relieve stress and discomfort. They are also **hard drugs** – drugs of addiction.

Cocaine is a white powder ('snow') made from the leaves of the coca shrub. It is a stimulant, making the user feel more energetic, confident and cheerful for a short while, followed by tiredness. 'Crack' is derived from cocaine and is rapidly addictive.

Amphetamines ('speed') are rarely used as medicines these days because they are addictive. They are stimulants, making the user feel 'high', more wide awake and lively. This is followed by depression, irritability and the need for sleep.

Solvents such as lighter fuel, cleaning fluid and some glues produce vapours which, when inhaled through the nose or mouth, depress the activity of the nervous system, relieving anxiety. Solvents can damage the liver and brain and lead to death.

Figure 1 Withdrawal symptoms. When the addict's drug supply ceases, the body reacts with symptoms which include depression, vomiting, abdominal pain and weakness.

QUESTIONS

1 Explain the meaning of: (i) drug abuse, (ii) tolerance, (iii) withdrawal symptoms, (iv) drug dependence, (v) pusher.

2a What does the effect of a drug depend on?
 b List four risks of drug-taking.
 c When does drug-taking often start?

d What must a user do to give up the drug habit?

3a Name six types of misused drugs.
 b (i) Name a hallucinogen. (ii) What is meant by a 'trip'?

c (i) Name six opiates. (ii) What is their main effect? (iii) Why are they 'hard drugs'?
d Name two stimulants and for each describe: (i) the effects, (ii) the after-effects.
e What are solvents and what effect do they have?

Smoking

In smoking, the dried leaf of the tobacco plant is burnt, usually in a cigarette, but sometimes in a pipe or cigar.

Tobacco smoke

Tobacco smoke is a mixture of gases, tar droplets and particles of ash, and it contains substances known to be harmful. These include the following:

◆ **Tar** – the sticky brown substance which stains fingers and teeth. (Tar is known to produce cancer when applied to the skin and lungs of animals used in experiments.)
◆ **Nicotine** – a habit-forming drug to which many people quickly become dependent.
◆ **Carbon monoxide** – a gas which is readily absorbed into the blood, taking the place of oxygen – the blood therefore carries less oxygen. (Carbon monoxide is the poison in car exhaust fumes.)

The effects of passive smoking Passive smoking – breathing in air containing other people's smoke – is a health hazard:

◆ Non-smokers who have lived or worked with smokers for a long time, have an increased risk of lung cancer.
◆ The children of smokers are more likely to get bronchitis, pneumonia and other chest infections.

Figure 1 Compared to non-smokers, young people who smoke up to six cigarettes weekly suffer more frequently from coughs and colds, and are more likely to become short of breath after exercise.

The Photo Co-op

Disadvantages of smoking

Smoking:
◆ is a major health risk: see opposite.
◆ quickly becomes a habit.
◆ is a very difficult habit to break.
◆ is expensive.
◆ stains fingers and teeth.
◆ is a fire hazard.
◆ leads to shortness of breath.
◆ causes 'bad breath'.
◆ during pregnancy can harm the unborn child.
◆ results in 'fag ends' and ash-trays to clear up.
◆ produces a strong smell which clings to clothes and lingers in rooms.
◆ affects non-smokers who are sensitive to smoke, are prone to bronchitis, or have heart disorders.
◆ makes the smoker objectionable to many non-smokers.

Every time a smoker sucks at a lighted cigarette, smoke is drawn through the cigarette, and some of it becomes trapped in the tobacco or filter tip. The further down a cigarette is smoked, the greater is the amount of harmful substances released into the smoke. The last third of a cigarette (the 'fag end') produces more tar and nicotine than the other two thirds put together.

When smoke passes through the mouth and into the lungs:

(**a**) The tar droplets stick to the sides of the air tubes which become coated with tar.

(**b**) The tar, gases and ash irritate the mucous membrane which lines the tubes, causing increased amounts of mucus to be produced. This results in coughing to remove the sputum, especially first thing in the morning – 'smokers cough'. (A regular cough is always abnormal.)

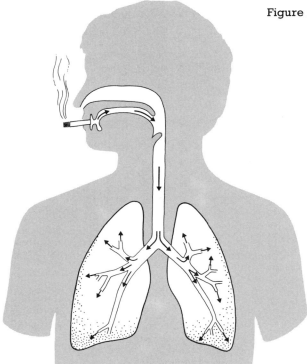

Figure 2 Smoking

(**c**) Nicotine and carbon monoxide pass through the lung wall and into the blood in the same way as oxygen, and within one minute they have travelled to all parts of the body.

(**d**) Tar, ash and phlegm accumulate and block the smaller air tubes, causing shortness of breath.

(**e**) Some of the phlegm may become infected with bacteria and pus collects. This is one of the causes of bad breath.

(**f**) Smoke damages the white blood cells which normally scavenge and remove dirt from the lungs.

Diseases linked with smoking

If a child smokes, the earlier it starts the greater the risk to health in later years. Smoking day after day, year after year, puts increasing strain on certain tissues and makes them more prone to disease, eg:

lungs – bronchitis, emphysema, pneumonia, cancer,
heart – heart attack,
digestive system – peptic ulcers,
legs – gangrene and amputation.

Non-smokers also suffer from these diseases but their chances of illness are very much less than those of smokers.

The smoking habit

The smoking habit usually begins early in life. Anyone who reaches the age of 20 without smoking is unlikely to start.

Reasons for starting to smoke
◆ Wanting to be like friends who are smoking.
◆ Following parents' example.
◆ Reaction against being told not to smoke.
◆ Curiosity.
◆ Wishing to appear 'grown up'.
◆ Easy access to cigarettes.

Reasons for not smoking
◆ No wish to become dependent on cigarettes.
◆ Aware of the health risks.
◆ Find it unpleasant.
◆ The cost is too high.
◆ Other people disapprove.
◆ Makes it easier to get a job – some employers do not want smokers.
◆ Having had a heart attack.
◆ The fire risk.

Giving up smoking

Giving up smoking requires, first of all, a strong desire to break the habit and then enough will-power to do so. Many people find it very difficult or impossible – until they have had a heart attack!

Because people smoke for different reasons, there is no one method of stopping the habit. It may be helped by:
◆ dummy cigarettes,
◆ tablets that give cigarettes a nasty taste,
◆ chewing gum, sometimes containing nicotine,
◆ eating sweets, apples etc instead,
◆ hypnosis,
◆ counselling,
◆ attending a clinic for advice and support.

When a heavy smoker gives up the habit, the body will have recovered from most of the effects of smoking within a year.

Sniffing and chewing tobacco Snuff is powdered tobacco which is sniffed up into the nose and the nicotine from the snuff is absorbed into the body. Some people **chew tobacco**. This causes irritation of the lining of the mouth but the main effect is again due to nicotine in tobacco getting into the body.

Smoking during pregnancy

When a pregnant woman smokes, chemicals from the smoke such as carbon monoxide and nicotine cross the placenta and enter the unborn baby's blood stream.

Heavy smokers – those who smoke more than 20 cigarettes a day – are more likely to have:
◆ a miscarriage,
◆ a still-born baby or one who dies in the first week after birth,
◆ a smaller, weaker baby.

The effect of smoking is greater during the latter part of pregnancy – mothers who give up smoking by the fourth month produce babies with birth-weights similar to those whose mothers have never smoked.

FURTHER WORK

1 Carry out a survey on smoking amongst people who do not mind answering the following questions:

Have you ever smoked? (Yes or No)
If the answer is Yes:
 1. At what age did you start?
 2. Why did you start?
 3. If you have given up, at what age did you do so?
If you still smoke
 4. How many per week?
 5. Have you tried to give it up?
 6. For what reason?
 7. Why do you think you failed?
If you have given up:
 8. Why did you give it up?
 9. What helped you to give it up?
 10. What benefits have you gained?

2 Use an apparatus similar to the 'smoking' machine on p. 217 to demonstrate the presence of tar in cigarette smoke.

QUESTIONS

1a Name three harmful substances in tobacco smoke.
 b Explain why there is a greater amount of harmful substances in the 'fag end' of a cigarette.
 c Explain why smokers are liable to:
 (i) 'smokers cough', (ii) shortness of breath, (iii) bad breath.
2 Thirteen disadvantages of smoking are listed. Rearrange them in order, starting with the one you consider to be the greatest disadvantage and ending the least disadvantageous.
3a List the diseases linked with smoking.
 b Compared to non-smokers, what illness are young people more likely to have if they smoke up to six cigarettes weekly?
 c What is meant by passive smoking?

 d Describe two health hazards of passive smoking.
4a At what age does the smoking habit usually begin?
 b List reasons for starting to smoke.
 c List reasons for not smoking.
 d Name seven suggestions which may be helpful to someone who wants to give up smoking.
 e When a heavy smoker gives up the habit, how long does it take for the body to recover from the effects of smoking?
5a How do chemicals from smoke reach an unborn baby?
 b Give three dangers of smoking heavily throughout pregnancy.
6a What is snuff?
 b Give two effects of chewing tobacco.

Effects of alcohol

10 cm³ alcohol (ethanol) = 1 unit

Sensible drinking
Many people consider that the sensible upper limit per week is:
20–25 units for adult males;
10–13 units for adult females

Alcohol-related illnesses
are likely to develop with the regular drinking of
8+ units per day – males;
5+ units per day – females.

10 cm³ = 10 ml

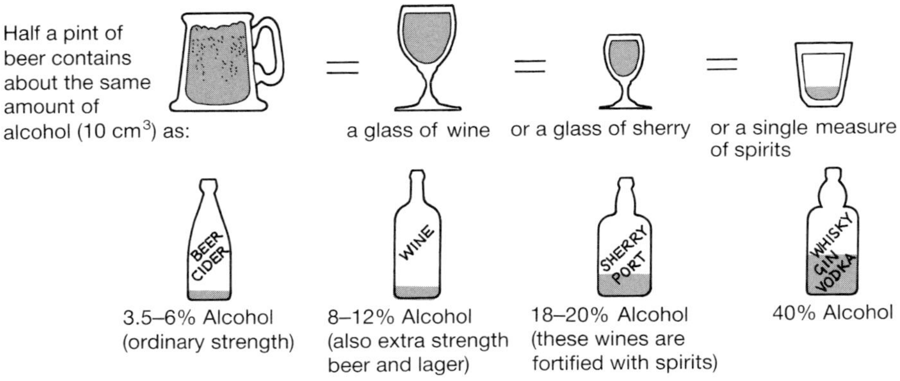

Half a pint of beer contains about the same amount of alcohol (10 cm³) as: = a glass of wine = or a glass of sherry = or a single measure of spirits

BEER CIDER — 3.5–6% Alcohol (ordinary strength)

WINE — 8–12% Alcohol (also extra strength beer and lager)

SHERRY PORT — 18–20% Alcohol (these wines are fortified with spirits)

WHISKY GIN VODKA — 40% Alcohol

Figure 1 (from drawings by Simon Gooch)

Many people enjoy drinking alcohol from time to time. They may feel it helps them relax, relieves worry, overcomes shyness, eases mild pain and generally makes them feel better.

Effects of alcohol on the brain

Alcohol:

◆ is a **sedative**, that is, it slows down the activity of the brain.
◆ **removes restraints** that people place on their behaviour. This may result in easy chatter and loud laughter, or may sometimes cause them to become sentimental or aggressive.
◆ **numbs the pain centre** of the brain and makes the drinker less aware of discomfort.
◆ **reduces muscle coordination**, resulting in clumsiness, staggering, and slurred speech.
◆ **affects judgement**, making it impossible to see 'straight' or to judge distances.

Alcohol affects people differently

The effects of alcohol vary with different people: **Fig 2**, and with the same person on different occasions. Factors causing these differences include:

◆ the amount which is drunk and the speed of drinking.
◆ whether the person is used to drinking alcohol.
◆ whether the person has food in the stomach – an empty stomach allows quicker absorption.
◆ the size of the person – the larger the person the greater the dilution of the alcohol.
◆ whether certain medicines or drugs have also been taken.
◆ the general character of the drinker.
◆ the mood of the drinker at that particular time.
◆ how alert or tired the drinker is.
◆ whether male or female – females generally require smaller quantities of alcohol than males to experience the same effects.

Drunkenness A person is drunk when he no longer has control over his actions. When sufficient alcohol has been taken to slow down all parts of the brain, the person falls into a drunken stupor (deep sleep).

A person may be so drunk that afterwards he/she cannot remember what happened – promises, fights etc may be completely forgotten.

Unmoved   Unsteady   Unconscious

Figure 2 The effect of the same amount of alcohol on three different people (from drawings by Simon Gooch)

Hangover Heavy drinking may be followed by a hangover – feelings of headache, weakness, nausea and tiredness. This may be made worse by mixing drinks, having a late night, or the combination of alcohol with medicines or drugs.

Alcohol has a dehydrating effect, therefore non-alcoholic liquid, eg water or soft drinks, taken after heavy drinking helps to reduce a hangover.

'Hair of the dog' or **livener** is an alcoholic drink taken to relieve the feelings of a hangover – it just puts more alcohol into the body and numbs the senses again.

Sobering up Inexperienced drinkers easily get drunk on small quantities of alcohol. Strong coffee or a cold shower may help them to sober up, but will have little effect on heavy drinkers – they can neither reduce the level of alcohol in the blood nor speed up the rate at which the liver destroys it.

Long-term effects of heavy drinking

Alcohol-related illnesses include:

Gastritis (gaster – stomach; itis – inflammation) Alcohol irritates the lining of the stomach which then becomes inflamed causing:
   nausea (feeling sick),
   vomiting (being sick),
   loss of appetite.

Malnutrition Large quantities of alcohol affect the stomach and appetite, so heavy drinkers tend not to have a full and balanced diet. Although they can get enough calories from alcohol, they may suffer from lack of vitamins, particularly the B vitamins.

Cirrhosis of the liver Large amounts of alcohol damage the liver, causing it to become shrunken and distorted (p. 88). A woman's liver is more easily damaged by alcohol than that of a man.

Dementia Alcohol destroys brain cells and may permanently reduce mental ability.

Obesity Alcoholic drinks are energy foods rich in calories – 1 pint of strong beer has nearly as many calories as 1 pint of milk. If the body does not need all the calories they are turned into fat, so alcohol can make a person fat in the same way as too many cakes, biscuits or chips.

Alcohol and sport

Footballers, cricketers and others who take their sport seriously do not drink alcohol before playing. They know that the effect of alcohol on the brain results in:
   slower reactions,
   lack of concentration,
   uncoordinated movements,
   poorer judgement.

Effects of alcohol on the skin

Alcohol causes the small blood vessels in the skin to dilate (open), which results in a rush of warm blood to the surface. This makes the skin look flushed and gives the person a false feeling of 'being hot'.

It is a mistake to give alcohol to people suffering from the cold unless they are in a warm place. When the warm blood gets to the surface of the skin, the body loses more heat. For this reason, it is undesirable to take alcohol before going out into severe cold.

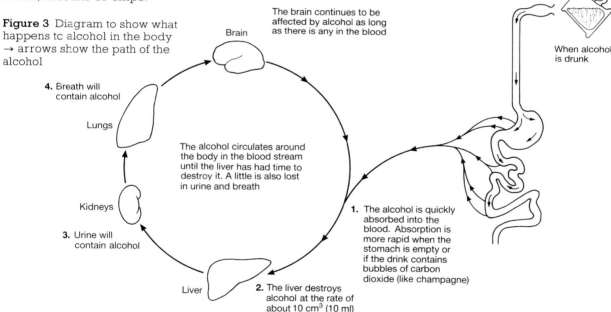

Figure 3 Diagram to show what happens to alcohol in the body → arrows show the path of the alcohol

Brain — The brain continues to be affected by alcohol as long as there is any in the blood

When alcohol is drunk

4. Breath will contain alcohol

Lungs

The alcohol circulates around the body in the blood stream until the liver has had time to destroy it. A little is also lost in urine and breath

Kidneys

3. Urine will contain alcohol

Liver

1. The alcohol is quickly absorbed into the blood. Absorption is more rapid when the stomach is empty or if the drink contains bubbles of carbon dioxide (like champagne)

2. The liver destroys alcohol at the rate of about 10 cm³ (10 ml) an hour

QUESTIONS

1a Give five effects of alcohol on the brain.
 b Alcohol affects people differently. List nine factors which can cause differences.
 c Why do people who take sport seriously not drink alcohol before playing?
2a When can a person be described as being drunk?
 b Why does strong coffee have little effect on sobering up heavy drinkers?
 c Describe the symptoms of a hangover.
3a Describe what happens to alcohol in the body either with a diagram to show what happens, or by listing the events (Fig 3, 1–4).

 b What effect does alcohol have on the skin?
 c Why is it a mistake to give alcohol to a person suffering from the cold?
4 Describe the links between alcohol and:
 (i) malnutrition, (ii) cirrhosis of the liver, (iii) chronic gastritis, (iv) putting on weight.

FURTHER WORK

1 (i) How much alcohol does 1 unit of alcohol represent? (ii) Name four different types and quantities of alcoholic drinks that contain 1 unit of alcohol. (iii) How long, on average, does it take the body to destroy 1 unit of alcohol?

(iv) How long will it take the body to get rid of the effects of 4 pints of ordinary beer?
(v) A person with more than five units of alcohol inside him is likely to exceed the legal limit for driving. If a person drank 4 pints of beer (ordinary strength) in three hours, would he then be likely to be above or below the legal limit for driving? If he was drinking extra strength beer, how many hours would he have to wait until he was below the legal limit? (vi) How much alcohol in the form of whisky could a man consume per day and still keep within sensible limits? How much wine could a woman drink?

2 Complete Exercise 4, p. 194.

Problems caused by alcohol

Social problems may be the cause of heavy drinking, but heavy drinking frequently causes social problems such as:

Anti-social behaviour Alcohol lessens the control which people have over their behaviour, for example:
- A person may become aggressive and be more likely to fight or bully. Wife-beating and baby battering often follow drinking.
- A thief may find that alcohol gives the 'courage' to steal to provide the money for more drinking.
- A drunken person may have no consideration for others or their safety, or may indulge in vandalism.

Self-neglect Persistent heavy drinkers may fail to feed themselves properly or keep clean.

Absenteeism A person with a hangover may be:
   too ill to go to work,
   late for work,
   inefficient when he gets to work,
   accident-prone.
Such a person may lose his job.

Poverty Quite often, people who spend a lot of money on drink do not have enough left for necessities. They are frequently also heavy smokers – more expense and more poverty.

Unwanted pregnancy When a girl has had too much to drink she may not care what happens to her, or bother about contraception.

Spread of sexually transmitted diseases (STDs) Drunken behaviour that leads to casual sex can also lead to the spread of gonorrhoea, AIDS etc.

Unhappy home One person with an alcohol problem affects the whole family in one or more of the ways mentioned above.

Road accidents

Small amounts of alcohol increase the danger of accidents because judgement is impaired and reaction times are slowed. The effects of alcohol on driving is shown in **Fig 2**, but drunken pedestrians and cyclists also cause accidents.

In certain circumstances the police may require a driver to take a **breathalyser test**. If the test indicates that the driver may be 'over the limit' (is likely to have more than the legal amount of alcohol in his blood), he is taken to a police station for further breath or blood tests. Convictions for drunken driving can lead to a driving ban, heavy fines, imprisonment, and much dearer insurance cover when the ban ends.

Figure 1 People with an alcohol problem (from drawings by Simon Gooch)

A. This man regularly gets drunk

– Is he drinking to forget about his worries?
– What is his home life like?
– Has he been convicted of drunken driving?
– Does his job encourage drinking?
– Does he admit to a drinking problem?
– Is he in danger of becoming an alcoholic?

B. This boy drinks too much.

  Is he trying to:
– look grown-up?
– drink as much as his friends?
– forget problems at home or school?
– get self-confidence?
– impress a girlfriend?

C. This woman drinks secretly

– Is she lonely?
– Is she depressed?
– Has she marital problems?
– Has she lost her job?
– Is she worried about her health?

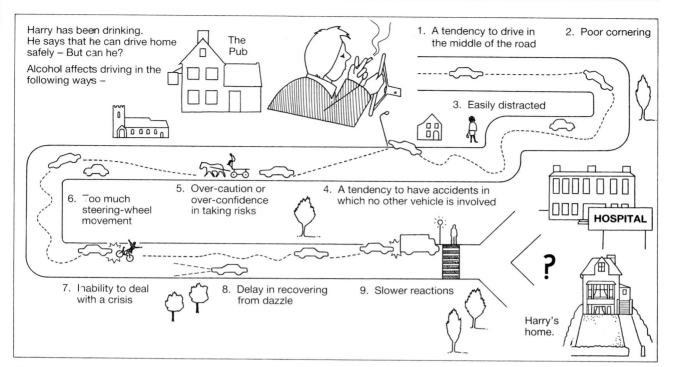

Figure 2 How driving is affected by alcohol (after Peter Kneebone, from drawing in D. R. Lawrence, Clinical Pharmacology, Churchill Livingstone)

Alcoholism

What is an alcoholic?   This is a person who cannot control his (or her) drinking. Once an alcoholic starts to drink he cannot be certain of being able to stop when he wants to.

Warnings signs of alcoholism   Any of the following may be a warning sign of alcoholism:
◆ frequent heavy drinking,
◆ craving for drink in the mornings,
◆ missing time from work because of drinking,
◆ needing a drink to face difficult situations,
◆ blackouts (unconsciousness) due to drinking.

Delirium tremens (DTs)   DTs occur in alcoholics, often when they are suddenly deprived of alcohol, for example, on being confined to bed following an accident. They become very ill and, amongst other symptoms, develop the shakes, and have hallucinations – 'see' things which are not there such as big, black spiders on the walls or ants crawling up their legs.

Meths drinkers   Alcoholics sometimes turn to methylated spirits as a quick, cheap way to get drunk. Meths is a poison which destroys various organs in the body, particularly the eyes and liver, until it finally causes blindness and death.

Figure 3 (from a drawing by Simon Gooch)

Where to go for help

1. A doctor – for advice and treatment in the same way as for any other illness.
2. Alcoholics Anonymous – an informal association for people with alcohol problems (drinkers or their relatives). The number to ring is in the telephone book.
3. National Council for Alcoholism – gives information and advice to alcoholics, families and employers.

QUESTIONS

1   What is the link between alcohol and:
(i) anti-social behaviour – give three examples,
(ii) self-neglect, (iii) absenteeism,
(iv) poverty, (v) unwanted pregnancy,
(vi) spread of STDs, (vii) unhappy homes

2a   Why do even small amounts of alcohol increase the danger of road accidents?
b   List, or draw a diagram to show, nine ways in which alcohol affects driving.

c   What penalties can follow a conviction for drunken driving?

3a   Describe an alcoholic.
b   Give five warning signs of alcoholism.
c   What is meant by DTs, and when do they occur?
d   Why may alcoholics drink meths?

4   Give three sources of help for alcoholics.

FURTHER WORK

1   Fig 1 shows three people with an alcohol problem. From your experience of life, or from information obtained from magazines, books and television, make a list of possible reasons for a drink problem in: (i) men, (ii) women, (iii) teenagers.

2   Make a collection of newspaper reports to show the range of social problems linked with alcohol.

3   Discuss 'Teenage drinking is on the increase – does it matter?'

Section 6 EXERCISES

1 Match each of the terms with the correct statement in the list below.

(a) **aseptic carrier contagious germs incubation infectious hepatitis larynx placebo stress vector**

harmless substance given in place of medicine
voice box
psychological pressure
pathogenic microbes
time between entry of germs and appearance of symptoms
disease which is spread by contact
animal which transmits disease
a cause of jaundice
harbours an infectious microbe without ill-effect
free from germs [10]

(b) **active immunity AIDS antigen chicken pox DPT nicotine nits rubella scabies VD**

body produces its own antibodies
stimulates antibody production
German measles
triple vaccine
the virus also causes shingles
acquired immune deficiency disease
sexually transmitted diseases
caused by itch mites
eggs of lice
habit-forming drug [10]

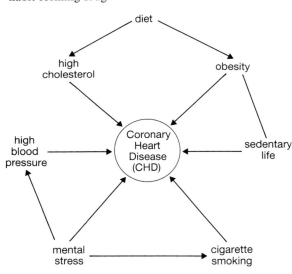

2
(a) CHD results from certain arteries becoming partially or completely blocked. Name these arteries. [1]
(b) Describe the sequence of events leading to a heart attack using the phrases given below:
a part of the heart muscle; oxygen shortage; blockage; blood supply; coronary artery; heart muscle. [5]
(c) Describe two modifications to the diet which could help reduce the risk of a heart attack. [2]
(d) Fats are essential items in the diet. State two functions of fats in the human body. [2]
(e) Name two other ways besides CHD in which health may be adversely affected by the smoking of cigarettes. [2]
(f) What is meant by a sedentary life? [1]
(g) State two ways in which mental stress may increase the risk of a heart attack. [2]

3 The diagram shows organisms which can affect the health of humans.

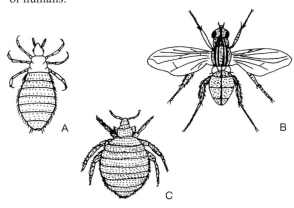

(a) Use this simple key to identify A, B and C from the diagrams.

1. Has wings 2
   Does not have wings 3
2. One pair of wings .... Housefly
3. Has four pairs of legs .... Scabies mite
   Has three pairs of legs 4
4. Abdomen longer than its width .... Headlouse
   Abdomen round .... Bed bug [3]

(b) State two characteristics observed in the diagram which are found in all these animals. [2]

(c) (i) Name one disease transmitted by the mosquito. [1]
(ii) Briefly describe those measures which have been taken to reduce or prevent the spread of this disease. [4]

(WJEC: GCSE Biology (Human) Specimen)

4 A person was given a drink of alcohol and then asked to give blood samples over the next five hours.
The table below shows how much alcohol was found in the blood at that time.

Time in hours from drinking	0.0	0.5	1.0	1.5	2.0	3.0	4.0	5.0
Percentage alcohol in blood	0.00	0.07	0.14	0.15	0.11	0.07	0.05	0.04

(a) Use the figures in the table to plot a curve on graph paper. [4]
(b) Use your graph to answer the following:
(i) What percentage of alcohol is likely to be in the blood at 2.5 hours? [1]
(ii) On the graph, draw in the expected curve up to 7 hours. What percentage of alcohol does your curve show at 7 hours? [2]
(iii) How long after the drink would you expect the alcohol to have its maximum effect on the body? [1]
(iv) During which half hour does the percentage of alcohol in the blood decrease at the greatest rate? [1]

(c) (i) In what way does alcohol affect muscular responses? Explain your answer. [2]
(ii) Name one organ of the body which may be damaged by an excess of alcohol. [1]

(LEAG: GCSE Human Biology Specimen)

5 (a) How would you explain to someone who has little knowledge of the hygienic handling of food the dangers of each of the following?

(i) Storing raw meat in the same container as a pork pie. [3]

(ii) Not thoroughly thawing frozen food, such as a chicken, before it is cooked. [2]

(iii) Using a chipped and cracked wooden surface on which to prepare food. [2]

(iv) Refreezing a food such as ice cream which has been removed from the freezing cabinet and allowed to thaw. [2]

(b) Explain the difference between pasteurisation and sterilisation of milk. [3]

(SEG: GCSE Biology (Human) Specimen)

6 (a) Explain what is meant by active immunity to disease. [4]

(b) How can active immunity to tuberculosis be acquired? [4]

(c) Give an account of the ways in which the body is protected against disease-causing organisms, other than by immunity. [8]

(MEG: GCSE Biology (Human) Specimen)

SECTION 7
Humans within their Environment

Living things

Living things are called **living organisms**. They differ from non-living things in carrying out the following essential activities, often referred to as the **characteristics of living organisms**:

◆ **Feeding.** Food is required for growth and to provide energy.

◆ **Respiration.** Food is broken down to release energy. Oxygen is usually required for this process, and carbon dioxide given off.

◆ **Excretion.** The waste products of living cells must be removed to prevent poisoning of the organism.

◆ **Growth and repair.** Growth takes place until a certain size is reached. Repair continues throughout life, becoming less efficient with age.

◆ **Movement.** All living organisms are capable of some degree of movement.

◆ **Response to stimuli.** Living things are sensitive to stimuli such as light, heat, chemicals and touch. In general, animals respond by movement and plants by growth.

◆ **Reproduction.** Life continues because living things are able to reproduce.

◆ **Death.** All living organisms eventually die.

Classification of living things

There are many different varieties of living things, and more are still being discovered. They can be classified – placed into groups – in various ways, eg plants, animals, fungi or bacteria. Each of these large groups – **kingdoms** – is then sub-divided into smaller and smaller groups, with all members of a group having certain basic features in common. A **kingdom** is sub-divided into **divisions** or **phyla** (singular – **phylum**), **classes**, **orders**, **families**, **genera** (singular – **genus**), and **species**.

Binomial system for naming species This is a system for giving each species a scientific name based on Latin which can be recognised all over the world. The scientific name has two parts, and is usually printed in italics. The first part is the name of the **genus** in which the species has been placed; the generic name starts with a capital letter. The second part is the name of the **species**; the specific name starts with a small letter. For example, humans are known as *Homo sapiens*.

Differences between plants and animals

The fundamental difference between plants and animals is their method of obtaining food (nutrition). Plants make food by the process of photosynthesis, whereas animals find their food, eat and digest it. All other differences between plants and animals, for example, movement and sensitivity, are connected with the difference in the method of nutrition.

Photosynthesis

Photosynthesis is the process by which the green parts of plants use energy from sunlight to combine **carbon dioxide** with **water** to make sugar, with oxygen given off as a waste product. The process can be summed up as follows:

Carbon dioxide + water + sunlight $\xrightarrow{\text{chlorophyll}}$ sugar + oxygen

$$(6CO_2 + 6H_2O + \text{light energy} \longrightarrow C_6H_{12}O_6 + 6O_2)$$

Conditions necessary for photosynthesis Photosynthesis takes place inside plant cells, and it only occurs when four factors are present:

◆ **Sunlight.** Photosynthesis cannot take place in the dark.

◆ **Chlorophyll.** Photosynthesis only takes place in the green parts of a plant.

◆ **Carbon dioxide.** This gas is obtained from air in addition to that which is continuously produced by the plant as a by-product of respiration.

◆ **Water.** The cells of the plant must have water to function, and additional water is required during the daytime for photosynthesis.

What happens to the sugar When the factors listed above are available, a plant makes sugar continuously in the parts containing chlorophyll. The sugar is then either removed to other parts of the plant, or converted to starch for temporary storage within the cells in which it has been made. When photosynthesis ceases, as happens during the night, the starch is gradually converted back to sugar again, and most is removed.

Sugar is required by the living parts of a plant for:

◆ **respiration** to supply energy for the cell's activities;

◆ **growth.** Sugar is used to make other carbohydrates including **cellulose** for cell walls, and to make protein for protoplasm.

◆ **storage.** The sugar is:
    stored in fruits (eg grapes), roots (eg sugar beet) etc.
    converted into **starch** for storage in potatoes, wheat grains, rice etc.
    converted into **fat** for storage in peanuts, olives, etc.

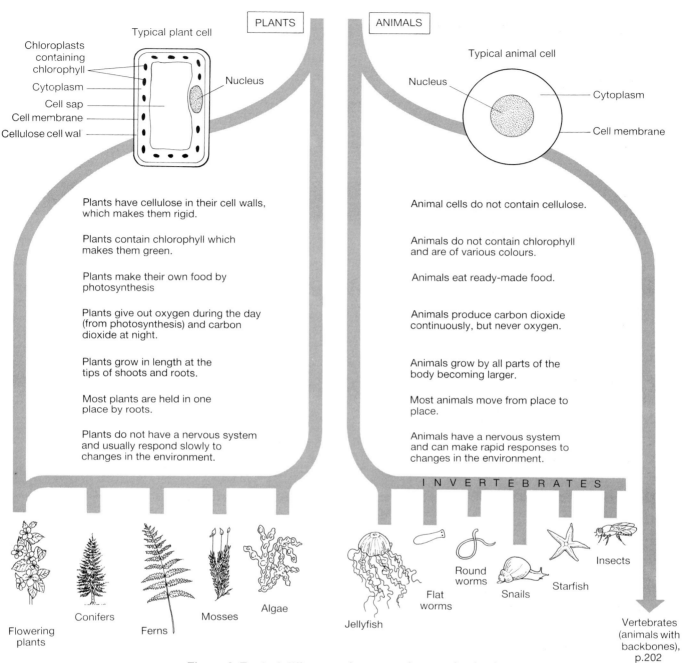

Figure 1 Typical differences between plants and animals

Vertebrates (animals with backbones), p.202

QUESTIONS

1 List eight characteristics of living organisms.

2a What is the fundamental difference between plants and animals?

b Copy and complete the chart, using information from **Fig 1** above.

3a What is photosynthesis?

b Give the equation which sums up photosynthesis.

c Name four factors essential for photosynthesis.

d Describe the uses which a plant may make of the sugar it produces.

Differences between plants and animals

	Plants	Animals
Food		
Colour		
Cellulose		
Movement		
Nervous system		
Oxygen		
Carbon dioxide		
Growth		

FURTHER WORK

1 Describe experiments to show that each of the following is necessary for photosynthesis: (i) light, (ii) chlorophyll, (iii) carbon dioxide.

2 Describe an experiment which shows that oxygen is produced during photosynthesis.

Interdependence

All living things are dependent on other living things for their survival. Some examples are shown in **Fig 1**.

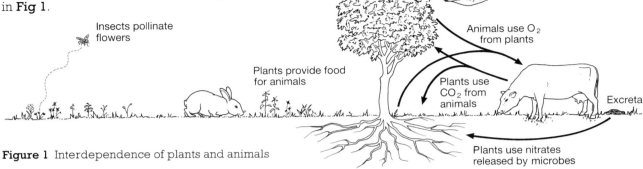

Insects pollinate flowers

Plants provide food for animals

Birds spread seeds

Animals use O_2 from plants

Plants use CO_2 from animals

Excreta

Plants use nitrates released by microbes

Figure 1 Interdependence of plants and animals

Food chains and webs

Food chains A food chain is a chain of organisms in which the first group is used as food for the second group, and the second group is used as food for the third, and so on. The food chain illustrates that all food originally comes from plants, eg:

(i) Humans eat beef, milk, butter and cheese, but, as cattle feed on grass, the beef, milk, butter and cheese must have originated as grass.

(ii) Humans eat large fish which eat smaller fish which eat plankton, and plankton contains minute plants.

Food web Food chains usually interconnect to form a network of food chains called a food web: **Fig 2**.

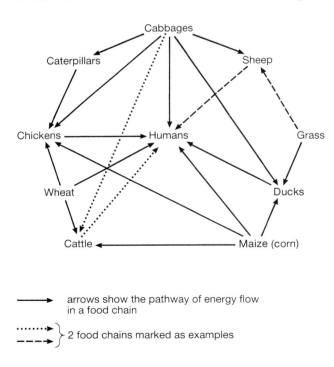

arrows show the pathway of energy flow in a food chain

}⋯⋯▸ 2 food chains marked as examples
---▸

Figure 2 Food web based on food eaten by humans.

Producers Green plants are producers – they produce food, and are the first stage in a food chain.

Consumers Animals are consumers – they consume (eat) food:

Primary consumers – **herbivores** – are animals which eat plants

Secondary consumers – **carnivores** – are animals which eat primary consumers.

Omnivores ('all'-eating animals) eat both plant and animal food and are both primary and secondary consumers. Humans are omnivores.

Predators are animals which hunt other animals for food.

Decomposers are microbes which feed on dead plant and animal remains and break them up into simple substances. Plants absorb these substances and use them for growth.

Transfer of energy Food is a means of transferring energy as well as materials. As energy is transferred from one organism to another it becomes converted into different forms: **Fig 3**.

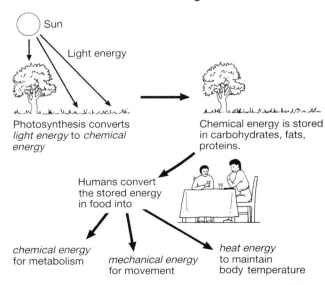

Sun

Light energy

Photosynthesis converts *light energy* to *chemical energy*

Chemical energy is stored in carbohydrates, fats, proteins.

Humans convert the stored energy in food into

chemical energy for metabolism

mechanical energy for movement

heat energy to maintain body temperature

Figure 3 A diagram to illustrate how energy from the sun is transferred to human activity

A food chain is a series of energy transfers, with a considerable amount of energy being lost at each transfer: **Fig 4**. Therefore a food chain rarely has more than three or four links since there is not enough energy to maintain more.

Recycling of materials

Materials are continuously being recycled between organisms and the environment as they are used and re-used. Nitrogen and carbon are examples of elements which move from living to non-living things and back again over and over again.

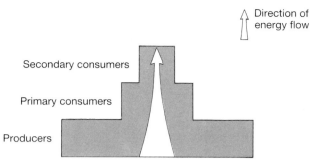

Direction of energy flow

Secondary consumers

Primary consumers

Producers

Figure 4 Pyramid of energy – indicates how much energy is lost at each stage

Carbon is present in carbon dioxide (CO_2) in the air

CO_2 is released from food in **respiration**

CO_2 is used by plants in **photosynthesis** to make food. Carbon becomes part of carbohydrates, fats, proteins.

Plants use stored food as energy source

Carbon is part of food eaten by animals

Plant and animal death

Plant and animal matter in the soil provides food for **microbes**

Fuels – wood, peat, charcoal – come from plant material and contain carbon. The same applies to **fossil fuels** – coal, oil and natural gas. **Combustion** (burning) of fuels releases CO_2

Figure 5 The carbon cycle

Carbon cycle Carbon, as well as being part of carbon dioxide, also forms part of carbohydrates, fats, proteins, coal, oil, and natural gas. **Fig 5** shows how carbon is in continuous circulation between the air and living things and the materials that come from them.

Nitrogen cycle The **nitrogen cycle** is the way in which nitrogen circulates continuously between living things and the environment: **Fig 6**.

Figure 6 The nitrogen cycle

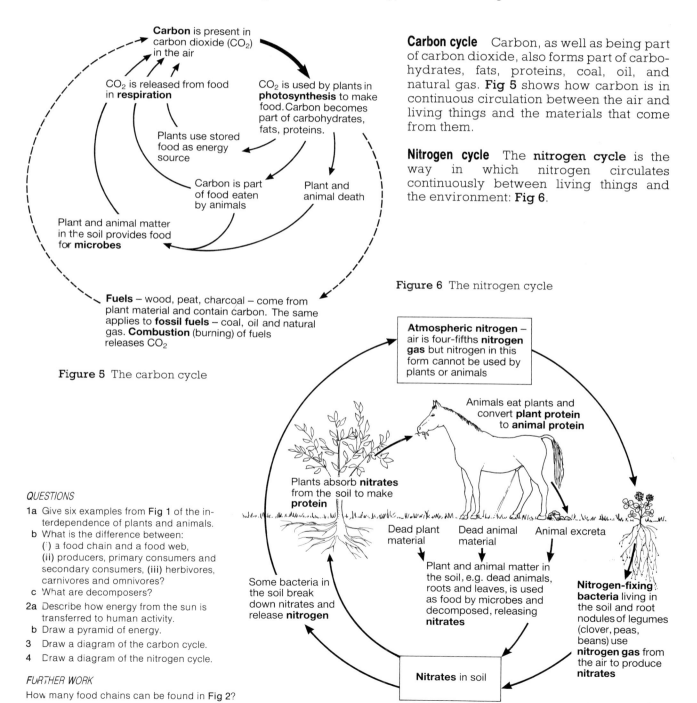

Atmospheric nitrogen – air is four-fifths **nitrogen gas** but nitrogen in this form cannot be used by plants or animals

Animals eat plants and convert **plant protein** to **animal protein**

Plants absorb **nitrates** from the soil to make **protein**

Dead plant material

Dead animal material

Animal excreta

Some bacteria in the soil break down nitrates and release **nitrogen**

Plant and animal matter in the soil, e.g. dead animals, roots and leaves, is used as food by microbes and decomposed, releasing **nitrates**

Nitrogen-fixing bacteria living in the soil and root nodules of legumes (clover, peas, beans) use **nitrogen gas** from the air to produce **nitrates**

Nitrates in soil

QUESTIONS

1a Give six examples from **Fig 1** of the interdependence of plants and animals.
 b What is the difference between:
 (i) a food chain and a food web,
 (ii) producers, primary consumers and secondary consumers, (iii) herbivores, carnivores and omnivores?
 c What are decomposers?
2a Describe how energy from the sun is transferred to human activity.
 b Draw a pyramid of energy.
3 Draw a diagram of the carbon cycle.
4 Draw a diagram of the nitrogen cycle.

FURTHER WORK

How many food chains can be found in **Fig 2**?

Bacteria, viruses and fungi

Bacteria

Bacteria are found almost everywhere – in air, water and food, and on the outside and the inside of the bodies of plants and animals. They range in size from 0.5 to 1.5 μm in diameter and, being microscopic, can only be seen with the aid of a microscope.

Each bacterium is a single cell with a cell wall and cytoplasm. There is no definite nucleus, but nuclear material (DNA) is present. Substances necessary for life are absorbed through the cell wall and unwanted substances are excreted by the same route.

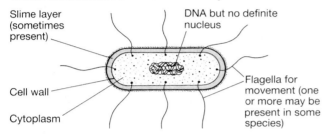

Figure 1 Structure of a typical bacterium

Types of bacteria   There are many different types of bacteria and each species has its own particular shape, size, and conditions in which it can survive and grow. (Bacteria which cause food poisoning are discussed on p. 86).

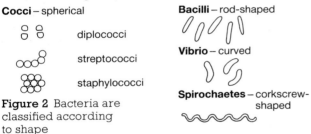

Cocci – spherical
- diplococci
- streptococci
- staphylococci

Bacilli – rod-shaped

Vibrio – curved

Spirochaetes – corkscrew-shaped

Figure 2 Bacteria are classified according to shape

Reproduction   After growing to its full size, a bacterium reproduces by dividing into two (binary fission). In the right conditions this can take place about every 20 minutes. In the course of 24 hours, one bacterium can multiply to produce a **colony** – a group of many millions of bacteria which is easily visible to the naked eye.

Surviving unfavourable conditions   When conditions become unfavourable, bacteria which are not killed either remain inactive or, in the case of some species, produce **spores**: Fig 3. Bacterial spores can withstand drought, high temperatures, and antiseptics. Most are killed by:
- being boiled for ten minutes or more, depending on the species,
- sunlight,
- strong disinfectant,
- irradiation with gamma rays.

Conditions for growth   Bacteria will only grow and multiply when the following conditions are right:

Water   Moisture is essential, and most bacteria are also capable of living in water.

Food   Different bacteria require different types of food. Some feed only on one type of food, whereas others are able to feed on a wide range of material.

Temperature   Most bacteria grow best at moderate temperatures of 25 to 38°C, although a few prefer higher or lower temperatures. Most are killed by heat above 60°C, but spores can survive in boiling water, some for several hours. Low temperatures stop most bacterial activity but do not kill them, and when the temperature rises, the bacteria become active again.

Sunlight   Direct sunlight often kills bacteria or slows down their growth. Greatest bacterial activity takes place in the dark, such as within soil or rubbish dumps.

Oxygen   Some bacteria – **aerobic bacteria** – require oxygen in order to grow, as they respire in the same way as plants or animals. Others – **anaerobic bacteria** – will not grow in the presence of oxygen, and this accounts for the great amount of bacterial activity which takes place in rubbish dumps and in the sludge in sewage works – places into which air cannot penetrate. These are the bacteria which produce foul-smelling gases.

Importance of bacteria to humans   A few bacteria are harmful to humans but many more are essential or useful.

Harmful bacteria are those which:
- cause disease to humans,
- cause disease to animals and plants which are food for humans,
- make food inedible.

Useful bacteria are those which:
- live in the large intestine and produce **vitamin K**.
- are used in the **production of foods**, eg cheese, yoghurt, sauerkraut, vinegar.
- are used in **industrial processes**, eg curing of tea leaves, tanning of leather.
- make **antibiotics**, eg streptomycin.
- make **amino acids** (for animal feedstuffs), **proteins** (for human food), **enzymes** (eg for biological detergents), **medicines** (eg insulin).

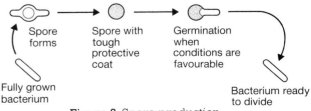

Spore forms

Spore with tough protective coat

Germination when conditions are favourable

Fully grown bacterium

Bacterium ready to divide

Figure 3 Spore production

◆ **decompose rubbish** and break it down into very small particles. This not only removes rubbish – leaves, excreta, rotting food, unwanted paper – but also provides food which can be used by plants.
◆ plants.

Viruses

Viruses are even smaller than bacteria, ranging in size from 10 to 300 nm, and are only visible with an electron microscope. There are many types and they are all parasites on plants or animals.

Each virus particle consists of a single strand of DNA or RNA surrounded by a protein coat. It only becomes active and multiplies when inside the right type of living cell. The cell then bursts and a large number of new virus particles are free to infect other cells. As the virus spreads, it damages tissues and causes disease.

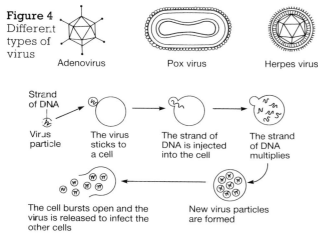

Figure 4 Different types of virus

Adenovirus   Pox virus   Herpes virus

Figure 5 How a virus reproduces

Fungi

There are many kinds of fungi. They include single-celled yeasts: (**Fig 6A**), various moulds consisting of a network – **mycelium** – of branching threads – **hyphae** (**Fig 6C**) – and the very much larger mushrooms and toadstools formed from inter-woven hyphae. Fungi do not contain chlorophyll and therefore are unable to photosynthesise. They obtain food either as parasites on other living organisms, or as saprophytes on dead plant or animal matter. Some fungi contain cellulose in the wall, and reproduction is often by spores.

Importance of fungi to humans

Harmful fungi are those which:
◆ cause skin diseases, eg athlete's foot, thrush.
◆ damage food crops, eg potato blight.
◆ turn food bad, eg mould on bread, jam, oranges, tomatoes.
◆ damage useful materials, eg dry-rot in wood, mould on leather.
◆ are poisonous when eaten, eg toadstools.

Useful fungi are those which:
◆ make antibiotics, eg penicillin.
◆ can be eaten as food, eg mushrooms.
◆ are useful in food production, eg yeast for making bread rise, blue mould in cheese.
◆ are used to make vitamins (B-group) or enzymes (eg amylase – used in brewing).
◆ are decomposers – they assist in the breaking down of rubbish.
◆ produce alcohol. The fermentation of sugar by yeast is a form of anaerobic respiration

$$sugar \rightarrow alcohol\ (ethanol) + carbon\ dioxide$$

Antibiotics An antibiotic is a substance produced by one type of microbe which destroys or stops the growth of another type of microbe. Antibiotics are widely used as medicines to combat bacterial diseases. Examples are:
◆ **Penicillin**, produced by the mould *Penicillium*, destroys various common and dangerous bacteria.
◆ **Streptomycin**, produced by the bacterium *Streptomyces*, is used to treat tuberculosis.
When antibiotics are freely used, there is the danger that the germs they are intended to destroy will produce mutations which are resistant to that antibiotic. A new antibiotic will then be needed against the disease.

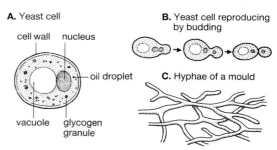

A. Yeast cell
cell wall   nucleus
oil droplet
vacuole   glycogen granule

B. Yeast cell reproducing by budding

C. Hyphae of a mould

Figure 6

QUESTIONS

1a Where are bacteria found?
b Describe a bacterium.
c Draw a diagram to show the structure of a typical bacterium. **(i)** How are bacteria classified? **(ii)** Draw some examples.
e How do bacteria reproduce?
f What is a colony?

2a Describe the effect on bacterial growth of: **(i)** water, **(ii)** food, **(iii)** temperature, **(iv)** sunlight.
b What is the difference between aerobic and anaerobic bacteria?
c What happens to bacteria when conditions become unfavourable?

d Use labelled diagrams to describe spore production.
e **(i)** Name three conditions which spores can withstand. **(ii)** How can spores be killed?

3a Name three ways in which bacteria are harmful to humans.
b Name six ways in which bacteria are useful to humans.

4a **(i)** Describe a virus particle. **(ii)** Draw some different types of virus.
b **(i)** When does a virus become active? **(ii)** Describe, with diagrams, how it reproduces.

5a How do fungi obtain their food?
b Name five types of: **(i)** harmful fungi, **(ii)** useful fungi.
c What are antibiotics and why are they useful?

FURTHER WORK

1 How many bacteria could theoretically be produced in 12 hours from one bacterium if divisions took place every $\frac{1}{2}$ hour?

2 Carry out the experiment described on p. 216 to demonstrate the presence of microbes in soil, water, dust, air etc.

3 Complete Exercise 2, p. 214.

Human origins

This topic gives the generally accepted view of the origins of man, that humans evolved from primitive creatures over many millions of years by a series of gradual changes. **Evolution** means slow change and development.

There are people who do not agree with this view. They believe that man and other living creatures were created in their present form. Some believe that this happened only once; others that creation took place several times, with the earlier creatures dying out and being replaced with new ones.

Theory of evolution

Scientists estimate that there has been life on earth for about the last 2 billion years (2 000 000 000). The first forms of life to appear were very small and simple. Gradually, these changed to give rise to many different types of microbes, plants and animals. Many which do not exist today are found as fossils.

Characteristics of mammals

Characteristics typical of mammals include:
◆ The young are fed on milk from mammary glands.
◆ The young develop within the uterus and are supplied with food and oxygen through the placenta until they are born.
◆ The body is covered with hair.
◆ A diaphragm separates the thorax and the abdomen.
◆ There are two sets of teeth – a milk set and a permanent set.
◆ Ear flaps (pinnae) are present.
◆ They are able to regulate body temperature.

Characteristics of primates

Characteristics typical of primates include:
◆ opposable thumb (thumb can move to be opposite the fingers),
◆ prehensile (grasping) hands and feet,
◆ finger nails, not claws,
◆ 32 teeth in the permanent set,
◆ one pair of mammary glands,
◆ stereoscopic vision.

Figure 1 Stages in human evolution

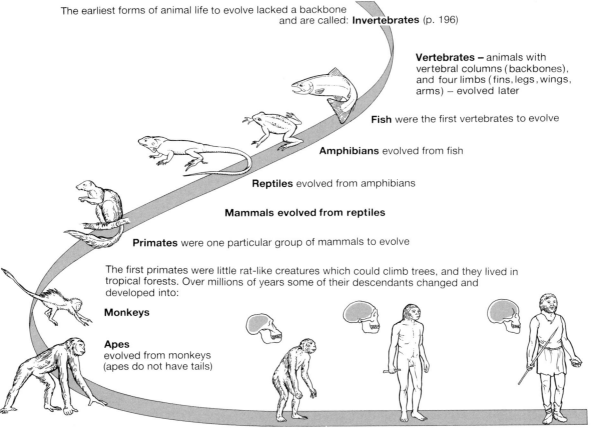

The earliest forms of animal life to evolve lacked a backbone and are called: **Invertebrates** (p. 196)

Vertebrates – animals with vertebral columns (backbones), and four limbs (fins, legs, wings, arms) – evolved later

Fish were the first vertebrates to evolve

Amphibians evolved from fish

Reptiles evolved from amphibians

Mammals evolved from reptiles

Primates were one particular group of mammals to evolve

The first primates were little rat-like creatures which could climb trees, and they lived in tropical forests. Over millions of years some of their descendants changed and developed into:

Monkeys

Apes
evolved from monkeys
(apes do not have tails)

Humans
evolved from ape-like animals

Part ape-like/part human

Early man
(*Homo erectus*)

Modern man
(*Homo sapiens*)

Main trends in human evolution

Millions of years were required for humans to evolve from their ape-like ancestors, during which time the following developments took place:

♦ A **larger brain** developed in comparison with body size, particularly those areas of the fore-brain concerned with intelligence and speech.

♦ **Bi-pedal gait** – walking on two legs – left the hands free to carry food, tools, etc.

♦ **Upright stance** – standing on two legs with the body held vertically gave extra height and range of vision.

♦ **Changes in skull shape** accompanied changes in the brain and in the diet, eg enlarged forehead, reduced eyebrow ridges, a more prominent chin and smaller teeth.

♦ The **hairs** of most parts of the skin became much finer and almost invisible.

♦ The **hands** became capable of delicate movements for making and using complicated tools.

♦ A **change in diet** occurred, from fruits and shoots to one relying more on tougher seeds, grasses, roots and meat which could be partly digested by cooking.

♦ **Working in groups** made food-gathering, hunting, defence and farming more efficient.

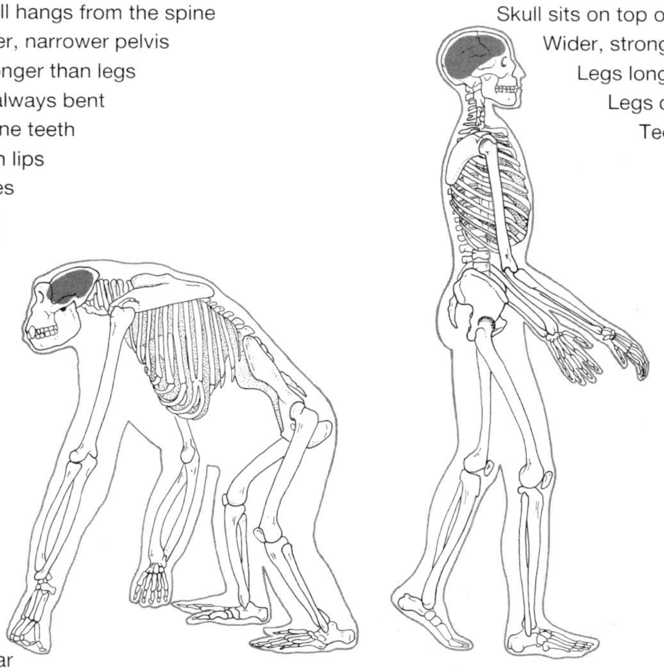

Apes	STRUCTURE	Humans
Dense hair covers most of the skin		Dense hair covers only a small part of the skin
Skull hangs from the spine		Skull sits on top of the spine
Longer, narrower pelvis		Wider, stronger pelvis
Arms longer than legs		Legs longer than arms
Legs always bent		Legs can bend and straighten
Large canine teeth		Teeth all about the same size
Thin lips		Thick lips
Small buttock muscles		Large buttock muscles
Flattened nose and protruding jaws		Protruding nose and flattened jaws
Face larger than cranium		Cranium larger than face
Smaller brain		Larger brain
Large eyebrow ridges		Small eyebrow ridges
Feet have a 'thumb' – good for climbing		Feet have an arch – good for walking
Legs and arms are used for walking		Only legs used for walking

	BEHAVIOUR	
Collect or hunt for their food		Produce food by farming
Do not have a fixed home base		Make homes in houses, tents or caves
Do not use fire		Use fire for warmth and cooking
Are restricted to a particular environment		Have learnt how to survive in a variety of environments
Can use simple tools but not make them		Make complicated tools
Use a limited range of sounds for communication		Have a highly developed power of speech
Have a length of pregnancy similar to humans, but the childhood phase is only half as long		Have a very long childhood, which provides more time for learning
Have a certain amount of reasoning power and learning ability		Have reasoning power and learning ability developed to a much greater extent. Humans also have a cultural life involving art, science and religion

Figure 2 Comparison of apes and humans

QUESTIONS

1 Using **Fig 1** as a guide, describe the course of evolution from invertebrates to humans.

2a List features characteristic of mammals.
b List features characteristic of primates.
c Describe the main trends in human evolution.

3a List in two columns the 14 differences in structure between apes and humans shown in **Fig 2**.
b List in two columns the 8 differences in behaviour between apes and humans given in **Fig 2**.

FURTHER WORK

1 The theory of evolution is based on evidence obtained from fossils, comparative anatomy, embryology, breeding experiments and genetics. Find one piece of supporting evidence from each of these categories.

2 Who were Charles Darwin and Alfred Wallace, when did they live, and what part did they play in formulating the theory of natural selection and the origin of species?

Population

Population is a world issue. Although the population of the world is increasing rapidly: **Fig 1**, there is a finite amount of food, fuel, housing and living space. No country exists in isolation – people, radio waves, aeroplanes and pollution cross boundaries, so the actions of one country have an effect on conditions in another country.

Factors which influence population size

Birth rate   The number of live births per 1000 people per year depends on such factors as:
◆ the extent to which birth control methods are used,
◆ the age at which child-bearing starts,
◆ the average number of children per family.
The population increases when the birth rate exceeds the death rate.

Life expectancy   The average length of life of individuals within a population is influenced by good nutrition or malnutrition, good or poor medical services, epidemics, famine and war.

In Britain, the average life span for females has increased from about 52 years to 77 years within this century. For males it has increased from 48 to 72 years.

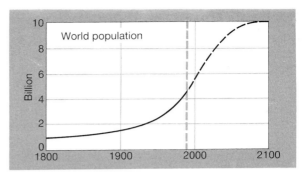

Figure 1 Graph showing the recent rapid increase in the world's population

Death rate   The number of deaths per 1000 people per year declines with improved water supplies, sanitation, diet, disease control and medical care.
Immigration increases the population.
Emigration decreases the population.

Structure of the population

This depends on the numbers of people in the different age groups: **Fig 2**. A pattern which gives a steep-sided pyramid: **2A**, indicates that the bulk of the population are young people. The pattern changes as larger numbers of people survive to old age; **2B**. Much of the wealth of a country is created by the young adults and the middle-aged, and consumed by children, old people and mothers.

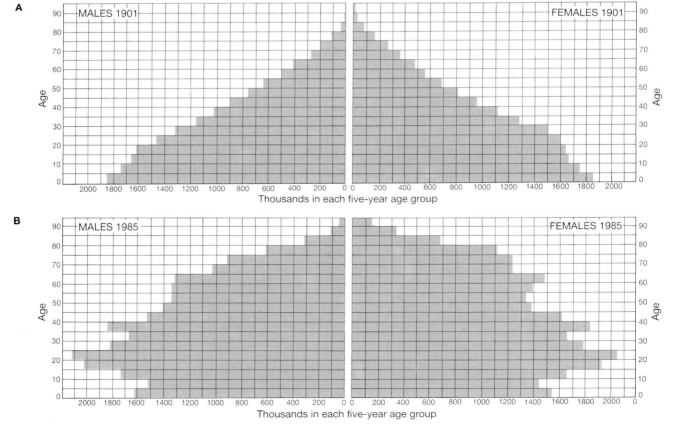

Figure 2 Population pyramids for England and Wales showing the structure of the population by age and sex in **A** 1901, **B** 1985.

Developed countries

These countries have modern farming, industries and services. They have about a third of the world's population and control about 90% of the world's wealth. The overall population of the developed countries is increasing slowly, but the rate of increase has fallen. In some countries it is remaining stable, and in others is slightly decreasing.

Main causes of death
- Heart disease
- Old age
- Cancer

Developing countries

These countries lack a sophisticated agricultural, industrial and financial basis for their economy. Consequently, the income per head of population is low and there is widespread, and often severe, poverty. Birth rates tend to be high and, with an increase in medical care, result in a rapid increase in population. Such countries at present have a large percentage of children who have not yet reached child-bearing years.

Main causes of death
- Infection
- Malnutriton
- Accidents

Problems caused by a rapidly expanding population
Increasing population puts increasing pressure on:
- clean water supplies,
- food supplies,
- waste disposal services,
- land for housing,
- land for food production,
- land for industry,
- medical services.

The world's food problem   There is enough food in the world to feed everyone, but millions of people are under-nourished or starving due to:
- poverty which prevents the purchase of an adequate diet,
- drought and other natural disasters,
- war and the disruption of trade,
- inadequate facilities for transporting 'food mountains' to the hungry,
- destruction of crops by pests such as locusts,
- a cash crop economy where crops are grown for export in place of crops needed by the local population.

Tumours

Cells in most parts of the body are continually dying and being replaced, eg the epidermis of the skin is entirely replaced about every 30 days, and red blood cells about every 120 days. New cells are produced by cell division (p. 24), and normally cell replacement keeps pace with cell loss.

A tumour begins when one cell, or a group of cells, divides more rapidly than is necessary, producing an excess number of cells which form a swelling – a **growth** or **tumour**.
- A **benign tumour** is slow growing and contained within a thick, fibrous capsule.
- A **malignant tumour – a cancer** – rarely has a capsule around it. It tends to grow quickly and spread into other tissues and organs nearby, or a small part may separate and be carried in the blood stream or lymph to grow in a different part of the body.

Causes of cancer   Various factors are linked with cancer in that their presence increases the risk of cancer developing in some individuals, eg:
- smoking – mouth, throat, lung and bladder cancer,
- excessive sunlight – skin cancer,
- asbestos dust – lung cancer,
- ionising radiation, eg leukaemia,
- viruses.

The delay between exposure to a cancer-producing agent (**carcinogen**) and the development of cancer may be 20 years or more.

Treatment
- Surgery removes the tumour.
- Radiotherapy destroys the cancer cells.
- Chemotherapy – treatment with drugs – stops the cancer cells from dividing.

Early detection and treatment makes it more likely that the cancer can be completely cured. Some cancers are very treatable with very high cure rates.

FURTHER WORK

1   Analyse the population pyramids in **Fig 2**. (i) Were there more children aged 0–5 in 1901 than there were in 1985? (ii) State whether there were more males than females in each of the following five-year groups in 1901: 0–5, 20–25, 40–45, 60–65? Do the same for 1985. Compare the answers obtained for 1901 with those for 1985. (iii) Estimate the total population of England and Wales in 1901, and in 1985 (each little square represents 100 000 people). Find the percentage increase. (iv) Compare the shapes of the two pyramids. List the differences and suggest reasons for them.

2   **Fig 1** is a very vague graph. Could it be improved? Do you think it is possible to count the world's population with any degree of accuracy? Give reasons for your answers.

QUESTIONS

1a Draw a graph to show the world's rapidly increasing population.
  b What problems are caused by a rapidly expanding population?
2a List the factors which influence population size.
  b Describe the general differences between developed and developing countries including the main causes of death.

  c What are the main factors leading to the starvation of millions when there is enough food in the world to feed everyone?
3a How does a tumour begin?
  b What is the difference between benign and malignant tumours?
  c Give five causes of cancer.
  d Name three treatments for cancer.
  e What is the advantage of early detection and treatment of cancer?

Water supplies and sewage

Water circulates continuously between the atmosphere, land and sea. It evaporates into the atmosphere from the oceans, rivers and land, and is also given off by plants as they transpire. The water is then carried as vapour by air streams and may form clouds before returning to earth as precipitation (rain, snow, etc). It may pass through soil, rock, and the bodies of plants and animals before evaporating into the atmosphere again. The continuous re-cycling of water means that it is constantly being polluted and then purified by evaporation.

Water treatment

The aim of a Water Treatment Plant is to supply the local population with water which is clean and suitable for drinking (**potable**). The water should be:
◆ free from germs,
◆ free from harmful chemicals.
It is desirable that it should also:
◆ be colourless,
◆ be tasteless,
◆ be without smell,
◆ be free from suspended particles,
◆ contain small amounts of certain beneficial minerals.

Safeguarding the water supply

◆ The faeces of humans and animals are almost certain to contain microbes capable of causing disease. So:
   rules apply to catchment areas (the areas from which water is obtained) to prevent people or animals from polluting the land and hence the water.
   care has to be taken when water mains are fractured to prevent the water becoming contaminated by sewage.
◆ People employed at a Water Treatment Plant must observe strict rules of hygiene. They are also tested regularly to check that they are not typhoid carriers.
◆ Samples of treated water are regularly tested to check that it is free from harmful microbes and chemicals.

> **Chemicals in the water supply** These can be beneficial, harmless or harmful, often depending upon the amount present.
>
> **Magnesium** and **calcium** compounds cause 'hardness'. When they are present it is difficult to get soap to lather because the soap combines with the minerals to form scum. 'Soft' water lacks these compounds.
>
> **Iron** stains clothes washed in water containing it.
>
> **Phosphates** from detergents encourage algal growth in the distribution system.
>
> **Spa water** contains various substances which may have a medicinal value.

A. Screening – to remove large objects
The water passes through a mesh to remove, fish, worms, insects, leaves, water weed and other floating matter.

B. Aeration – to remove smells and tastes
Unwanted smelly gases are able to escape from the water as it is sprayed into the air. At the same time, oxygen is absorbed for the oxidation of unwanted chemicals, eg iron to iron oxide, which can then be removed by filtration.

E. Chlorination – to destroy germs
Small quantities of chlorine are added to the water to kill harmful bacteria and other microbes.

Distribution If the reservoir is not at a higher level than the buildings it supplies, the water is pumped to a high level, eg in a water tower, to provide a head of pressure. Gravity causes water to flow through the pipes and into houses and other buildings. When a tap is turned on, water is forced out.

F. Chemical conditioning – to remove harmful chemicals and add useful ones
Chemicals which may be added include: sulphur dioxide to remove excess chlorine; fluoride to prevent tooth decay, if there is not enough natural fluoride; lime to reduce hardness or acidity.

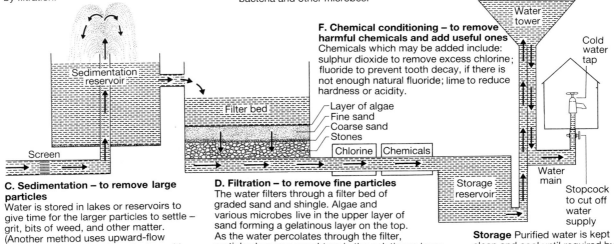

C. Sedimentation – to remove large particles
Water is stored in lakes or reservoirs to give time for the larger particles to settle – grit, bits of weed, and other matter. (Another method uses upward-flow sedimentation tanks where the impurities are removed by chemicals such as ferric sulphate.)

D. Filtration – to remove fine particles
The water filters through a filter bed of graded sand and shingle. Algae and various microbes live in the upper layer of sand forming a gelatinous layer on the top. As the water percolates through the filter, particles become caught up in the gelatinous layer. (Another method uses rapid gravity filters.)

Storage Purified water is kept clean and cool until required by being stored underground in enclosed reservoirs.

Figure 1 Water Treatment Plant: Water treatment includes some or all of the processes **A–F shown here**, depending on how clean and pure the water is when it enters the plant.

Testing for *E. coli* *Escherichia coli* bacteria live only in the colon (large intestine) of humans and are found in large numbers in the faeces. These bacteria are normally harmless, but they live and thrive in the body under the same conditions as microbes which can cause disease. Because bacteria can survive in water, the presence of *E. coli* in the water supply indicates contamination by sewage. Such water is condemned and the source of contamination investigated.

Diseases spread by water contaminated with sewage

These include typhoid, paratyphoid, cholera, dysentery, and gastro-enteritis. Water intended for drinking which does not come from a water treatment plant can be made safe from germs by boiling for ten minutes.

Sewage treatment

Sewage is more than 99% water and comprises all the liquid waste removed from lavatories, baths, wash-basins and kitchen sinks together with industrial and agricultural waste. It is dangerous to health as it provides a breeding ground for the germs it contains, and therefore needs to be treated and made harmless.

Sewage usually flows through a **sewerage system** – a network of pipes (**sewers**) and pumping stations – for treatment in a **Sewage Treatment Plant**. Small quantities of sewage may be dealt with in a **septic tank**.

The main object of sewage treatment is to turn sewage into much cleaner water. Much of the organic matter – faeces, leaves, paper, rags – in sewage is broken down and removed by bacteria.

◆ **Aerobic bacteria** form a slimy film around the clinker in a filter bed. As the effluent (liquid waste) filters through, the particles of organic matter which it contains are used as food and destroyed by the microbes:

$$\text{Organic matter} + O_2 \xrightarrow[\text{bacteria}]{\text{aerobic}} CO_2 + H_2O + \text{nitrogen compounds}$$

Worms and insects move around inside the filter bed feeding on the microbes and this prevents the filter from becoming clogged.

◆ **Anaerobic bacteria** break down sludge. This process can be used to:
  reduce the quantity of sludge,
  turn sludge into fertiliser,
  produce methane gas – a useful fuel.

$$\text{Organic matter} \xrightarrow[\text{bacteria}]{\text{anaerobic}} \text{methane } (CH_4)$$

Screening
Raw sewage passes through a screen which sifts our large objects, eg plastic cartons, paper, rags.

Filter bed
The effluent is sprinkled over the filter bed which is filled with clinker or other rough hard material and is ventilated so that fresh air can penetrate inside – important because of the oxygen it contains.

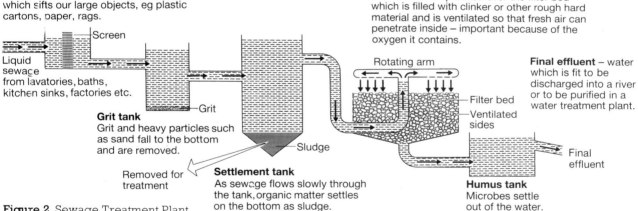

Final effluent – water which is fit to be discharged into a river or to be purified in a water treatment plant.

Grit tank
Grit and heavy particles such as sand fall to the bottom and are removed.

Settlement tank
As sewage flows slowly through the tank, organic matter settles on the bottom as sludge.

Humus tank
Microbes settle out of the water.

Figure 2 Sewage Treatment Plant

QUESTIONS

1 (i) Name two conditions of water which make it fit to drink. (ii) Name five other desirable qualities.

2a Name six processes which may take place in a Water Treatment Plant. Give a reason for each process.
 b Give examples of objects removed from water by screening.
 c How can smells and tastes be removed from water?
 d What happens in a sedimentation reservoir?
 e Draw a diagram of a filter bed and describe how it works.
 f Name three chemicals besides chlorine which may be added to water.
 g What is the purpose of a water tower?

3a What is meant by: (i) sewage, (ii) sewers, (iii) sewerage system, (iv) effluent?
 b Describe the processes in sewage treatment shown in **Fig 2**.
 c Name 4 types of organic matter in sewage.
 d In the treatment of sewage, what use is made of: (i) aerobic bacteria, (ii) anaerobic bacteria?

4a Describe ways of safeguarding the water supply.
 b Name 5 diseases spread by water contaminated with sewage.
 c Why is water tested for *E. Coli*?

FURTHER WORK

1 In industrial countries the average consumption of water for all purposes is about 250 litres (approx 50 gallons) per person per day. For what purposes is water used? Give reasons why the demand for water is increasing throughout the world.

2 Draw a diagram to illustrate the Water Cycle (the continuous circulation of water) which includes the information given in the paragraph at the top of the opposite page.

3 Investigate samples of water from various sources, eg tap, pond, sea, river, rain, distilled. Copy and complete the table below.

Sample	Appearance	Smell	Result of filtering	Result of evaporation	pH*	*a pH below 7 indicates acidity
Tap water						

Pollution

Pollution is the contamination of the environment with toxic or harmful products. It is a problem in all industrial countries because large populations and the modern way of life produce vast quantities of waste matter.

Pollution of the air

This is caused mainly by the burning of coal, wood, oil, petrol etc. Smoke, dust and ash are produced as well as invisible gases such as carbon dioxide, carbon monoxide, sulphur dioxide and nitrogen oxides. The main sources of air pollution are
◆ chimney smoke from homes and factories,
◆ exhaust from cars and lorries,
◆ factory dusts.

Smog It is a combination of fog with smoke from coal fires and factory chimneys. Smog used to be common over industrial cities in Britain until 'smokeless zones' were introduced by the Clean Air Acts of 1956 and 1968.

Many cities in other parts of the world suffer from **photochemical smog** – a yellowish haze created by the interaction of sunlight with chemicals from vehicle exhaust fumes.

Pollution of the upper atmosphere

Ozone layer There is a layer of ozone (a gas) around the earth about 25 km up, which acts as a filter by absorbing most of the sun's ultra-violet rays, thus preventing damage to plants and animals. The ozone layer can be damaged by exhaust fumes from aircraft, and chemicals (chlorofluorocarbons-CFCs) from aerosols and refrigerators.

Carbon dioxide The burning of fuels – coal, oil, gas, wood, releases large amounts of carbon dioxide into the air. This rises into the upper atmosphere and forms a layer around the earth where it has a '**greenhouse effect**' by trapping heat from the sun in the earth's atmosphere. One possible effect is an increase in air and ground temperature worldwide.

Acid rain is rain polluted by sulphuric and nitric acids. Sulphur dioxide and nitrogen oxides are given off as gases when fuel is burnt, eg emissions from power stations, exhaust fumes from vehicles. These oxides turn into acids in the atmosphere and return to the earth in rain hundreds of miles away, killing forests and making lakes acid so that fish are destroyed.

Pollution of the land

This is caused by:
◆ **Refuse dumping** – which results in large areas of derelict land.
◆ **Pesticides** – chemicals poisonous to pests are also often poisonous to many other animals.
◆ **Insecticides** (pesticides for killing insects) which are not readily destroyed such as DDT,

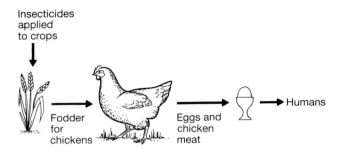

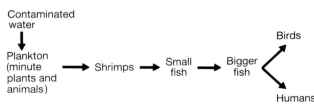

Figure 1 Progress of pollution through a food chain. Some poisonous chemicals which are harmless in small doses can build up in the body and eventually cause ill-health.

aldrin, and dieldrin persist in the soil for many years and:
  cause the emergence of insects resistant to the pesticide which was intended to kill them.
  alter the balance of nature, eg by killing insects necessary for pollination.
  get into food chains; **Fig 1**, then build up in plants and animals and cause them harm.

Pollution of rivers, lakes, ponds and streams

This is caused by:
◆ Seepage of impurities from refuse tips into the sources of river water.
◆ Nitrates used by farmers as fertilisers being washed into rivers and lakes and causing overgrowth of weeds and algae.
◆ Overflowing of lagoons which store slurry – the liquid excreta which comes from the factory farming of pigs and cattle.
◆ Discharge of untreated sewage. The enormous numbers of bacteria in the sewage use up the oxygen in the water so that it is no longer available for the plants and animals which normally live there. These die off and the river becomes a 'dead river'.
◆ Seepage of effluent from grass stored on farms in silos to make silage for cattle feed. Silage effluent is highly acidic.
◆ Discharge of large amounts of phosphates from detergents used in factories and homes, encourages algal growth.
◆ Discharge of effluent from factories which contains poisonous chemicals, eg the heavy metals mercury, lead and cadmium, which get into food chains and accumulate in the bodies of animals, including humans, **Fig 1**.

All the factors mentioned above may also cause the pollution of **ground water** which may be used as a source of supply for Water Treatment Plants (p. 206) or for irrigation.

Pollution of the sea

This is caused by:

♦ Dumping of poisonous chemicals and radio-active substances in the sea. These could be absorbed by fish and eaten directly or indirectly by humans.

♦ Discharge of raw sewage into the sea from houses and industry. This is unsightly and spoils beaches and bathing, but it quickly becomes diluted and is unlikely to be harmful to health.

♦ Discharge of oil from ships. The oil floats on the surface and if washed onto the beaches makes them unusable, thus depriving people of a recreational facility. Oil also harms sea birds; it:
   poisons them when eaten,
   soaks into their feathers, reducing insulation and causing hypothermia,
   stops them from flying.
   Oil also kills shellfish.

Noise pollution

Traffic, aircraft, industry, discos and radios all produce a considerable amount of noise. The effect of noise on different people varies considerably, but generally it makes them less efficient, and it can be a cause of deafness or ill-health.

Radiation pollution

Radiation pollution occurs when levels of radiation rise significantly above the normal background level. It can be caused by radioactive waste from nuclear power stations and fall-out from nuclear explosions (radiation: p. 212).

Radioactive waste

♦ **Traces of radiation** may be found in emissions from nuclear power stations, either in gases which come from the chimneys, or in water discharged from the cooling systems. It is desirable that these are kept to the minimum and well below the level of natural background radiation.

♦ **Radioactive materials** from nuclear power stations or hospitals are usually buried underground or dumped on the bottom of the ocean.

Fall-out When a nuclear explosion takes place, radioactive dust is thrown up into the air, and it is called 'fall-out' when it returns to earth: **Fig 2**. These radioactive substances may then be absorbed by plants, eaten by animals, get into the water supply, or remain in the soil for many years. The area affected will depend on how far the fall-out travels – which is governed by the height to which the dust is thrown, the force and direction of the wind, and rainfall.

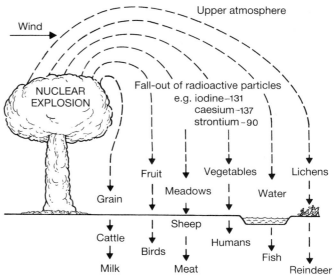
Figure 2 Fall-out and food chains

The harm caused by fall-out depends on:

♦ the amount of fall-out produced.

♦ the half-lives of the radioactive substances in the dust (p. 217).

♦ whether radioactive substances enter food chains.

♦ how long the substances remain in plants or animals.

Fall out from nuclear weapon tests in the 1950s and '60s still contributes a small amount of radiation to the general background level, **Fig 1**, p. 212. Nuclear weapons are now tested deep underground, with no fall-out. Nuclear war would result in massive fall-out.

Detecting radiation

♦ A **geiger counter** is an apparatus which clicks at great speed when near a highly radioactive substance, and less often for background radiation.

♦ A **scintillation counter** is another apparatus for measuring radiation.

♦ **Badges**, such as those worn by people who work in nuclear reactors, contain a film which records the amount of radiation to which the wearer has been exposed.

c How may solid waste with a long radiation half-life be disposed of?
d Name three methods of detecting radiation.
4a What is meant by fall-out?
b What factors govern the area which is affected by fall-out?
c List four factors on which the harm caused by fall-out depends.
d Draw a diagram to show the effect of fall-out on food chains.

FURTHER WORK

1 Collect newspaper reports of pollution. For each, note: (i) cause, (ii) effects, (iii) actions required to remedy the situation.

2 Compare the forms of pollution which may be created when power is obtained from the use of: (i) coal, (ii) oil, (iii) nuclear fuel.

QUESTIONS

1a What is meant by pollution?
b Name three main sources of air pollution.
c Describe acid rain and its harmful effects.
d Name an insecticide which persists in the soil, and give three possible effects.
e Draw a diagram to show the progress of pollution through a food chain.

2a Name seven ways in which rivers and lakes can be polluted.

b When ground water is polluted, give two ways in which the pollution may be passed on.
c In what ways can sea birds be affected by oil pollution?
3a Describe causes and effects of noise pollution.
b Name two types of emission from nuclear power stations in which traces of radiation may be found.

Conservation

Conservation is the protection and maintenance of habitats. A **habitat** is a place where an organism or a group of organisms naturally lives. Habitats can be any size from a desert to a cow pat, or even smaller, and usually contain a mixture of plants, animals, fungi and lichens.

People living in hunter-gatherer societies are small in numbers and have little impact on the environment. Nomadic grazing of animals causes some changes to natural habitats, but greater changes take place with the introduction of farming. These changes have, in the past, resulted in the creation of man-made and semi-natural habitats including hedgerows, copses and ponds. Today, with modern technology, farming often destroys traditional habitats and creates conditions where wildlife cannot survive. (**Wildlife**: animals and plants living in natural conditions).

Farming also enables large quantities of food to be produced. It can be used to feed large numbers of people and so permits the growth of towns and cities. This results in further loss of large areas of natural habitat and changes in the environment, and the creation of new but artificial habitats.

Destruction of habitats

Natural habitats change only slowly over a long period of time unless they are destroyed by alteration of climate or by human action. When this happens the effects can be far reaching.

Modern farming methods can be damaging to wildlife

◆ Chemical sprays and pesticides kill wildlife and flowers, and often pollute rivers and lakes, killing fish and destroying river habitats.
◆ Draining of wetlands destroys the natural habitats of marshland plants, butterflies, and migrating birds which stop and feed there.
◆ Removing hedgerows and trees destroys the nesting place of birds so that the countryside becomes empty of birds and birdsong. Natural pests, which were formerly controlled by birds, have to be controlled by pesticides.
◆ The use of artificial fertilisers means that animals no longer have to be kept to manure the land, so farmers can grow single crops over vast areas, which provide only a limited variety of habitats for wildlife.

Changes to woodland and forests can be destructive

◆ Replacement of mixed woods by conifers destroys the varied habitat suitable for many plants and animals, and replaces it with just one uniform habitat suitable for only a few species.
◆ Destruction of tropical rain forest in the Amazon basin, Africa and Asia destroys the habitat of large numbers of plant and animal species, and

they disappear. Scientists believe that such widespread destruction has also caused climatic changes in other parts of the world, mainly to rainfall patterns, and this may be responsible for the increasing number of droughts and enlargement of the desert areas.

Neglect of man-made habitats

◆ Moorland previously grazed can become overgrown by fern.
◆ Meadows can be overgrown by bramble.
◆ Ponds can become silted up.
◆ Woods require careful management to allow regrowth and to encourage wildlife.

Land and habitats are lost to meet the needs of an increasing population through:

◆ building housing, factories and warehouses,
◆ constructing roads, airports, railways, car parks,
◆ providing leisure facilities – sports grounds, golf courses, camp sites,
◆ flooding valleys for reservoirs to supply more water,
◆ effluent and waste which pollutes the air and rivers (p. 208).

Urbanisation is not always destructive. Suburban gardens provide new man-made habitats for birds and butterflies, and wild flowers thrive on the banks of motorways.

Reasons for conservation

Encouraged by television and by travel, people have become more aware that we share the earth with other animals and plants and that we have a duty to ensure their survival and preservation for future generations.

Apart from the fact that many people derive pleasure from observing the great variety of plants and animals, conservation makes sense when it is realised that:

◆ A green environment is an aid to health.
◆ Many wild plants are a possible source of new medicines.
◆ Wild species may be hardier and more disease resistant than the cultivated variety. Genes from wild species may be useful in producing new varieties, some of which may be able to grow in new places, eg rice which will grow in parts of the world where it could not grow before.
◆ Many pests are kept in check by other wild creatures. If this balance is upset, pests can increase.
◆ Some species are useful as monitors of pollution.
◆ Fish stocks can be preserved by preventing over-fishing.
◆ Conservation areas and game reserves attract tourists, to the economic advantage of the area.

Actions to aid conservation

Managing wildlife involves:

◆ Scientific study of **ecology** – the relationship between living organisms and their environment – to try to avoid mistakes, correct errors, and improve degraded areas (those poor in wildlife).
◆ Education to increase awareness of the need for conservation.
◆ Suitable ways of collecting and disposing of rubbish.
◆ Nature reserves to protect endangered species.
◆ Farming methods which provide variety of habitat.
◆ Preserving species by not picking wild flowers, taking birds' eggs, or killing rare animals.
◆ **Gene banks** to prevent the disappearance of species:

Kew Gardens has a gene bank where seeds of plant species in danger of becoming extinct are stored.

Zoos and wildlife parks can rear animals which are in danger of becoming extinct and even to re-stock their normal habitat.

Managing waste

Conservation can be aided by arrangement for the disposal of **refuse** – household rubbish – which is basically of two types:

Organic matter – food, paper, rags, bones – which rots away as it is destroyed by microbes.
Inorganic matter – tins, bottles, iron, plastics, ashes – which does not easily break down and therefore persists for a much longer time.

Methods of disposing of refuse

Dumping

◆ Refuse can be tipped into holes or on to the ground, squashed, and then covered with soil. The organic matter (food, paper etc) may encourage rats and flies, and may smell unpleasantly, but it will eventually rot away. If the tipping has been properly controlled, the land can eventually be reclaimed and put to good use.

Problems Dumps look unsightly, refuse can be blown around, and flies and rats are encouraged. Also, toxic chemicals may seep into the water supplies. There is also the possibility of a build-up of methane, creating a danger of fire or explosion.

◆ **Dumping in the sea.**
◆ **Burying** deep underground.

Incineration Refuse can be incinerated – burnt and reduced to a small amount of ash. The heat produced can be used to power the incinerator or for domestic heating.

Problems Fumes are produced, some of which may cause air pollution and acid rain.

Recycling Refuse is first sorted to salvage paper, rags, bottles, bones, and metals of different types. These materials can be recycled – used again. The rest is then either dumped or incinerated.

Problems This type of treatment is much more difficult to organise and requires expensive equipment.

QUESTIONS

1a What is meant by: (i) conservation, (ii) habitat, (iii) wildlife?

2a Give four examples of ways in which modern farming methods can be damaging to wildlife.
 b Give two examples of ways in which changes to woodland and forest destroys habitats.
 c Give three examples of the ways in which man-made habitats change when neglected.
 d Suggest reasons why land and habitats are lost to meet the needs of an increasing population.

 e Give two examples of how urbanization provides new habitats.

3a List seven reasons for conservation.
 b What actions can be taken to aid conservation?

4a Describe the two types of matter in household refuse.
 b Name three methods of disposing of refuse, and give the problems.

FURTHER WORK

1 Describe three actions which have been taken in support of conservation locally, nationally or internationally.

2 Gardens are naturally suitable habitats for certain plants. Describe ways in which gardeners modify the habitat so that plants naturally suited to other habitats can grow well.

Radiation

This topic deals only with **ionising radiation** – radiation which comes from outer space, X-ray machines and radioactive substances. This radiation produces electrically charged particles called **ions** in the materials it strikes. Since 'ionising radiation' is commonly referred to simply as 'radiation', this practice has been adopted here.

Background radiation

There is a small amount of radiation all around us – natural background radiation. It comes from radioactive substances on, or in, the Earth, and within our own bodies. It also arrives on earth as cosmic rays from sources in space such as the Sun. Humans and all forms of life have evolved in an environment with natural background radiation, and radiation is thought to be one of the causes of the mutations which have helped the progress of evolution.

These days, in addition to natural background radiation there is a very small amount of man-made radiation, **Fig 1**.

Types of radiation: Fig 2

Alpha particles These cannot penetrate the skin, so only enter the body when inhaled, swallowed, or through a wound.

Beta particles These can pass into the body through the skin, and can also be inhaled, swallowed, or enter through a wound. They can be stopped by a thin layer of water, glass or metal.

Gamma rays and **X-rays** These can travel through people. They can be stopped by a moderately thick layer of lead or concrete.

Neutrons These are present in cosmic rays and also in nuclear reactors or nuclear explosions. They easily pass through the human body, but can be stopped by a thick layer of lead or concrete.

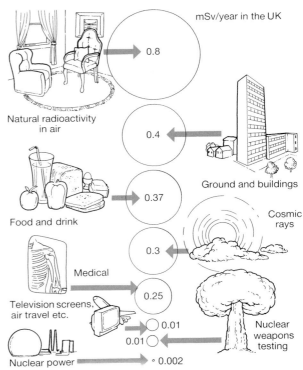

mSv/year in the UK

Natural radioactivity in air — 0.8

Ground and buildings — 0.4

Food and drink — 0.37

Cosmic rays

Medical — 0.3

Television screens, air travel etc. — 0.25

0.01

0.01 — Nuclear weapons testing

Nuclear power — 0.002

Figure 1 Background radiation – the general level from both natural (top 4 drawings) and man-made sources

Effects of radiation

Radiation can cause changes in living cells, chiefly to the DNA of the genes.

Immediate effects

The immediate effects of radiation are related to the dose:

◆ Very small doses – the DNA is repaired and there is no effect.
◆ Small doses – a few cells are killed, and they are replaced.
◆ Medium doses – many cell deaths occur and part of a tissue may be destroyed.
◆ Large doses (rare except for nuclear disasters and some forms of medical treatment) result in widespread damage, for example:

Tissue	Effects of large doses of radiation
Bone Marrow	Stops production of blood cells, leading to anaemia, poor clotting and poor resistance to infection.
Skin	**Radiation burns** – no new skin cells are formed and the old skin peels off (much like ordinary burns but heal less well).
Hair	Cells in the growing region are destroyed and the hair falls out.
Gut lining	Stops replacing itself, leading to diarrhoea, vomiting and internal bleeding.
Ovaries and **Testes**	Damage to the cells which form the sperm or eggs may result in sterility.
Foetus	A baby in the early stages of development in the uterus is in danger of being deformed or killed.

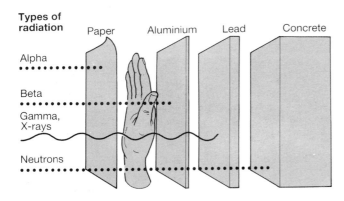

Types of radiation	Paper	Aluminium	Lead	Concrete
Alpha				
Beta				
Gamma, X-rays				
Neutrons				

Figure 2 Different types of radiation have different degrees of penetration and therefore require different kinds of protective shield to block them

Delayed effects

In theory, there is no 'safe' amount of radiation. There is a remote chance that even the smallest amount may cause one tiny change in a cell's DNA which alters a gene, producing a mutation (p. 130). Should this cell survive and divide, the mutation will be passed on to other cells. If the mutation took place in a:

◆ **body cell** there is a slight chance that, given time, it may give rise to cancer.
◆ **reproductive cell** it may affect future generations.

Radiation damage

Generally, the harm caused by radiation depends on:

◆ The **amount of radiation** received:
  High doses produce radiation sickness within days or weeks.
  With low doses, the body is usually able to repair the damage within days or weeks.
◆ The **type of radiation** – alpha particles and neutrons are much more damaging than beta particles and gamma rays.
◆ **Age** – children, including those unborn, are more at risk than adults because they are actively growing.

Measuring radiation

The **becquerel** (Bq) is the unit for measuring the **amount of radioactivity** in soil, water, milk, air, etc.

There are two different units for measuring radiation in people – grays and sieverts. For many types of radiation they are essentially the same.

◆ **Gray** (Gy) – measures the amount of radiation absorbed by the tissues. The gray is the unit most used for measuring the early effects of radiation. The following is a rough guide:
  up to 3 grays – no obvious signs of ill-health.
  3–8 grays – signs of radiation sickness; bone marrow would be damaged. Treatment is needed to help the clotting of blood in wounds, and to protect against infection.
  8–12 grays – radiation sickness – diarrhoea, vomiting, and death from bone marrow failure.
  more than 12 grays – death within 3–5 days from loss of fluid in vomiting and diarrhoea.

◆ **Sievert** (Sv) measures the effect of the radiation on the tissues. The sievert is the unit most used for measuring delayed effects.
  1 millisievert (1 mSv) = one thousandth of a sievert.
  0.02 mSv is the dose from a chest X-ray.
  2 mSv is the typical annual dose from natural background radiation, but it may be as high as 100 mSv in people who live in some houses in granite areas.
  15 mSv (0.015 Sv) is the maximum radiation dose that workers are allowed to receive in one year.

Note: The SI units – becquerel, gray and sievert – have replaced the curie, rad and rem.

Medical uses of radiation

Radiation is widely used in medicine for:

Medical diagnosis

◆ **Radioactive isotopes** are used in very small, low-energy doses to trace blood flow or the functioning of some organs and tissues in the body. A minute quantity of the isotope (one with a short half-life – see p. 217 – and which the body excretes easily) is injected into the blood stream and its whereabouts is traced with a scintillation counter or geiger counter (p. 209).
◆ **X-rays** show the shadows cast by the bones and organs, eg lungs. In a **barium meal**, the shadow is cast by barium sulphate.
◆ **CT** (computerised tomograph) **scanner** – a form of X ray which shows a series of cross-sections ('slices') through the body.

Treatment

◆ In very large doses, **gamma rays** or **neutron beams** damage rapidly dividing cells, and, when focused on a cancer, can be used to treat it.
◆ **Iodine-131** taken by mouth for an over-active thyroid becomes concentrated in the gland and damages the cells, and so reduces the amount of hormone produced.

Sterilisation of medical equipment

◆ Gamma rays are used to kill bacteria and other microbes to prevent infection (eg syringes, catheters – tubes for removing fluid from the body – are sterilised).

QUESTIONS

1 From **Fig 1**, list the sources of:
  (i) natural radiation,
  (ii) man-made radiation.

2a Describe the types of radiation shown in **Fig 2**, and the kind of protective shield which blocks them.

3a (i) How does radiation affect living cells?
 b Give the immediate effect of:
   (i) a very small dose of radiation,
   (ii) a small dose, (iii) a medium dose.
 c Describe the effects of a large dose of radiation on:

(i) bone marrow, (ii) skin, (iii) hair, (iv) gut lining, (v) ovaries and testes, (vi) foetus.

4a Why, in theory, is there no safe amount of radiation?
 b How does the delayed effect of radiation in a body cell differ from that in a reproductive cell?
 c Name three factors on which the amount of damage caused by radiation generally depends.
 d Give three effects of radiation sickness.

5a Name the SI unit for measuring the amount of radioactivity in soil or water.
 b Name two SI units for measuring radiation in people. Explain what they measure and when they are used.
 c Give the radiation dose: (i) from a chest X-ray,

(ii) from natural background radiation per year (iii) that workers are allowed to receive per year.

6 Give examples of the medical uses of radiation for: (i) diagnosis, (ii) treatment, (iii) sterilisation of equipment.

FURTHER WORK

1 List the uses to which radiation can be put. Discuss the advantages and disadvantages.

2 Use a geiger counter to measure radiation in different parts of your locality and note any differences.

213

Section 7 EXERCISES

1 Match each of these terms with the correct statement in the list below.
(a) **anaerobic bacteria chlorophyll colony evolution excretion food chain omnivorous oxygen photosynthesis vitamin K**

    removal of the waste products of living cells
    manufacture of sugar by green plants
    green pigment in plant cells
    waste product of photosynthesis
    feeds on both plant and animal matter
    a series of energy transfers
    a group of bacteria derived from one parent cell
    can live without oxygen
    produced in the large intestine
    slow change and development   [10]

(b) **antibiotic becquerel bipedal gait carcinogen chemotherapy conservation ecology pollution potable primates**

    the group of mammals to which humans belong
    walking on two legs
    protection and maintainance of natural habitats
    study of the relationship between living organisms and
      their environment
    contamination of the environment
    unit for measuring radiation
    cancer-producing agent
    treatment with drugs
    destroys microbes
    suitable for drinking   [10]

2 A pupil prepares a sterile agar plate in a petri dish and then coughs on to it. The dish is sealed and incubated at 37°C for 72 hours. The pupil arrives early for his next lesson, unseals his dish and opens it to examine it closely.

(a) Describe how a sterile agar plate is prepared.   [2]

(b) Explain why 37°C is the temperature chosen for incubation.   [1]

(c) The diagram shows the two kinds of micro-organism seen growing on the agar.

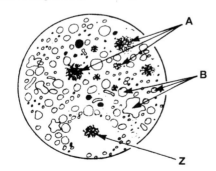

(i) Name these types of micro-organism (A and B).   [2]
(ii) Explain the reason for the clear area around Z.   [1]

(d) State two rules about microbiological experiments which were *not* followed by this pupil.   [2]

(e) The experiment illustrates that 'coughs and sneezes spread diseases'. State two ways by which such a spread can be reduced.   [2]

(WJEC: GCSE Biology (Human) Specimen)

214

3 (a) The diagram shows a food web.

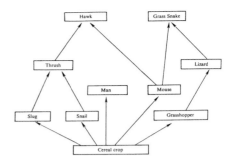

(i) Select from the food web a complete food chain consisting of **four** organisms.   [1]
(ii) Explain how the energy from the sun is made available for man through this food web.   [5]
(iii) Construct a diagram to show the circulation of carbon in nature. Using examples from the food web, incorporate *named* examples of a producer, a primary consumer (herbivore) and a secondary consumer (carnivore).   [8]
(iv) Name a class of organisms, *not included in the food web*, which are necessary for the complete circulation of carbon in nature.   [1]
(v) Explain what is likely to happen to the concentration of oxygen in the air surrounding the plants of a cereal crop during a 24-hour period of the growing season.   [7]

(b) The element nitrogen is absorbed from the soil by plants.
(i) In what form is this element absorbed?   [1]
(ii) Name a compound containing nitrogen which is made within the plant.   [1]
(ii) Explain why the amount of nitrogen in the soil normally remains constant in nature.   [6]

(AEB: Human Biology)

4 In 1980 a severe earthquake destroyed the Algerian city of El Asnam leaving an estimated 20 000 people dead and much of the city reduced to rubble. Apart from making immediate preparations to provide shelter and food for the homeless, the authorities were extremely concerned about the possible spread of disease.

In what ways may the following:
(a) sewage disposal,
(b) use of vaccines,
(c) potable water supply,
contribute to protection of the population from disease. In each case, discuss the measures that might be taken and the biological significance underlying them.   [19]

(AEB: O(A) level Biology of Man)

5 Explain briefly the difference between:
(a) breathing and respiration
(b) digestion and absorption
(c) fertilisation and conception
(d) antibody and antigen
(e) dominant and recessive
(f) mental illness and mental handicap
(g) antibiotic and antiseptic
(h) active immunity and passive immunity.   [16]

6 (a) The list below gives some of Man's effects on the environment. The table contains methods by which these effects may be controlled or prevented. Match each effect to its method of control/prevention by writing the appropriate letter in the table. One example has been done for you.

List – Man's effects on the environment
A increased lead in the air
B sea birds poisoned by mercury
C piles of waste paper
D large animals becoming extinct
E death of fish in rivers due to lack of oxygen
F mineral content of the soil reduced

Method of control of prevention	Letter
Reduction of lead content of petrol	A
Use of fertilisers	
Sewage treatment	
Re-cycling	
National Parks created	
Treatment of effluent before discharging	

[5]

(b) In many areas farmers have moved hedges in order to create larger fields. How does this affect wildlife? [1]

(MEG: GCSE Biology (Human) Specimen)

Supplement

Skin sensitivity test for two-point discrimination

Apparatus Unwind a paper clip and bend it into a U-shape with the points 1 cm apart. This clip can be used to test the sensitivity of different areas of the skin. Both points are applied to the skin at the same time, with equal pressure on each point, and the subject (the one being tested) says whether he or she can feel two, or only one, point.

Method Work in pairs. Write a list of the parts of the skin you intend to test (fingertips, palm, wrist, bend of elbow, neck), placing them in order, with the one you think most sensitive at the top and the one you think least sensitive at the bottom. Test the skin of each partner in turn, with the subject (the one being tested) keeping his or her eyes closed. Record against the list whether one or two points were felt or if the subject was not sure.

Result Did your results confirm your original list? Are different results obtained when the space between the two points is altered, for example to 0.5 cm or 2 cm?

Energy in food

This experiment demonstrates that energy contained in food can be released as heat energy and that the amount of heat energy released differs for different foods. Foods only burn when they are very dry and when sufficient oxygen is present.
  (i) Compare the energy values of different foods.
  (ii) Give reasons why measurements obtained in this experiment will not be accurate.
  (iii) Carry out this experiment using a crucible or tin lid in place of a wire mesh basket. Does this affect the experiment? If so, in what way and why?

Skin tests

1 Study your skin with a magnifying glass. Where can you see:
  (a) the most hairs,
  (b) no hairs,
  (c) the roughest skin,
  (d) the smoothest skin,
  (e) the deepest wrinkles,
  (f) the largest blood vessels,
  (g) no blood vessels?
2 To find out where the sweat pores are, paint a small area of the hand with iodine. Wait until it dries. Then Sellotape a piece of starch paper over the iodine. Examine after one minute. Purple spots indicate the positions of sweat pores.
3 Using a paintbrush, lightly touch the skin of the hand. Note the areas which are
  (a) most sensitive,
  (b) moderately sensitive,
  (c) least sensitive.
  Carry out this test on the arm and the face. What is the effect of touching a hair?
4 Find the pH of the skin by placing a drop of Universal Indicator on your hand. Wash your hands with soap, then test again for pH. Find the pH of the soap, also of any hand creams, face creams, washing up liquids, etc. What is pH and is it likely to be of importance in connection with the skin?
5 Describe acne and the treatments that may be helpful.

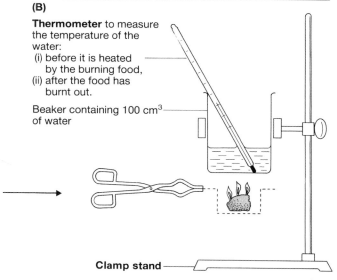

(A)
Wire mesh basket containing 1 g of food, eg peanut, bread, crisps, dried potato

Tongs

Heat the food until it catches fire, then place the burning food underneath a beaker containing 100 cm³ water (see right)

(B)
Thermometer to measure the temperature of the water:
(i) before it is heated by the burning food,
(ii) after the food has burnt out.

Beaker containing 100 cm³ of water

Clamp stand

Food tests

To test for starch
(i) Add a drop of iodine solution (potassium iodide) to the food.
(ii) If a blue black colour appears, starch is present.

Tests for sugars
When simple sugars such as glucose are heated with Benedict's solution they react to give a colour change. These sugars are called **reducing sugars**. They reduce the copper sulphate which gives Benedict's solution its blue colour and form a green, yellow, orange or red precipitate.

Double sugars such as sucrose are **non-reducing sugars** because they do not react with Benedict's solution until they have first been split into simple sugars by heating with hydrochloric acid.

To test for a simple sugar (monosaccharide, reducing sugar, eg glucose)
(i) Make a solution of the food.
(ii) Pour a little into a test tube.
(iii) Add a little Benedict's solution.
(iv) Heat to boiling point in a water bath.
(v) If the contents of the test tube change to green, yellow, orange or red, a simple sugar is present.

To test for a double sugar (disaccharide, eg sucrose)
(i) Make a solution of the food.
(ii) Pour a little into a test tube.
(iii) Add a few drops of dilute hydrochloric acid.
(iv) Heat in a water bath at boiling point for 2 min.
(v) Remove from the water bath, allow to cool, then neutralise by adding a few drops of sodium hydrogencarbonate solution.
(vi) Add an equal quantity of Benedict's solution and return to the water bath.
(vii) If the contents of the test tube change to green, yellow, orange or red a double sugar is present.

To test for fat
Fats are insoluble in water but soluble in ethanol, methylated spirits, etc. All apparatus must be clean and dry.
(i) make a solution of the food with a little ethanol.
(ii) Filter the liquid into a dry test tube.
(iii) Pour the filtered liquid into a little water.
(iv) If the liquid turns cloudy, fat is present.

A simpler test for fat
(i) Rub the food on to a piece of thin paper. Allow any moisture to dry.
(ii) Hold the paper up so that light can shine through it.
(iii) If the food has left a translucent mark, it contains fat.

To test for protein – Biuret test
(i) Make a solution of the food to be tested.
(ii) Pour a little of the solution into a test tube.
(iii) Add an equal amount of Biuret A (sodium hydroxide solution).
(iv) Add one drop of Biuret B (copper sulphate solution).
(v) If a violet or pink colour appears, protein is present.

To test for vitamin C (ascorbic acid)
(i) Use a syringe to put 1 cm³ DCPIP (a blue dye) into a test tube.
(ii) Using a second syringe, draw up exactly 2 cm³ of fruit juice (or other liquid) into the syringe.
(iii) Squeeze the plunger of the second syringe carefully so that separate drops of fruit juice are added to the blue dye. Shake the test tube regularly.
(iv) If the dye becomes colourless, this shows that vitamin C is present in the liquid being tested.
(v) Note the volume of liquid from the syringe required to decolour DCPIP. The smaller the amount of juice required to remove the colour, the greater the amount of vitamin C it contained.
(vi) Compare the amount of vitamin C in different types of fruit juice, squash, milk, carrot juice and liquid extracted from other vegetables, being sure to wash the syringe thoroughly before each test.
(a) How can you make the experiment more accurate?
(b) Devise an experiment to find if vitamin C is affected by (i) boiling, (ii) storage.

Culturing microbes

Many bacteria and fungi will grow on nutrient agar in a petri dish. (Viruses will only grow inside living cells, for example a hen's egg or kidney tissue, so cannot be cultured in this way.) Nutrient agar is a jelly made from seaweed which provides food and moisture for microbe growth. The following procedure can be used to test for the presence of microbes in various substances or to show the effect of antibiotics in inhibiting microbe growth.

Equipment Two or more sterilised petri dishes containing nutrient agar are required. One of the dishes should be used as a *control*, so must remain unopened. If microbes grow in the control, it shows that the dishes and agar used in the experiment were not sterile.

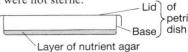

Inoculate Lift the lid of the dish sufficiently to add a drop of tap water, milk or other liquid, or to add a little dust, soil, antibiotic disc or other substance. If the air is being tested for the presence of microbes, remove the lid from the petri dish for five minutes.

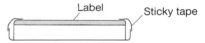

Seal Tape the two parts of the dish together. Turn the dish upside down and use a chinagraph pencil to label it with your name, the date, the substance added/control.

Incubate Leave the dishes in a warm place for a few days to encourage microbe growth.

Examine for microbe growth (without opening the dish) *Fungi* will be seen as a fuzziness above the agar or as branching threads growing in the agar. *Bacteria* can be seen as individual colonies or groups of colonies. Each different type of bacterium and fungus has its own particular colour, shape and set of conditions under which it will grow.

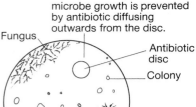
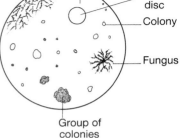

Disposal The microbes grown on the agar could well be a source of disease. Therefore the dishes must not be opened under any circumstances. When the experiment is over, autoclave the unopened dishes before disposing of them.

Testing a leaf for starch

1 Place a leaf in boiling water for one minute to kill and soften it. Then TURN OFF THE BUNSEN BURNER. (Ethanol is highly inflammable.)

2 Remove the leaf from the water and place it in a test tube containing ethanol (alcohol).

3 Stand the test tube in the boiled water. As the ethanol heats up and boils (it boils at a lower temperature than water) the chlorophyll will dissolve out from the leaf, leaving it more or less white. This makes any colour change caused by iodine easier to see.

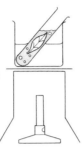

4 Place the leaf in the hot water to soften it again.

5 Remove the leaf, spread it flat in a petri dish and cover it with iodine solution. Any parts which turn blue/black have starch in them.

Half-life

Different forms of the same element are called **isotopes**. Some isotopes are stable, others (the radioactive isotopes) are unstable and give off radiation (energy) as they gradually change to a stable form. Each radioactive isotope has a fixed time for its radioactivity to decay by half. This is known as the half-life. In two half-lives radioactivity is reduced to a quarter, and in ten half-lives to about one-thousandth.

Half-lives vary for different substances from a fraction of a second to thousands of years. The half-life of:

iodine 132 is 6 hours
radon 222 is 4 days
iodine 131 is 8 days
strontium 90 is 28 years
caesium 137 is 30 years

If one of these substances gets into the body, it will continue to give off radiation at a steadily decreasing rate, unless the substance is removed in excreta.

Smoking machine

This apparatus can be used to 'smoke' a cigarette by moving the plunger in and out at appropriate intervals. The cotton wool can then be removed and examined for tar.

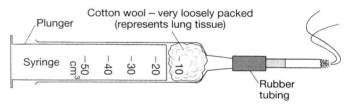

Plunger

Cotton wool – very loosely packed (represents lung tissue)

Syringe

Rubber tubing

Index

Bold numbers indicate pages on which main coverage appears.